WM

WITHDRAWN

INDIAN LIFE ON LONG ISLAND

T.F. Spry

THE FIRST WHITE MAN ARRIVES

Notice the round wigwam with the hole
in the top to let out the smoke. Also in
the front you can see a stretching and
drying frame for animal pelts.

By
JACQUELINE OVERTON
Author of LONG ISLAND'S STORY

Illustrated by
THOMAS F. SPRY

IRA J. FRIEDMAN, Inc.   Port Washington, N. Y. 1963

INDIAN LIFE ON LONG ISLAND

FAMILY
WORK
PLAY
LEGENDS
HEROES

EMPIRE STATE HISTORICAL PUBLICATION XXIII

EMPIRE STATE HISTORICAL PUBLICATION XXIII

Library of Congress Catalog Card No: 63-12957

Manufactured in the United States of America

SECOND PRINTING September 1966

PUBLISHER'S FOREWORD

The author of this book, Miss Jacqueline Overton, had been for many years, before her untimely death, the librarian of the Robert Bacon Memorial Children's Library in Westbury, Long Island. Her classic work "Long Island's Story" is considered one of the outstanding contributions to Long Island history.

Just twenty-five years ago the chapters making up this book first appeared as a series of articles in the *Nassau Review-Star*. It had been Miss Overton's fond hope that someday the articles could be assembled and presented as one cohesive and comprehensive work on a subject about which she knew so much. She had often discussed with Mr. Ira J. Friedman her plan of having the articles published in book form. Unfortunately she never saw her wish realized.

Through the kind cooperation of the *Long Island Press* (successors to the *Nassau Review-Star*) and Miss Overton's family we are proud to offer this book as tribute to the memory of Jacqueline Overton—beloved librarian, competent historian, accomplished author and a friend to all who knew her.

CONTENTS

LIST OF ILLUSTRATIONS

INDIAN LIFE ON LONG ISLAND

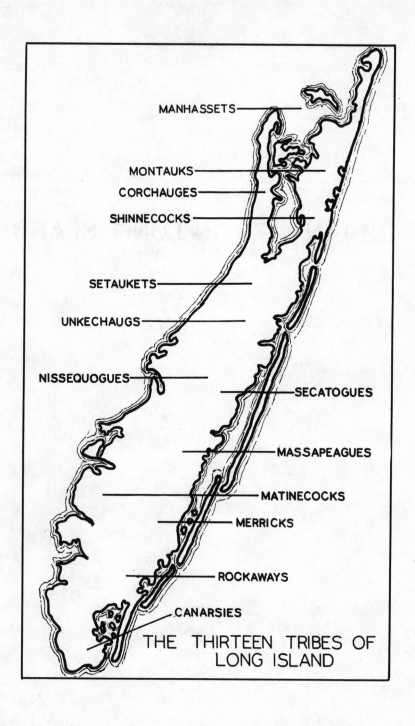

THE THIRTEEN TRIBES OF
LONG ISLAND

MANHASSETS

MONTAUKS
CORCHAUGES
SHINNECOCKS

SETAUKETS

UNKECHAUGS

NISSEQUOGUES
SECATOGUES

MASSAPEAGUES

MATINECOCKS
MERRICKS

ROCKAWAYS

CANARSIES

CHAPTER 1

THE THIRTEEN TRIBES

The first white people to come to Long Island were Henry Hudson and his men.

On a September day in 1609 they dropped the anchor of their ship, the Half Moon, off the place we now call Coney Island and prepared to come ashore in small boats to catch fish and see what the land and the people were like.

At that time only Indians lived on Long Island and these Indians probably had never seen a white man before or a ship such as the one they came in, a ship unlike their own canoes, a ship carrying as they said "big white wings." As the Indian men, women and children crowded down to the shore no doubt they were afraid as well as curious. After all this might not be a ship but some strange bird from the sky or sea-monster from the water.

These Indians had heard of white men, they were strong, they could do big things, good and evil. It might be well to greet them as friends when their boats reached the shore and give them a present of some green tobacco.

We know that they did this because Robert Juet, mate of the Half Moon, kept a journal of the trip and wrote of this first meeting of the white men with the Indians of Long Island. "They seemed very glad of our coming and brought green tobacco and gave us of it for knives and beads."

If Hudson had stayed on Long Island instead of sailing away in a few days as he did, he would have found that there was not only the Canarsie (Can-ar-see) tribe that greeted him but thirteen or more tribes or big families of Indians living from one end of the Island to the other.

Here are the names of the principal ones beginning at the western end of the Island:

> Canarsies (Can-ar-see)
> Rockaways (Rock-aways)
> Merricks (Mer-ricks)
> Matinecocks (Mat-tin-e-cocks)
> Massapeagues (Mas-sa-peaques)
> Nissequogues (Niss-e-quogues)
> Secatogues (Sec-a-taugs)
> Setaukets (Se-tau-kets)
> Unkechaugs (Un-ke-chaugs)
> Corchauges (Cor-chaugs)
> Shinnecocks (Shin- ne-cocks)
> Manhassets (Man-hass-ets)
> Montauks (Mon-tauks)

These all belonged to the great general tribe known as the Delaware Indians.

If you look on a map of Long Island you can tell about where each tribe settled and which one lived where you do now.

The CANARSIES claimed all the land within what is now the Borough of Brooklyn and part of the town of Jamaica. On the shore of Jamaica Bay is a place to this day called Canarsie.

This tribe must have made much wampum for vast shell heaps have been found in their terrritory.

The ROCKAWAY tribe lived in the southern part of what is now Hempstead, part of Jamaica and all of Newtown. A portion of the Rockaway Indians were known as the MASPETHS. Their settlement was at the head of Maspeth Creek in Newtown. They had also a settlement on Hog Island in the Rockaway Bay. The shell banks of the Rockaway Indians were also big.

Mangwobe was their Sachem in 1650.

In 1643, the explorer, De Vries, visited this tribe and wrote in his diary, "At evening we arrived at Rechqua Akie (old spelling for Rockaway) where we found the chief who had one eye, with two or three hundred Indians and about thirty houses. They led us into his house and treated us as to what they had as oysters and fish which they catch here."

The name Rockaway meant Sandy Place.

The MERRICK Indians lived on the South Shore east of the Rockaways and their land extended inland as far as the bounds of the town we now call Oyster Bay. Part of Mineola, Westbury and Hempstead belonged to the Merricks also, as well as the town that now carries their name. They had a settlement likewise on Hick's Neck and other necks of land near by. A good portion of their land extended over the Hempstead Plains and the name Merrick means, "plains country."

On the North shore the MATINECOCKS owned all the land east of Newtown as far as the western line of Smithtown. This originally must have been a big tribe and a roaming one and had settlements at Flushing, Glen Cove, Cold Spring Harbor, Dosoris, Huntington and Northport as well as the place we now call, Matinecock.

They were great fishermen as well as makers of wampum but in 1650 when vanTienhoven visited their part of Long Island, he wrote that only about thirty families were left and that "a great number of Indian plantations now lie waste and vacant."

By the year 1654 much of their territory had been sold to white people.

There were hills on the land of the Matinecocks and their name stood for "hilly country".

The MASSAPEAGUE tribe made their largest settlement on the South Shore around the place later called Fort Neck. When the white men came they found two forts there. The remains of one is said to be still in existence. The other, which was built on a salt meadow, has long since been washed away by tides and storms, and water now covers the place where it stood. Their territory ran east to the bounds of the present town of Islip and north to the middle of the Island.

At Fort Neck in 1653, the only big battle between the whites and the Indians on Long Island took place. That was when Capt. John Underhill and his men attacked the Fort. You will hear more of that later.

The name Massapeague means "the great waterland" or "the land on the great cove."

Their Sachem in 1640 was Tach-a-pausha.

East of the Nissequogue River as far as Stony Brook and from the Sound to the middle of the island lived the NISSEQUOGUE Indians.

In a Dutch record of 1645 their land was called Nis-inck-queg-hacky, which meant "a place where the Matinecocks now reside," showing that this tribe must once have been part of the Matinecocks.

Near the Nissequogue River great shell heaps and fire holes have been found. Their name also means "the clay country." Probably the clay on the banks of the river was the kind the Indians liked best for making their pots, and the marsh lands about held the grasses they gathered for making many things.

The SECATOGUE Indians lived on the South Side of Long Island east of the Massapeague tribe. They claimed the country as far east as Patchogue. There is a point of land today called Secatogue Neck where their Sachem is supposed to have lived. The name Secatogue means "black or colored land" and the meadows there have sometimes been called Black Grass Meadows.

From what is now the village of Stony Brook east to Wading River and south to the middle of the island lived the SEATALCOTS or SETAUKETS. They were a strong tribe and lived along the shores of the creeks and bays that abound in this part of Long Island.

The first white settlers found War-a-wak-my, their Sachem, living on "land at the mouth of the creek" which is what the name Setauket stands for.

To the UNKECHAUG Indians belonged all the land on the South Shore from Namkee Creek (between Blue Point and Bayport) to the river in Eastport.

Several small groups of Indians made up the Unke-chaug tribe. These groups lived in different localities and gave their names to the section.

One of these small groups was called the PAT-CHOGUES and another the POOSEPATUCKS.

A few of the descendants of the Poosepatuck Indians still live on Mastick Neck.

There were other groups living in Bellport, Brookhaven Village, South Haven, and the Moriches, but the Sachem and the largest part of the tribe lived in Unkechaug which was part of Mastic.

For many years Tabacus was their Sachem and his name is often found on Indian land deeds for this part of Long Island.

On the North Shore the country adjoining the Setaukets, from Wading River east to Oyster Ponds, or as we say now, Orient Point, belonged to the CORCHAUGUES. They lived along the north shore of Peconic Bay also and probably claimed Robins Island, too. In 1640 their Sachem was Mom-o-we-ta.

At this eastern end of Long Island four Indian forts were built, one by the Corchauges, another by the Manhassets, a third by the Shinnecocks and a fourth by the Montauks. By signal fires from one to the other the four tribes could be brought together within a few hours.

The SHINNECOCK Indians lived on the hills that still carry their name and along the shores of Great Peconic Bay and Shinnecock Bay.

Their Sachem in 1640 was Nowedonah, a brother of Poggattacut of Shelter Island and Wyandanch of Montauk.

A small remnant of this tribe still lives on a reservation in the Shinnecock Hills.

The MANHASSET tribe lived on Shelter Island, Ram Island and Hog Island.

The first white settlers found the Manhasset's chief, Poggattacut, was the Grand Sachem over all the tribes on Long Island (with the exception of the Canarsies). In other words, he was Grand Sachem of Paum-man-ak-e, as the Indians called Long Island.

Poggattacut was not inclined to be very friendly toward the white men.

The most powerful tribe of all Long Island Indians lived from East Hampton to the end of Montauk Point.

This tribe was the MONTAUKS and to them belonged also the island that we now call Gardiner's Island.

Before you finish the story of the Indians of Long Island you will have heard more about the Montauks and their splendid Sachem, Wyandanch, who after the death of his older brother Poggattacut became Grand Sachem of Paumanack.

We are told that the Montauk Indians "were tall and of proud and lofty movement, active of body, straight as the arrow."

The people of these thirteen tribes or families on Long Island were alike in many ways. They all spoke the Algonquin language, dressed like one another, and lived and worked the same.

A trail or a stream set up, marked the bounds where the land belonging to one tribe stopped and another began. That was all the fence they needed for an Indian in those early days, before the white man settled here, would seldom trespass on another's land to hunt or fish.

As you have read, each tribe had its own chief or sachem and over them all was a "Grand Sachem."

A sachem represented the people of his own tribe and when matters of importance were to be settled many Sachems met together. Sometimes a tribe had two Sachems, the elder for council and advice and the younger for action. Sachems had the power to declare war, make peace, sign treaties, and receive foreign visitors as well as to settle disputes between strong and weak tribes.

If a Sachem died and left no son, his wife took his place. She was then called the Sunk Squaw or Squaw Sachem. If he left a baby son its mother became Squaw Sachem until the child was of age.

Strong tribes for one reason or another often demanded tribute from weaker ones. This tribute was like our taxes today.

The powerful Mohawk Indian tribe of upper New York State claimed the Canarsie Indians belonged to them and demanded an annual tribute of skins and wampum, which they dared not refuse.

All the other Long Island tribes paid tribute to the Pequot Indians in Connecticut, a warlike tribe that was always stirring up trouble.

It was part of the Sachem's duty to see that this tribute was collected and delivered.

CHAPTER **2**

WHAT THE INDIANS LOOKED LIKE

If it were not for some of the records kept by the early Dutch and English travellers we would have a hard time telling just what the Indians of Long Island did look like or how they dressed, because they left no pictures behind them.

The mate of the Half Moon wrote: "They go in deer skin, loose well dressed. They grease their bodies and hair very often and paint their faces with several colours, as black, white, red, yellow, etc. which they take great pride in, everyone being painted in a different manner."

If you imagine the Long Island Indians dressed in war-paint and feathers, you are going to be disappointed. They wore very few feathers and though they painted their faces, the Indians here seldom painted them for war, since they were a peace-loving tribe.

Master Charles Wooley, a minister of the Church of England, spent two years between 1678 and 1680 in these parts and it is he who told us many things about the dress and manner of the Indians.

AN INDIAN FAMILY

Our Long Island Indians were very fond of their
children and family ties were very strong.

T. F. Spry

"Most of them," he says, "are between five or six feet high, straight bodied and strongly composed. In complexion of a clayish colour, the hair of their heads generally black lank and long hanging down—Their hair being naturally black they make it more so by oyling, dyeing and daily dressing, yet though they be very careful about the hair of their heads yet they will not endure any upon their chins, where it no sooner grows than they take it out by the roots or scrape it off with a kind of razor made out of bone."

Sometimes the young men burned off the hair on their heads with hot stones leaving only a brush of hair from the forehead to the nape of their necks. Sometimes also the hair was allowed to grow long from the crown of their heads. This was known as a scalp-lock which a warrior always defied his enemy to take.

Indian women wore their hair in a braid over either shoulder. On these braids they often slipped a little ring made of deer's hair colored red. They were very vain of these rings.

All Indians were very proud of their brown skins and from the time they were little children they took very good care of them.

Master Wooley tells us that they kept their skins smooth "by anointing them with the oyl of fishes, the fat of eagles and the grease of rackoons, which they held in summer the best to keep their skins from blistering by the scorching sun and their best armour against the musketto." In winter this same oil protected their skins from cold.

They painted their faces and sometimes their bodies. First because it pleased them and they thought it made them look handsome, and second because they believed it pleased the unseen spirits that might be about and frightened off the evil spirits of sickness and other bad things.

Painting the face was a form of magic to the Indian and he liked magic. It made him feel strong.

There were different styles of painting for different occasions. Each chief had his own style that no one else might copy. Every color had its own meaning.

Red meant power, success or war.

Black usually meant death or sorrow.

Blue was for defeat or trouble.

Yellow for joy, travel, bravery.

White meant peace.

Of course there were no ready-made paints for an Indian to buy. He must make every color for himself out of the juices of plants, clay or other things. Some colors were made by pounding, rubbing or grinding stones. This stone dust when mixed with grease shone like metal when smeared on the skin.

Other colors were made from plants like the poke-berry. They bruised the berries and squeezed out the juice on the inside of a flat piece of bark. The bark was then put in the sun to dry. When dry the surface of the bark was scraped off like dust and the dust put into little bags. Pokeberry juice made a fine purple color.

Red was made from natural iron rust and black came from soot and charcoal, also from the stain found in the bloodroots, a lovely little flower, seldom found on Long Island now, though years ago patches of woods were snow white with its blossoms in April and May.

Powdered shells made white and clay made yellow. Sumac roots and hemlock bark when boiled made yellow too. Green and blue were usually made from the juices of flowers and berries.

Colors were mixed with grease in small stone paint cups. This grease made the color easier to smear on the face. Some of the men tattooed patterns on their faces and bodies with hot stones or pricked in the color with thorns.

For clothing the men wore a kind of leather breeches shaped like an apron and fastened above the waist with a deer skin thong or a snake skin.

On their legs were leather leggins and on their feet moccasins usually fashioned out of deer hide. At times their feet were only covered by a strip of hide, or corn husks or rushes were bound about them.

In summer this was all they wore except perhaps a necklace of dyed deer hair or a string of beads made of shells or copper or some ornament worked out of stone. Since all Indians liked jewelry, stones were very often drilled and strung and worn as necklaces. Still other stones were shaped and polished and grooved and probably worn as ornaments. These are known as banner stones.

Having no pockets the Indian was likely to hang almost anything around his neck, even his knives and his pipe made of clay and his tobacco pouch (they were all great smokers). On his shoulders when going hunting he carried a six foot bow and a quiver of arrows and when he was on the warpath he added a stone axe or a club made of wood.

In winter they covered the upper part of their bodies with a robe of deer skin, bearskin, wolf or wildcat. Sometimes it might be a shawl of turkey feathers woven upon a net. So skillful were some Indians in making these feather garments that it is said they shed rain as a bird's feather does. Not until the white men settled among them did the Indians wear blankets.

Snow shoes helped them to travel in the winter. Master Wooley describes them in "deep snow," he says, "the

SPEARING FISH

Notice the scalp-lock. The hair was removed
by burning with hot stones. The Indians made
fine baskets and our fisherman is carrying one.

T. F. Spry-

Indians wear broad shoes much the shape of the round part of our rackets which we use at tennis, which travel without sinking in the least."

Preparation of furs and skins was women's work and it was no small task after her lord and master brought in the deer or wildcat or beaver to make its skin ready to be worked into a garment.

First it must be fleshed. That meant that all the flesh and fat were scraped off the inside of the skin with a tool made of bone.

If it was to be used as a hide all the hair must be taken off. This was done by pegging the skin down to the ground, hairy side up, over another skin which had already been oiled. Then all the hair was scraped off and the inside turned and scraped also.

Now the skin must be dressed, that is have something rubbed into it that would preserve it and make it wear well. The mixture the Indian women used to rub into the skins was made of the animal's brains and liver boiled together and mixed with grease and salt. This they rubbed into the inside of the skin by hand. Bundles of dry grasses were then piled in the middle of the skin and hot water was poured on. When it was all thoroughly soaked the four corners of the skin were gathered together and it was tied up like a ball and hung up to dry over night.

The following day the skin was shaken out and twisted like a rope until the moisture was wrung out. It was then stretched over a slanting frame made of wood and scraped with a bone tool, like the blade of a hoe. After that it was left to dry and bleach in the sun for a few days. Then to make it smoother it was rubbed again with a round piece of bone.

Next a string made of sinew was stretched between two trees and the skin drawn back and forth across it until it was as soft and easy to handle as a piece of velvet. Last of all it was cleaned with water in which white clay or chalk had been mixed much the same as you clean your white shoes in the summer.

The women wore a kind of skirt made of a single square piece of fringed leather or woven hemp open at the side. For dress they made a skirt trimmed with shell beads sewn on it in pretty patterns or "in pleasant wild works" as one old writing tells us. The hemp skirts were woven out of the fibre of a plant that grew along the banks of streams. It looked like milkweed and Indian children were sent out to gather it in armfuls for their mothers to weave into skirts, mats, blankets and fishnets. To this day we call the plant Indian Hemp and also Dogbane since the juice of the plant was sometimes used to poison some poor old sick dog.

As for what the children wore —they spent the first year of their life swaddled in a fur or a hemp blanket strapped to a board and hung on their mother's back. When they learned to walk they were not bothered for a few years by having to wear any clothes at all in summer and in winter they dressed much as their fathers and mothers did.

CHAPTER **3**

INDIAN HOMES AND LIFE IN AN INDIAN VILLAGE

The Long Island Indians made their homes near streams, or around the bays and inlets of the South Shore beaches and the necks and harbors of the North Shore.

Footpaths led from one settlement to another; paths which since their day have widened into great roads like the one that now runs through Brooklyn called the Kings Highway, or the one that runs along the South Shore now called the Montauk Highway. Within each settlement smaller paths ran in all directions, the broadest and best worn one being the way that led to the shore, the spring, or the fishing ground.

Paths were no more than two feet wide below since Indians seldom walked side by side, but travelled one behind the other. Overhead a path was always well cut back to leave a clear way for carrying either a big bundle or a canoe on the shoulders.

They did not live in tents and teepees as the Indians did on the western plains, but in huts called wigwams which looked like beehives turned upside down, and were made of bark or flags or grass.

When one of these houses was to be built the men cut down the young trees or saplings and after taking off the branches planted the poles in the ground in a circle the size they wanted the house to be. Then the branches were bent over and fastened together and the framework was covered with strips of bark or thatched with with grass and the cracks plastered with mud. There were two doors, each about three feet high, one to the north and the other to the south. When the wind blew they closed up one door with bark and hung a deer skin or a mat over the other. A hole was always left in the roof to let the smoke out. This chimney was made larger or smaller by drawing a mat over it.

Long narrow wigwams were sometimes built in which several families lived.

Seventy years after Henry Hudson visited Long Island, two missionaries, Jasper Dankers and Peter Sluyter, came here and wrote so good a description of a visit to an Indian village and how the Indians built their wigwams, that I am going to let them tell it to you in their own words. The tribe they visited must have been the Canarsies. They were staying in Gowanus, now part of the Borough of Brooklyn, and went for a walk along the shore with a man named Gerrit.

"Early this morning we went along the shore to the west—We soon heard a noise of pounding or thrashing and found an old Indian woman busily employed beating Turkish beans out of the pods by means of a stick, which she did with astonishing force and dexterity. Gerrit inquired of her in the Indian language, which he spoke perfectly well, how old she was and she answered eighty years, at which we were still more astonished that so old a woman should still have so much strength and courage to work as she did.

"We went thence to her habitation where we found the whole troop together consisting of seven or eight families. Their house was long and low, about sixty feet long and fourteen or fifteen feet wide. The bottom was earth, the sides and the roof were made of reed and the bark of chestnut trees, the posts or columns were limbs of trees stuck in the ground and all fastened together. The top or ridge of the roof was open about a foot wide from one end to the other to let the smoke escape in place of a chimney.

"On the sides of the walls of the house, the roof was so low that you could hardly stand under it. The doors at both ends were so small and low that they had to

LIGHTING A FIRE

This was a long and hard task and because of this the fires at home were seldom allowed to go out.

T. F Spry

stoop down and squeeze themselves to get through them. The doors were made of reed or flat bark . . .

"They build their fires in the middle of the floor according to the number of families which live in it, so that from one end to the other each family boils its own pot, and eats what it likes, not only the families by themselves but each Indian alone, whenever he is hungry, at all hours, morning, noon or night.

"By each fire are the cooking utensils, consisting of a pot, bowl or calabash and a spoon also made out of a calabash (gourd).

"They lie upon mats with their feet toward the fire. They do not sit much upon anything raised up, but for the most part sit on the ground or squat on their ankles –

"All who live in one house are generally one family, as a father and mother with their children and grandchildren.

"Their bread is maize (corn) pounded on a block by a stone, but fine. This is mixed with water and made into a cake, which they bake under the hot ashes.

"They gave us a small piece when we entered and although the grains were not ripe and it was half baked, we had to eat it or at least not throw it away before them, which they would have regarded as a great sin or a great affront.

"We chewed a little of it and managed to hide it so they did not see. We had also to drink out of their calabash, the water which was their drink, and which was very good . . . .

"We gave them two jewsharps, which much pleased them and they immediately commenced to play upon them.

"Some of the chief men were busy making shoes of deer leather which they understand how to make soft by working it in their hands."

Small torches made of pitch pine "cloven into little slices" were used at the times to light up a wigwam.

Of course the Indian had no matches like ours with which to light his fires. Either he struck two hard stones one against another until sparks flew big enough to kindle a flame or he made fire by rubbing two sticks together. A stick was twirled between the palms of his hands while at the same time its point was pressed into a piece of soft wood until the friction made it hot enough to smolder.

Lighting a fire this way, as you see, was slow business so a fire in the wigwam was not allowed to go out very often and it was part of the woman's work to see the fire was tended and wood kept on hand.

At times a fire was built outside large enough for the whole village to cook over.

When an Indian went hunting or left home for a time you may be sure he carried the means of making a fire with him.

Fire was used for more things than cooking, smoking fish and keeping warm. It was used as a tool as you will learn later when you read how they made their canoes.

Every year they burned over the small trees and underbrush because fire worked more quickly than stone hatchets and when the undergrowth was cleared, fresh green would spring up to attract the deer. This was called "brushburning." It may have been good for the hunting but it was bad for the big trees.

Fire was used to cure stiff joints and other ailments. Stones were heated red hot and then placed in a little hut built near the water. The sick person lay inside until he was dripping wet with sweat. Then he dashed out and threw himself in the cold water. This was supposed to cure because it made their bodies clean and drove away the poison.

So great a respect had an Indian for fire and what it meant to another that he would never willingly pass between another person and the fire because it would shut off the heat and light.

Long Island Indians lived by fishing and hunting and raising small crops of corn, beans, pumpkins, squash, melons and tobacco.

Their fishhooks were made of bone and they likewise used nets to catch fish. Sometimes they speared fish at night by torchlight. This was called "wigwas."

They seemed to have understood how to make ground right for their planting because it is known they planted a dead fish as fertilizer in every hill of corn and used cracked-up clam shells when more lime was needed in the soil. Planting time arrived "when leaves of the white oak were large as a mouse's ear."

Master Wooley tells us, "they dig their ground with a flint ... and put five or six grains into the hole the latter end of April or the beginning of May. Their harvest is in October."

When corn or maize was half a foot above the ground the Indians placed beans around it and let them grow together. The cornstalk served as a beanprop and the beans ran upon it. They throve well this way and the two were gathered at the same time. Pumpkins and squash were also planted in the same ground and the vines ran about between the hills of corn.

Great care was taken to keep the birds from destroying their garden crops. Hawks were often tamed to keep the small birds from the fields. Crows did much damage in cornfields but Indians seldom killed them because they believed that long ago it was the crow that brought

DEER HUNTING WITH BOW AND ARROW

Deer were very plentiful on Long Island when the Indians were the only inhabitants. We know that it is winter from the skin worn by the Indian brave.

T.F.Spry

their first grain of corn in one of its ears and a bean in the other all the way from the Southwest.

The men hunted and fished, gathered clams and oysters and built canoes. The women not only helped build and tend the fires but cooked and worked in the fields. A man would have thought it beneath him to plant and hoe and dig.

The women must have been good farmers for an account written by a traveller in 1654 says, "Another work is their planting of corn wherein they exceed our English husbandmen keeping it so clear with their clamshell hoes as if it were a garden rather than a cornfield not suffering a choking weed to advance its audacious head above the infant corn or an undermining worm to spoil his sprouts."

In September and October when crops were gathered in, shallow pits were dug near each wigwam. These were lined with grass mats and in them stored the dried corn, nuts, beans, etc. that were to last them through the winter. The white men called these pits "Indian barns."

When a food pit was emptied it was used as a hole in which to throw clam shells, bones, broken cooking pots and all sorts of odd trash. Cattle often stumbled into these holes and broke their legs. At last the white men passed a law that all "Indian barns" must be covered up. To this day food pits are being unearthed on Long

Island and it is sure proof that where one is found Indians must have lived.

Clams, oysters, and many kinds of fish were to be had in great quantities. Some were eaten fresh, others dried or smoked on a pole over the fire and kept for months at a time. Meat bones were always broken in slivers and the good marrow dug out and eaten.

Deer was most important game to the Indian and deer were plentiful on Long Island in the early days. Deer not only made good meat for eating, but the skin made fine clothing, the bones were readily fashioned into tools and the antlers of the bucks were useful to make knife handles and other things.

And what else did Indian mothers cook over the fire besides fish and game? From the accounts of some travellers things went into the pot that you and I would not care to eat—skunks, raccoons, possums, turtles, frogs, but the Indian found them tasty. The tail of the beaver was thought to be a great dainty.

All sorts of dishes were made out of corn, beans, and squash. No meal was quite right without a kind of porridge made of corn called mush. Mush might be found cooking over the fire at all hours. If you eat succotash today you are eating a dish Indian women taught white women to make out of beans and corn. The coarse grains of parched corn which we call samp was also Indian food. They raised corn of several colors, red, blue, yellow, white.

Indians were great fruit and berry eaters. During the summer they feasted on juniper berries, huckleberries, strawberries, wild grapes, beach plums, apples and wild cherries. The strawberries lasted from "half May" to July. When autumn came they gathered hickory nuts and chestnuts and they also brought in acorns out of which they made a kind of flour paste and baked it as a pancake.

Indian women were very wise in knowing how to use dried mushrooms, groundnuts and various kinds of bulbs such as wild artichokes and wild onions and also herbs as food. Herbs or simples were likewise used to cure insect stings, snakebites and other ills. The Indian probably saved many a white person's life by teaching him how to use herbs for medicine. Of course you know it was the Indian that showed the white man the use of tobacco.

Indians seem to have had no fear of snakes except the rattlesnake. The Dutch traveller, Van der Donk told how he had seen them run after snakes, take hold of them behind their heads, and bite them in their necks to kill them. But of the rattlesnake they were fearful and if they were going far into the fields or woods they would carry with them an herb called rattle-wort which was a sure cure for rattlesnake bite.

"I witnessed," says Van der Donk, "an experiment made on Long Island with snakewort on a large rattle-snake, when a person chewed a quantity of green plant and spit some of the juice on the end of a stick which was put to the nose of the snake and it caused the creature to thrill and die instantly."

There was a greater variety of birds and animals to be found here in the early days than there are today. The Indian hunter shot wild turkey, heath hen, quail, partridges, pigeons, geese, ducks and other wild fowl for food. He trapped beavers, bears, raccoons, squirrels, rabbits, foxes, otters, muskrats, skunks, wolves and deer not only for food but for skins to make his clothing or to trade with Indians in other parts of the country.

An Indian never killed an animal just for what we call "the sport of the thing."

Their dogs were half-tamed wolves and no Indian village was complete without half dozen or more of them trailing after the children. They made themselves useful about the house killing the rats and chipmunks and field mice who found it very easy to get into a house made of bark.

There were no horses or other domestic animals such as cows, goats, pigs, chickens and cats until after the white men brought them.

The sun was the Indian's clock. It told him how the

INDIAN WOMEN CULTIVATING CORN

The Indian man thought it beneath him to have anything to do with agriculture. These hard tasks were left for the women and girls.

hours of the day passed and as the moon changed he reckoned how the month was going. The year he divided into four seasons as we do spring, summer, autumn and winter. They seem to have bothered themselves very little about how old they were, which after all is a very wise thing. However they may have done some rude form of counting since flat stones have been often found with knicks along their edges not deep enough to have been saw teeth but apparently made to reckon numbers. Not long ago such a stone was found near Wantagh.

They were fond of all sorts of games and dances and much given to playing jokes on one another.

Indians seem to have talked very little when they were with strangers but to have been much given to conversation and speech making when among their own tribe and had any question to settle.

They were most polite about this because we read, "when Indians met in council every one, even the women were allowed to speak and while anyone was speaking no one might interrupt, though he chose to speak for hours. When he was finished he was asked if that was all he had to say, and until he assented no one else was allowed to address the meeting."

CHAPTER **4**

THE INDIAN'S TOOLS AND
WHAT HE MADE WITH THEM

In the days before the white man came to Long Island the Indian made every tool and implement he used.

Furs and skins were prepared with tools made of bone or flint and were sewn together with needles made from the curved rib bone of some animal. Queer clumsy needles they must have been, six or eight inches long, sharpened at one end and an eye bored half-way the length of the needle. The fibres of plants or sinews of small animals served as thread.

Master Wooley says, "The Indians make thread of Nettles pulled when ripe, pure white and fine and likewise another sort of brownish thread of a small weed almost like a willow which grows in the woods, about three foot high, which is also called Indian Hemp of which they likewise make ropes . . . which wear as strong as our hemp, only it wont endure wet as well. They twist their thread upon their thighs with the palm of their hand."

In summer the boys and girls gathered the Indian hemp from the stream sides and the broad tough grasses that grew in the marshes. These were woven into fish nets and sacks as well as mats to cover the houses. Great care must have been taken in preparing this hemp because we are told "Their cordage is so even, soft and smooth that it looks more like silk than hemp."

William Woods in an old book called New England Prospects, written in 1634 says, "In summer they gather flaggs of which they make matts for houses and hemp and rushes with which they make curious baskets . . . these baskets be of all sizes from a quart to a quarter in which they carry their luggage."

They made their baskets also out of white oak and maple splints. Sometimes sweetgrass was woven in to make them look pretty and smell nice. Traps to catch eels were woven out of white oak splints in the shape of big funnels. Large bowls called mortars, in which things were crushed or chopped or mixed, were made from the section of the trunk of a sour gum or pepperidge tree, because the wood of both was tough. These were hollowed out by laying on live coals and scraping out the burned part until it was deep enough.

Crocks and pots for cooking were made from clay mixed with finely powdered shells or stone to make it tougher, pure clay being very brittle. These pots were often ornamented with designs made by scratching the wet clay with a stick or pressing a clam or scallop shell along its edge. They were usually shaped with a pointed bottom so they might more easily be propped up with stones while in use. Also the heat of the fire would more quickly cover a pot of such shape.

If a pot became cracked it was not thrown out but a hole was bored in either side of the break and the parts held together with a thong. In this way it was still strong enough to be used for storing dried things.

You may see some of these pots at the Museum of the American Indian in New York and also in the Woodland Hall at the American Museum of Natural History, also some of their rooms and scrubbing brushes made of wood shagged out at the end.

Forks and knives to eat with were quite unknown to the Indian. He used his fingers or scooped up his food with a clam shell or a gourd split in two like a ladle and such manners for him were quite as good as we think ours are. Gourds were also used as drinking cups.

We can hardly picture an Indian without his bow and arrow, nor could he think of himself without them and he therefore took good care of both of them after they were made.

To shape a bow with a stone knife was no simple matter after he had found just the right hickory sapling

MAKING POTTERY

Notice the rounded bone in the large crock.
This was used to grind meal. In the background can be seen the famous 'longhouse'
in which several families lived together. The
foreground shows miscellaneous tools.

T.F. Spry

to use. It must be a sapling so supple that it would bend double without breaking. Sometimes the wood for a bow was buried for a time to season or harden it. Then great care must be taken to choose a sinew strong enough to string it, one without any flaws.

Men usually had several bows and many arrows. The shafts of their arrows were of wood tipped by a feather and their arrow points were beautiful bits of work chipped from hard stones like flint or chert, the points and the edges being very sharp.

Arrow heads of all shapes and sizes are still being found on Long Island. Most of them are made from quartz because quartz pebbles were easy to find on the beaches. Sometimes one is found made of stone never seen in these parts. Then we know it must have been an arrow traded by some Indian from another part of the country or the stone for making it had come from off Long Island.

Arrow points and other Indian relics that are found near the surface of the ground probably were those thrown away after the white man came and offered them steel knives, guns and metal cooking utensils, etc. Those buried deep are far older.

The most common arrow heads found on Long Island are those made in the shape of a triangle with a stem.

By means of this stem the point could be so firmly fastened to the shaft by a twisted thong smeared with resin (tree gum) that it was not lost when the arrow was drawn out.

Those shaped like a triangle without any stem were war arrows. This type of point was very loosely fastened to the shaft so that when the shaft was pulled out of the wound the point was more likely to stay in and thus make the wound more deadly.

Other stones, shaped like long arrowheads, are found. These no doubt were knives and scrapers. Drills were also made out of sharpened flint.

Hoes, hammers and hand choppers were made from various sizes of round stones. A hollow or groove was worked into them on either side so they might more easily be held in the hand, or between the fingers. Axes and heavy hammers were fastened to long handles by twisted thongs or eel skins. An axe was worked down on one edge until it formed a blade. The Indians called this tool a tom-a-hea-kan and from that the white man formed the word, tomahawk.

Sometime ago a farmer was plowing his field near Jamesport, Long Island. He found one of these stone axes beautifully made. It weighed more than nine pounds.   You may see it yourself when you go to the Historical Society at Riverhead.

Some tools were made without grooves. These were called celts.

Think of the skill and patience it must have taken to peck some tools into the right shape with only another sharpened stone to work with!

Fire was one of the Indian's greatest tools when it came to building his canoe.

CHAPTER 5

THE INDIAN CANOE

Long Island Indians did not make canoes out of birch bark as the Indians of the lake districts did. Their canoes had to be heavy enough to go on rough water, so they made them of the trunks of good straight trees, usually pine, oak or chestnut, and it was a long job that took both patience and skill.

When the canoe was to be made the Indian went into the woods with his stone axe, his implements for making fire, his bow and arrow and a plentiful supply of corn cakes and prepared to stay for some time. On such trips their food was sometimes just parched corn meal. A quarter of a pound of the meal was enough to last them for the day. When hungry they just ate a handful and drank a little water.

Once again an old traveller has told about the building of a canoe so well, that I am going to give you his words.

"The manner of making their boats," he says, "is very wonderful. First they choose some long and thicke

BUILDING A CANOE

The large trees were felled by lighting controlled fires around the base. The trunks were also hollowed out by burning and scraping. At the right end of the canoe you can see a portion of the handle type arrangement. There was also such a handle at the other end.

tree according to the bigness of the boate which they would frame and make a fire on the ground about the Roote therof, kindling the same by little and little with dry moss of trees and chipps of woode that the flame should not mount up too high and burn too much of the lengthe of the tree.

"When it is almost burnt through and ready to fall they make a new fire which they allow to burne until the tree falls of its own accord. Then burning off the top and boughs of the tree in such wise that the bodie of the tree may keep its full lengthe, they then raise it up upon poles laid out crosswise on forked posts at such a reasonable height as they may handsomely (easily) work upon it.

"They then take the bark off with certain shells . . . then make a fire according to the lengthe of the tree, singeing at both ends. When they think it is sufficiently burned, they quench and scrape away with shells. Making a new fire they burn it again and so they continue sometimes burning, sometimes scraping until the boat has sufficient depth."*

Slow work you see, but though the canoe might be narrow when finished it was sturdy and well balanced enough to float on the rough waters of the Sound or the Great South Bay or the Ocean.

---

*Adapted from the account by Theodore de Bry in Grand Voyages Pt. 1, 1590.

Heavy loads were often carried in these boats and as many as six men paddled the ones that were used in hunting whales off the South Shore. When they went whaling two canoes were usually taken since it was dangerous business.

The missionaries, Danker and Sluyter said the Canarsie fishing canoe was "without mast or sail and not a nail in any part, though it is sometimes forty feet in length."

They used a short, heavy wooden paddle and stood upright when paddling which took great skill in balancing. Our canoes are pointed at both ends. The Indians seemed to have shaped their canoes with curious long bows and sterns almost like handles. No doubt these handles were of use when fishing and also made the canoe easier to carry from place to place over narrow paths.

Roger Williams gave a description of a Rhode Island Indian building his canoe which must have been very much like the way it was done here. He says, "I have seene a native goe into the woods with his hatchet carrying onely a Basket of Corne with him, and the stones to strike fire. When he had felled his tree, he made him a little house of the bark of it. He puts fire to his tree and allows the burning of it with fire in the midst in many places. His corne he boyles and hath the Brook by him and sometimes angles for a little fish, but so he continues burning and hewing until he hath within ten or twelve days (lying there at his work all alone) finished, and (getting Hands) launched the boate with which afterwards hee ventures out to fish in the ocean," and Roger Williams goes on to say:

"It is wonderful to see how they will venture in these canoes and how (being oft overset as I have myself been with them) they will swim a mile, yea, two or more safe, to land ... When sometimes in great danger I have questioned safety, they have said to me. Fear not if we be overset I will carry you safe to land."

The Montauk Indians often travelled in their canoes as far east as Boston and west to New York. Some of their canoes were large enough to carry eighty persons. It is said the one belonging to the Sachem Wyandanch required the strength of eight men to land it from the water and one time it was damaged at Gardiner's Island because there were not enough people to drag it out of the sea.

In the Museum of Natural History in New York you may see the remains of an Indian canoe found in digging a street some sixty years ago. There is another in the Museum of the American Indian. At the Museum of City of New York, and the Children's Museum in Brooklyn, you may see fine models of Indian villages with Indians working on a canoe.

CHAPTER 6

WAMPUM AND
HOW IT WAS MADE

The Indians of western United States wove beautiful blankets and made fine pottery, baskets and silver work.

The Indians of Long Island minted the money that was used as a means of exchange in all parts of this country.

This money was in the form of a bead called wampum, and was made from the shells of the clam or quohaug or the conch and the periwinkle, all of which were found in vast numbers on the beaches of the mainland of Long Island and on the shores of Shelter Island and along Gardiner's Bay. Indeed, the Indians called the Island Meht-anaw-ack or the Earshell Country and later the Dutch called it Sewan-hacky meaning Land of the Shells.

The name wampum came from the Algonquin word, wamp-umpe-ag. Wamp meant white, umpe meant string of shells and ag was for the plural to show there were many beads.

MAKING WAMPUM

The various types of shell fish around Long
Island's shores provided the Indian with
food. The shells served as ornaments and
tools and when made into wampum became
a form of money.

Wampum was a very precious article to the Indians as you will see and the making of it was really a fine art.

The men gathered the shells and the women fashioned them into beads. Great quantities of these shells were often gathered in summer and stored up to be made into wampum in winter.

With only a rude stone tool to work with, the Indian woman clipped the shell to the proper size, drilled a hole through it lengthwise and then polished it by rubbing on a large stone. Then the beads were strung on strings of hemp or sinew.

There were two kinds of wampum, white and black (blue). The black was the most valuable. It is said that "a black bead the size of a straw, bored lengthwise and well polished was the gold of the Indians." Do you wonder?

John Josselyn, who visited this country in 1633 says, "Their beads are their money, of which there are two sorts, blue and white. The first is their gold and the latter their silver."

Black wampum was usually made from the shell of the clam. If you break open a clam shell you will see that for about half an inch from the joint, the shell is blue black. This was the part the Indians used in making dark wampum, Suck-an-hock it was called from the Indian word suki, meaning black.

Among the steel tools which the white man brought was a little awl known as a mucksuck. The Indians saw at once how much more quickly this little awl would drill holes in shells than their own tools made of bone or stone and they were ready to give the white man almost anything in exchange for them, even land. So we find the word muxes, as it seems to have usually been written, often mentioned in land transfers.

In exchange for the land where East Hampton now is the Englishmen gave the Montauk Indians among other articles "one hundred muxes."

The Indian deed for Huntington dated 1653 says the Indians are to have "30 muxes and 30 needles."

The deed for Mastic Neck, Brookhaven dated 1657 says that Wyandanch was paid together with other items, "40 muxes and 40 needles."

In almost every deed for land along the shore the Indians were allowed to keep the right to "fish for the shells to make the wampum."

The white man thought of wampum as we do money but to the Indian in all parts of the country it meant far more than that. Every tribe had its Wampum Keeper who was either a sachem or an older man of the group.

For tribes to exchange wampum was like exchanging gifts. It showed that faith and friendship existed between the two or else that some very important question was to be settled or treaty signed.

When wampum was given in this way it was usually in the form of a belt, many strings being woven together This was done with great care and only skilled women were called upon by the Wampum Keeper to make belts.

Each belt was woven with special lines or figures or patterns ordered by the Wampum Keeper. Each of these, in the way it was placed upon the belt, meant something to the Indian, and the one who received it could read the belt as you or I might read a printed message.

At other times the wampum was merely strung on strings. One string or many might be tied together and the message sent by an Indian runner. "Sometimes the strings were tied to little sticks which were notched in such a way as to show the number of days before an answer was expected."

Should a messenger come before a council without bringing a belt or wampum strings, his own words were considered valueless.

Black wampum was exchanged in the council of the Sachems when death occured.

White wampum meant peace. White belts were always exchanged between tribes when peace was declared.

Should war be declared between tribes that had already exchanged white belts "then those who made the war painted their white belts red or perhaps even soaked them in blood before they sent them by a war runner. The tribe receiving it might send back its own white belt stained red."

If one Indian killed another, revenge was taken at once by the victim's family. Sometimes a family tried to make peace by giving a white belt "to wipe away all grief and establish the path of peace."

Thus wampum played an important part in the ransom of life. Captives were ransomed with wampum when all else failed.

Wampum was also used as an ornament, woven into skirts, strung into necklaces, tablets and earrings.

John Josselyn says, "They drill and string them to adorn the person of their sagamores and principal men and young women, as belts, girdles, tablets and borders for the women's hair, bracelets, necklaces and links to hang in their ears."

"Sometimes when a great compliment was intended for a chief, a wampum collar was woven for him that he might wear it around his neck or drape it over his shoulders."

After the white man came and found that wampum was the only common means of exchange, both the

English and the Dutch agreed to set a regular price upon wampum. Three black beads were worth a penny and six white beads the same amount. English merchants gave the Indians "10 shillings for a fathom of their white wampum and as much again for blue."

In 1673 six white beads equalled a penny (or silver as the Dutch called it) and three blue the same amount.

CHAPTER 7
THE INDIAN'S LANGUAGE

Every large tribe throughout the country had its own language. Sometimes it was so like that of a neighboring tribe that they could understand one another. In other cases the language was quite different.

The Long Island Indians spoke the Algonquin language, which was the same as generally spoken by all the tribes along the eastern coast of North America.

Like other Indians they had no written language. Their legends, their religions, lore and their history were all passed on from father to son, from man to man by word of mouth, which no doubt accounts for the fine long memories most of them had.

Sometimes they made records of hunting or fishing trips by scratching pictures on a smooth stone (a few such stones or pictographs, as they are called, have been found on Long Island but not many).

Each Sachem or chief seems to have had his own mark or sign that stood for his name. It might be a bow or arrow, a pipe or a hatchet or many other things. We find many deeds drawn up by white men and signed by such Indian marks.

Had it not been for some of the white men who cared enough about the Indian's language to use their words and put them down, you and I would have no way of knowing any of the words spoken by these people who lived here so many generations ago.

The Rev. John Eliot, who came as a preacher to New England in 1631 wanted to know the Indian language well enough to be able to teach them and to preach to them in their own tongue.

There were no books to help him and very few Indians able to teach him.

At last he met a young Indian by the name of Cockenoe.

Cockenoe belonged to the Montauk tribe and as a little boy had been taken prisoner by the Indians of Connecticut during a raid and later was bound out as a servant to a New England farmer who taught him to speak English.

Cockenoe had the gift of being able to help the white man and the Indian understand one another's language, in fact his name means Instructor or Interpreter and he was usually spoken of as Cockenoe de Long Island.

He went to live with John Eliot and helped him so much that Eliot not only was able to speak the language but translated the Lords prayer and the Ten Commandments and many parts of the Bible into the Algonquin tongue. He also wrote an Indian grammar and a primer and taught Cockenoe how to write in English.

Cockenoe also helped the white settlers to establish the bounds of various pieces of land which they bought from the Indians. Wyandanch, chief of the Montauks, spoke of him more than once as "My agent, Cockenoe." He must have known something about surveying because we read that in 1657 he laid out and marked the bounds of Hempstead, Huntington, Smithtown and Lloyds Neck and for these services he received

1 coat

4 pounds of powder

6 pounds of lead

1 Dutch hatchet and seventeen shillings worth of wampum.

In 1652, the year Shelter Island was settled by white people, a dispute arose between them and the Indians. The Indians claimed they had given the white men the right to live on only a part of the island.

Cockenoe went over to Hartford, Connecticut to plead the cause of his people before the Commissioners of the United Colonies of New England. "As no deed could be found showing that the Indians had sold their right to the Island" the case was decided against the white men and they were obliged to buy the land from the Indians a second time.

During the winter and the spring of 1651 and 1652 he lived on an Island off Westport, Connecticut. For years afterwards this island was called Cockenoe's Island on maps and coast charts. Cockonoe married the sister of the Grand Sachem, Wyandanch.

By the time Cockenoe was an old man many Indians had learned to speak the English language. The last we hear of him is in 1697 when with other members of the Montauk tribe he signed his name for the deed which gave their land to the people of East Hampton. "For all our tract of land at Montauket" it read.

How much longer Cockenoe lived we do not know nor where he lies buried among the hills of Montauk.

More than a hundred years later in 1791, Thomas Jefferson and James Madison made a journey on horseback and visited the home of General Floyd at Mastic. From the Indians living near by at Poosepatuck in the town of Brookhaven they gathered a list of 162 words in the Algonquin language.

Seven years later, 1798, John Lion Gardiner who lived on Gardiner's Island made a list of many words used by the Montauk Indians.

Here are a few of the words and what they mean if you want to learn for yourself.

saunchem —king
sacunska—queen
wonnux—white man
wonnuxk—white woman
mewauchum—Indian corn
mausqueseets—beans
ausgoote—pumpkin
tobaugsk—tobacco
niep—water
mashuee—canoe
yunks quash—young woman
squashees—little girl
weenai—old woman
cheesk—small
chiauk—large
wedaums—roast corn
seaump—pounded corn

And to count you say,

nucquit	1
neeze	2
nisk	3
yuaw	4
nepaw	5
conma	6
nusus	7
swans	8
passecucond	9
pyunck	10

Almost the only thing left of the Indian on Long Island today are local names. Names such as Canarsie,

Rockaway, Quogue, Syosset, Shinnecock, Ronkonkoma. Patchogue, Amagansett, Montauk and many more that you have grown so used to hearing and saying that they no longer sound strange.

Many of these names have been brought together in a book written by William Wallace Tooker called Indian Place-Names on Long Island.*

Mr. Tooker made a great study of the Algonquin language and in this book he not only gives us place names but tells the Indian meaning of them as well, "that we may have a proper remembrance of those who tenanted the woods and sailed the seas before us."

*Reprinted in 1962 by IRA J..FRIEDMAN, INC.

CHAPTER **8**

THE INDIAN'S RELIGION

The Indians who lived here so long ago worshipped out-of-doors, like all other Indians.

The out-doors was part of their religion for they had many gods or Manitos to pray to. These were spirits, spirits of the four corners of the earth and the winds that blew from them—spirits of the sea and the sky, the rain and the sun. Other spirits guarded their wigwams and their fires and there was a spirit for their beans, their corn, their pumpkins and their harvest in general and a spirit for the day as well as the night.

Over them all were two great Spirits, one good and another evil.

They made long prayers to these spirits, the same prayers their fathers and grandfathers before them had said and the Indian child learned them word for word from their parents or from some of the elders of the tribe.

In almost every Indian village was a witch-doctor or "Sheman" who might be either a man or a woman. Some tribes had a medicine man. These witch-doctors

T.F.Spry

A WITCH DOCTOR

Here we see an Indian Powwas, or witch
doctor mixing herbs for some potion. Notice
the pot with the pointed end stuck into the
ground. The shape also helped when stones
were used to prop up the vessel and also
made heating much easier.

were wise in the use of herbs for healing and the Indians firmly believed they were able to cast a spell strong enough to drive away evils of all kinds. The witch-doctors in this part of the country seem to have been called Powwas.

These Powwas were very powerful. They told the people what the spirits required of them, when a feast should be held, when presents should be made to old people, when sacrifices should be made to the gods and what kind.

The best sacrifice of all was supposed to be the fin or tail of a whale which they roasted. If a whale was found cast up on the shore, the Indians made it a time of great religious rejoicing.

Powwas claimed to hold interviews with the spirits in dreams. Evil spirits in particular were supposed to appear to them in different forms and through voices in the air.

If an Indian was sick he believed he had an evil spirit working in him and the witch-doctor was called upon to cast it out.

At times a whole village would hold a strange religious ceremony called a powwow to drive away evil spirits. A powwow often lasted several days and after the white people came they objected to them so strongly that in 1665 a law was passed which forbade the Indians to hold a powwow within the white man's territory.

Indians placed great faith in dreams and visions. When a man or a woman had a dream he or she told it like a story around the fire in the evening. Sometimes it was chanted in a song.

Singing was a very important part of an Indian's life. He believed that song in some way reached the many unseen spirits that might help him. He would very often make up his own songs and would use them while praying to the Manitos.

Before he went out to hunt he sang that he might be lucky and bring back much game. When he felt himself in danger he sang to gain courage. When women gathered herbs or planted corn they sang that the herbs might be helpful in healing and that the corn might grow to a great harvest. In his sports, in his games, when he was sad or when he was happy the Indian had his song for the occasion.

Every Indian boy at the age of about twelve was supposed to prepare for his Spirit Dream. This meant he must stay quite alone for several days and fast. During that time he must watch for his Spirit Helper. This might appear in one of many ways or forms. It might also come in a Vision Song. It might be a bird or an animal or even a person but when it came the boy would know that it would help him all the rest of his days. It would be like another god to pray to and he must never forget his Vision Song.

Before beginning his fast his mother told him what he must do and what he might expect.

Sometimes a boy fasted at home with his face painted black but more often he went away and remained alone night and day waiting for his dream. Should the dream fail to come he must try again at some other time.

If the vision came he returned home feeling very serious and thoughtful, ready to follow his Spirit Guide. He was no longer a boy but a young man and his next step was to go before the elders of the tribe to be taught the tribal laws.

There is a story of a young Indian boy named Siaka and his Spirit Vision that I am going to tell you even though Siaka lived a very long way off from this part of the country.

This is the way he told his dream.

"I painted my face white and went to the hilltop. At each of the four points of the compass I place a buffalo robe and some tobacco. These offerings were to show that I desired messages from the direction of the four winds and was anxiously waiting to hear the voice of some bird or animal speaking to me in a dream . . . An owl appeared in my dream. Just before day-break I saw a bright light coming toward me from the east. It was a man. His head was tied up and he held a tomahawk in his hand. He said, "Follow me" and in an instant he changed into a crow. In my dream I followed the crow to a village. He entered the largest tent. When he entered the tent he turned into a man again. Opposite the entrance sat a young man painted red who welcomed me."

After this Siaka was taught a Vision Song. These were the words.

"At night may I roam, against the wind may I roam,
   When the owl is hooting may I roam,
At dawn may I roam, against the wind may I roam
   When the crow is calling may I roam."

The owl told Siaka to look toward the west whenever he made a prayer and help would be granted and he would have a long life.

Siaka faithfully followed the owl, his Spirit Guide, all his life and became a brave warrior and did honor to his tribe and his people.

An Indian believed that after one died his soul travelled westward a long way off into the presence of Saw-wonn-un-toh the god of the west from whom came the harvest.

If he had been good in this world then he should enjoy himself forever, singing and dancing and having good hunting. But those who had done wrong, though they went the to same place, must work hard forever at the kind of work that was never finished like carrying water in a sieve or digging out a canoe with a round stone.

When an Indian was buried many things belonging to him were buried with him, sometimes even his dog. All other things which had been his were given away and his wigwam pulled down.

The name of the one who had died was never spoken again in the presence of his family.and he was mourned for about a year. During this time the women of the family kept their faces painted black and no one sang or danced or made jokes or laughed.

After a year the name of the one who had died might be given to someone else outside the family. To receive a name in that way was thought to be a great honor.

CHAPTER 9

INDIAN CHILDREN

The first name an Indian child was called by was a pet name given by its mother while the baby still hung on her back strapped to a board to make its little body grow straight.

Later a child was given the name he or she would be known by for the rest of their lives. This name might come from the place where they had been born or they might have done something brave and their parents would give them a name to remind everyone of their brave deed.

When this second name was given a family party was held with much dancing and eating and exchanging of gifts.

Family names were not handed down by the Indians as they are with us. No child was ever named for his father or mother; this would have brought bad luck.

Boys often took names for themselves after their

INDIAN YOUTH DUCK HUNTING

Long ago, as now, ducks were plentiful on
Long Island. The Indian boys had to learn
how to be independent at an early age. Even
a seven year old had to be able to shoot down
a flying bird with his own bow and arrow.

Spirit Dream. These were usually bird or animal names, such as, Little Owl, Young Deer, Flying Eagle.

Indian parents seem to have loved their children dearly and petted them a great deal. Many of the songs that have been passed on to us from the Indians in all parts of this country are lullabies Indian mothers crooned to their babies.

They may have been petted but they were not spoiled because Indian children were obliged to learn to take care of themselves when they were very young and be brave and endure cold and hunger and pain and fright without cry or complaint.

Food they might eat in plenty but they also learned how to go without food for days at a time when they were travelling or when food was scarce.

They must learn to keep silent before grown people and pay respect to the old people of the tribe. They must help with the work, gathering rushes, picking berries or digging clay for their mother's cooking pots. And as they worked their dogs ran around their heels, for every Indian family had a dog or two.

Even as babies they were taught to swim and almost as soon as they could stand they were taught to lift up one foot after another while their mother beat time and so gave them their first lesson in dancing.

By the time a boy was seven he must be clever enough with his bow and arrow to shoot a bird while it was flying.

He must be able to catch fish in his hands with fingers so skilful that they could feel the fish under stones where they hid.

Though Indian children did not have to go to school and learn to read and write they had to study many other things.

"They learned the ways of Nature. They were taught to know the trees, the plants, the wild fruits, wild animals and their ways, birds and their habits, insects and their doings.

A boy was expected to learn the cry of the wild creatures, to imitate the call of the wild turkey, the quack of the duck and the honk of the goose. He had to be trained in the use of various weapons ... the dagger, the spear, the scalping knife, and to make and sharpen all implements of which he made use."

By the time a boy was grown he knew all those things He knew also how to be still in the woods and trained his eyes to see and his ears to hear.

There is the story of the "amusement of some Indians when a white settler admitted that he could not tell the difference between the patter of a dog's feet or the walk of a wolf"which to the Indian seemed a simple thing to know.

Besides learning the laws of Nature the boy must learn the language of his tribe, their legends, beliefs, prayers and social customs, learn them word for word from the lips of some older man in the tribe.

A girl was not taught these things but she must be skillful in the ways of the household and the farm fields. She must learn to cook and clean skins and make wampum, weave baskets and nets and sew and care for babies. She must hoe the ground and plant the beans and corn and pumpkins. Indians believed that things grew better when a woman planted them.

From the time a child hung on a board on his mother's back to make him grow straight he was being taught things that would prepare him for life when he grew up. Every game he played or song he sang or dance he danced had some meaning to an Indian.

Young and old they loved to play games, especially the men.

Guessing games and games of chance were great favorites for most Indians were born gamblers. They used a kind of dice made from bones.

One indoor game was to guess where objects were hidden under a row of moccasins, another was Jack Straws.

Out of doors they played a kind of football (the girls were very fond of this game) and in winter they skidded sticks over the ice in the same way we play hockey. They played another game much like LaCrosse.

There is a picture in a very old book showing Indians playing a game that must have been something like tennis or basket ball. Little children had games of various sorts. Often they sang with them. In one of these a row of girls stood one behind the other, each girl with her hand on the shoulder of the girl in front. Thus they went around the village singing, "The deer follow one another."

For another game they sat in a circle and each little girl tickled the hand of the girls next to her singing "I catch but I cannot hold you" until they all rolled over laughing.

A favorite game was one called ,"pretend" in which they imitated the actions of the grown folks.

Singing, dancing and story telling were not only amusements they were part of an Indian's religious worship. They thought it pleased their gods to dance and sing for them.

The music of their dance songs sometimes was made up of only two or three notes and very few words, sung over and over again, now fast, now slow, each one dancing for himself.

A dance often lasted for an hour or more without stopping. A story too might go on from one night to another for a long time and the same stories were told over and over so that boys and girls grew up with them and in time were able to tell them to their own children.

CHAPTER 10

SOME LEGENDS AND STORIES
OF THE LONG ISLAND INDIANS

Counting the Indians

How many Indians were there on Long Island before the white men came?

No one knows.

One of the early settlers of East Hampton asked a very, very old Indian if he knew, and the old man answered; "Once there were as many as the spears of grass" and he stretched his hand over the ground. "If you can count these, then you will know how many Indians were here when I was a boy."

Turf and Twig, Giving Away the Land

When an Indian came to sign the deed that was to give away his right to a piece of land, he always brought with him a sod of earth and a twig from a tree and gave them both to the new owner. This was his way of wishing the new owner good luck with his crops.

101

Indian Summer

Cold frosty days came in early November and found Indians still camped near the sea where they had been all summer digging clams, building canoes, gathering rushes or picking berries.

"It is time to go back to the woods where it is warm," said the children. But the old folks shook their heads.

"Not yet" they said, "this will pass. It is just squaw Winter. Indian Summer has not yet come. Before the real winter comes we will have Indian Summer."

A few days later the air grew warm, almost as warm as June and a haze-like blue smoke hung over everything.

This the old people said was because a great Manito, son of the West Wind who travelled over the earth each autumn had once more visited his people the Algonquins to see how life was with them.

As he passed by he stopped to rest and built a fire which warmed the earth once more and the smoke as it drifted down over the hills and fields and the seashore looked like a beautiful blue haze.

This was Indian Summer.

The Magic Footprints

Once, long ago there was a Montauk chief so tall and so swift of foot that he took but three steps to cross from North Shore of Long Island to the South Shore.

One print of his foot was left behind him on Orient Point. Another was left behind him on a big rock on Shelter Island. The third and the last one before he jumped into the ocean he planted on Montauk.

They must have been magical footprints because the story goes that they fit the feet of all who found them though they might be as big giants or as small as babies.

The Devil's Jump

The Devil seems to have left his footprints in many places on Long Island.

A powwow was once held on Montauk Point to drive away an evil spirit who seemed to be working trouble.

In the midst of the feast and excitement the Evil One knowing he was outwitted and wanting to make his escape, jumped from off a granite rock leaving his footprints on the rock and three more on the ground where he had lighted.

There are those who will tell you they know where those footprints are today.

The Devil's Rock

Off Orient Point is a boulder called Devil's Rock. Once there was a huge footprint to be seen on its top. The way it came there was this.

One winter long before the time of white man, much snow fell and to add to their troubles a strange sickness broke out among the Indians.

Medicine men did their best but they failed. Then the Indians knew the Evil One was in their midst.

They held a powwow to drive him out. The Devil hid in the wood but it was no use. They found his great shadow lurking there and with a mighty yell drove him before them to the water's edge.

For one second the Devil's foot rested on the rock and then his huge form made the sky dark as he sprang across the Sound.

The Devil and the Stones

In the old old days, so the Indians used to tell, the fields of Long Island were covered with big rocks and stones. This made it hard for the Indians to plant their corn.

Just across the Sound the fields of Westchester and Connecticut were smooth and green, quite free from rocks.

One day the Devil was prowling about greedy as always and he decided to take both Connecticut and Long Island for his own and to drive out all the Indians living in both places.

He would help himself to Connecticut first, the fields looked so fine and green.

But in Connecticut he met his match. The Indians there had no mind to quit their homes in such haste and they chased the Old Boy before them to a place on the shore called Throgs Neck.

The tide was out which was lucky for the Devil and he beat his retreat across the Sound to Long Island stepping from rock to rock laid bare by low water.

Down he sat in the middle of the Island at a place called Coram. First he sulked, then he planned revenge.

Presently he rose and gathered together all the big rocks he could find the length and breadth of Long Island and piled them in a great heap near Cold Spring Harbor.

Then did the Devil take the rocks and hurl them one after another over on to the smooth green fields of Connecticut and Westchester.

This was a true story the Indians said. They vowed they could show the white men the print of the Devil's foot on the spot where he had stood to throw the stones.

Be that as it may perhaps this is the reason why there are so many stone walls around Connecticut fields today and why people on Long Island who want to make rock gardens send across the Sound to get the stones.

Sachem's Hole

Many, many years ago on the road between Sag Harbor and East Hampton there was a spot by the side of the road known as Sachem's Hole.

This is how it got its name.

Po-gatt-a-cut, Grand Sachem of Long Island, died on Shelter Island and was carried to the Indian burying ground on Montauk Point. Legend says he was carried upright.

On the road between Sag Harbor and East Hampton the bearers rested their burden on the side of the road near the third mile stone.

When they lifted the Sachem's body up again they found a hole in the ground where none had been before, a hole about a foot deep.

For almost a hundred years, as long as Indians lived to pass that way the hole was kept clean. No one of them passed without stopping to pick up out a stone or a twig or stray leaves that might have fallen in because the spot was sacred to them.

When the Turnpike between Sag Harbor and East Hampton was laid about the year 1860, Sachem's Hole was plowed up and lost except for this story.

Whooping Boys Hollow

Another spot on the Sag Harbor road north of East Hampton was called Whooping Boys Hollow.

Few cared to pass that way at night.

The son of an Indian Chief was said to have been murdered there and after dark the place was still haunted by his cries.

The Enchanted Lake

In the middle of Long Island lies a big lake still called by the name the Indians gave it, Ron-kon-ko-ma.

In the dryest weather the water of this lake never falls for it is fed far down beneath by hidden springs of fresh water.

But in the Indian's time Lake Ronkonkoma with its shining white sand banks was thought to be enchanted. It never went dry the Indians said because it had no bottom.

It was more than enchanted, it was sacred and under the protection of the Great Spirit. Hundreds and hundreds of fish flashed through its clear waters but they belonged to the Great Spirit, too and so no Indian ever fished in the Lake Ronkonkoma.

Betty's Dream

Once upon a time a poor Indian woman named Betty took her baby on her back and a bundle of rushes under her arm and started off to walk across Hempstead Plains to Westbury to see if she could find some one who wanted to have a new seat made for a chair. In exchange for this work she hoped she might get some meat for her husband who was sick.

The day was warm and Betty grew so tired that at last she sat down among the tall grasses to rest.

Then Betty had a dream.

A gate opened and she was in a garden, the most lovely garden she had ever seen. There were many people in the garden planting and working with their hands deep in the earth.

The trees above her head were loaded with fruit and when she held up her hands, fruit dropped into them that tasted "for goodness and sweetness sweeter than honey" and made poor Betty young and strong again.

When she awoke the baby was still asleep on her back and she picked up her bundle of rushes and walked on across the Plains with light free feet.

Every home welcomed Betty that day and wanted her work and she received meat in plenty for her husband and returned home rejoicing.

The Fire Place

The Fire Place, a small settlement known sometimes as Setauket South and now as South Haven took its name from the Indians.

This spot was a camping ground where the Indians met to exchange wampum and goods and to renew their council fires.

In the days when whales were plentiful off the South Shore of Long Island a whaling crew made its headquarters at Fire Place.

Their huts were on the outer beach and during the whaling season the men lived on the beach and watched the sea day by day ready to put out to sea when they saw a whale blow.

Their supplies came from the mainland and a watch was set for the signal fire to send a boat over when supplies were low. When a light flashed up at night the crew would row across the bay heading directly for the light. After they had shipped their supplies the fire was put out and another was kindled on the beach to guide them back.

The fires were lighted at Fire Place Neck.

Josiah Beman

There was a Montauk Indian by the name of Josiah Beman who was a preacher. A sad man he must have been for long before he died he wrote these lines which were to be placed upon his tombstone.

"Here Josiah Beman lies,
    And nobody laughs and nobody cries.
Where he's gone and how he fares
    Nobody knows and nobody cares."

Canoe Place

Mon-go-tuck-see, once a chieftain of the Montauks was a giant in size.

The story goes that he dug a canal from Great Peconic Bay to Shinnecock Bay so that the Indians might pass through with their canoes.

His canal is deep and wide now, wide enough for deep draft boats to go through but traces of the canal still remain in the name of the locality, Canoe Place, and legend has it that winds that blow about Montauk Point still sing the praises the giant chieftain.

There are other stories about Canoe Place.

At that spot the Indians are known to have had a portage (a path) over which they might carry their canoes a short distance overland between Great Peconic Bay and Shinnecock Bay. This saved them from having to paddle their canoes all the way around Montauk Point where the waters were usually rough.

The white men saw the wisdom of this and two hundred years later dug a canal at Canoe Place to bring their boats through. We now call it the Shinnecock Canal.

In Mattituck there was a lane known as Canoe Path where from creek to creek the Indains crossed with their canoes until they reached the shores of Mattituck Creek.

This canoe path with the one at Canoe Place gave the Indians a short way to travel by water from the North to the South side of the Island.

The Story of Jason

Many years ago when Sag Harbor was a big whaling port and many cooper's shops were kept busy making barrels to hold the whale oil, an old Montauk Indian called Jason Hoopte used to visit the town.

When the boys saw him coming they would shout, "Here comes Jason" and then run and hide in a doorway to watch him go by, tall and swarthy with his long hair floating in the wind. The sight of Jason always scared them a little and made the cold shivers run down their backs.

As soon as he was well passed they slipped out and followed him at a safe distance.

When Jason reached the cooper's shop he was greeted with much heartiness. With a great clatter the workmen put aside their wedges and hammers and wooden hoop drivers and joining hands made a ring around Jason and began to dance.

How they danced and shouted while the boys crowded to the window to watch the fun. They had seen the dance before and never wanted to miss it.

Round and round they danced and capered like men

bewitched until out of breath they stopped and wiped their sweating faces with their arms and shook hands with Jason who ambled out and took his way to Smith's Tavern on the Dock.

Mannatto Hill

Mannatto Hill lies in the center of Long Island in the township of Oyster Bay.

The Indians gave it its name. They said it was where the Great Spirit of the Algonquins lived.

This spirit could do strange and wonderful things.

Once, they said, there was a great drought. The Indians were dying for lack of water.

In their distress they prayed to the great Spirit Sachem on Mannatto Hill and he told them to shoot an arrow into the air and where the arrow fell to dig.

This they did and where the arrow fell they found a spring of sweet water.

Gunnunk's Garden

On the north neck of Montauk Point half way between Fort Pond and Culloden Point, at the foot of a range of hills known as Rocky Ridge is a swamp and a piece of land near by called Gunnunk's Garden.

The swamp and the garden took their name from an old squaw who made her home there.

She was called Luce Gunnunk and she was a very tall woman.

Daniel Tredwell's Diary

A hundred years ago a boy named Daniel Tredwell lived on the South Shore of Long Island and he kept a diary of the things he did from day to day. Here is a story of a trip he made with his father.

Friday, Sept. 20, 1839

"We went out to the Bay yesterday with my father— on the way out we passed many Indian shell heaps bleached as white as snow, which they resemble at a distance.

Some of them on the banks of the creek extend from fifteen to thirty feet upon the bank and under the water.

My father is greatly interested in these shells —and especially the one on our farm.

He has preserved with great care all arrowheads, stone axes, bones of animals, etc. He knew these shells to be the remains of Indians who had inhabited this country.

There was a difference in the shells found on the farm and those of the mounds nearer the ocean.

Those on the farm my father claimed were the remains of clams found opened for food. These on the shore were the remains of wampum manufacturie.

He knew this to be so because a large number of the shells on the farm had never been broken while on the other mounds a search failed to reveal any whole shells.

Among the shells found on the farm were many skimmer clam shells. None of these shells were found on the wampum heap. The shells of this clam were used by the Indians in working and hilling their corn. Later the white people used them as skimmers in taking the cream off the top of the milk. That is how it got its name skimmer.

The old people in our neighborhood said that the shell heaps on our farm were the remains of a great tribal feast or powwow —when a gigantic clam-bake was servd to the thousands of braves."

At another time this same boy writes:

"This day we spent searching and digging for Indian curiosities in the old shell heaps in the swamp lot —

We were rewarded with a few knives, arrowheads, as Mr. Potter the teacher called them, all imperfect specimens, that is having been used and more or less broken."

The following story of Isaac's Grotto was told by Miss Cornelia Hosford who lived at Sylvester Manor on Shelter Island.

Sylvester Manor had belonged to Miss Hosford's family for many generations.

Two Indian Princes or Isaac's Grotto

"About 1834 after the emancipation of slavery in New York State, two little Indian princes (the descendants of Pogatticut, Yoho and Wyandanch) named Isaac Pharoh and William Pharoh were what was called "bound out" to Mr. Samuel Smith Gardiner of Sylvester Manor until they should be twenty years old.

They were lively little rascals like any other little boys and one of their duties was to polish the mahogany dining room table. They had each a brick wrapped up in soft cloths and wet with something used for polishing. With these they rubbed and rubbed the tables. If they were left alone for a minute they ran out of doors and chased and tumbled over each other until they were caught and brought back to their work.

Later they were promoted to waving a peacock feather fan over Mrs. Gardiner's head during meals to keep off the flies.

These boys slept in the garret at the Manor House and on the rough boards today are drawings of ships made in chalk and also cut with a knife by William Pharoh who ran away to sea before he was free.

Isaac Pharoh remained with the family until his death.

Mr. Gardiner at one time brought a servant from New York, a very handsome and fascinating Irish girl with whom most of the young men on the Island, including Isaac, promptly fell in love. She used to make patchwork quilts and Isaac went to Greenport and bought some gayly printed cotton which he cut into squares for her. These she did not like and refused to look at, which made Isaac very mad indeed.

About 1840, Isaac constructed a grotto in a cliff on the east side of the creek. It was hollowed out and boarded and lined with stone and here in hot weather the young ladies of the house and their guests took their reading and embroidery and spent their mornings. There was no bridge across the creek then and the reed-grown sand flats had not yet appeared. The water of the harbor splashed gayly against a pebble beach at their feet and over a stretch of blue water they watched for Mr. Gardiner's sail boat to come back from Greenport and go up the creek and anchor off the old stone bridge.

Years passed and this grotto fell in and was lost to sight although it was remembered and talked about to the children of the next generation.

The summer of 1923 being confined to the upstairs piazza of the Manor House for several weeks I began to long to see the boats and the harbor. First I had fifteen elm trees about thirty feet high cut down but still the harbor was concealed by a fringe of trees. Then I had two more stretches of trees and shrubs cut down and still the harbor was not plain enough so I had the lower branches of an Austrian pine removed making it look like the stone pines of Italy. Now I could see the races and the pleasure boats in the harbor.

When I could walk out again to see what had been done Behold! where the trees had been cleared there was the ruins of Isaac's lost grotto."

The Winged Head

The last ghost said to have appeared to an Indian on Long Island was called the Winged Head.

The legend goes that one night a widow sat alone in her wigwam and in a little fire near the door she was roasting acorns and taking them from the burning embers and eating them for her evening meal.

In the doorway appeared a ghost, Winged Head. She did not see him.

He watched what she was doing and grinned.

Then the ghost stealthily reached out one of his claw-like hands and snatched some small coals from the fire and thrust them into his mouth, thinking that was what the widow was eating.

With an awful howl of pain he rushed out of the wigwam, disappeared across the plains and neither he nor his like were ever seen again.

CHAPTER 11

AFTER THE WHITE MAN CAME

The first white men visited Long Island in 1609.

They did not stay long that time but sailed away to make further explorations.

About twenty years later Dutch and English people began coming in numbers to make their homes here.

For the most part the Dutch settled the western half of the Island and the English the eastern part.

From the time of their coming the history of the Indians here is short and sad.

Though some of the white men tried to understand them and their ways of living, there were many like the Dutch minister who wrote to Holland in 1628, that the natives were "uncivil, and stupid as garden poles and served nobody but the Devil." He could not understand their speech so he said it was "a made-up childish language."

On the whole the white men wanted the Indians to live the way they did and the ways of the white men fitted the Indians no better than the white men's clothing did.

Strong drink that might agree with an Englishman or a

Dutchman was like so much poison to an Indian and made him do all manner of bad things. The white man's chief weapon, the gun, was dangerous in the hands of an Indian.

Many Indians left Long Island to live with tribes in other parts of the country. Many became sick —a dreadful epidemic of small pox in 1662 carried away a big number—others were killed. By the time of the Revolutionary War very few Indians were left on Long Island.

Today there are few fullblooded Indians on Long Island. Most have intermarried and are scattered about, or live near Mastic or on a small reservation in the Shinnecock Hills.

The first white settlers found 13 or more tribes on Long Island.

The Montauk tribe at the far eastern end of the Island was the strongest. The name Montauk means "the fort country" and before the day of the white man the Indians built a fort there on the west side of Nominick Hills overlooking Napeague Harbor. Later, in 1661, a new fort stood on what is still called Fort Hill, overlooking Fort Pond. Sharp eyes can still find traces of this fort today as well as Indian graves. Their land originally extended from what is now the Town of East Hampton to Montauk Point. This included Gardiners Island.

The Montauk Indians were tall and straight and fine looking. Their chief was Wyandanch, but over him was his older brother, Po-gatt-a-cut, who was Grand Sachem of all Long Island tribes except the Canarsies.

Small troubles arose between early settlers and the Indians but the only real battle between them occured in 1653. This was at a place called Fort Neck located on the south side of Long Island toward the western end, where the Massapeagues had built a fort.

Captain John Underhill, an Englishman in the employ of the Dutch, attacked this fort and more than three hundred Indians were killed. Before the battle all the Indian women and children were sent to a small island off shore called Squaw Island.

After the battle many Indians were buried on the brow of a hill near the fort. Years later a road was made over the spot and workmen found the earth red, quite red. People said it was because so many Indians had been killed there.

Grand Sachem Pogattacut lived on the south side of Shelter Island in a place still marked as Sachem's Neck on old maps.

As Grand Sachem his word was law. Without his consent no Long Island Indian might sell land or have dealings with other tribes.

The Indian sold his land for all kinds of things.

A piece of property near Glen Cove was sold for

    3 coats
    3 shirts
    3 hatchets
    3 hoes
    3 fathoms of wampum
    6 knives
    2 pairs of stockings
    2 pairs of shoes.

Another went for

    12 coats, each coat to be 100 yards of tucking cloth
    20 pounds of powder
    20 dutch hatchets
    20 knives
    10 shirts
    200 muxes (a tool used in making wampum)
    5 pairs of handsome stockings
    1 good Dutch hat and a great fine looking glass.

One of the early deeds for a sale of land on Long Island bears the mark of Pogattacut, Wyandanch and two more of their brothers, Mo-mo-weta, Sachem of the Corchauge tribe and Nowedonah, of the Shinnecocks.

This deed was drawn on April 29, 1648, when these chiefs signed away to the white men the land now covered by the township of East Hampton.

For this the white man paid

    20 coats
    20 hoes
    24 hatchets
    24 knives
    24 looking glasses
    100 muxes.

According to the wording of this old deed, the Sachems asked that their people "might keep the right to fish on any or all of the cricks and ponds and hunting upp and downe in the woods . . . they giving the English inhabitants noe just offence or injuries to their goods or cattle. Alsoe they are to have the finnes and tayles of all such whales as shall cast upp . . . Alsoe to reserve libertie to fish in convenient places for shells to make wampum Also Indians hunting any deer they should chase into the the water, and the English should kill them, the English should have the body the Sachems the skin."

Rights such as these were often granted to the Indians, but at other times they were forced to agree "to move away and never return to live."

There are many records of land transfers written on Long Island — too many to tell about. Most of these deeds are strange to look at and hard for us to interpret.

We have to remember that some of the early white settlers knew little about reading or writing and less about spelling. Even those who could write well found the Indian names and phrases hard to understand and harder still to spell. They just had to take them by sound which accounts for the reason why names and words are spelled in so many different ways.

Take the case of a land deed written for Huntington.

The Indians who lived where Huntington now is were the Matinecocks.

The man who wrote out the deed for the First Purchase spelled the chief's name, Ras-e-o-kan.

Three years later a deed was signed for more land and that time the chief's name was signed Ash-a-ro-ken. It was no doubt the same man and a fine long stretch of beach near Huntington carries the name to this day, though we do not know it that is the way the chief would have called it.

In the last Indian grant made in Flushing the Sachems claimed the right of "cutting bullrushes forever."

In the deed for the south part of the Town of Oyster Bay the Indians were to have the privilege "of hunting and gathering huckleberries as they shall see cause."

When the land in the Shinnecock Hills was divided, the Indians were allowed "to plow and plant and cut timber for fences and fuel, also to cut flags and bullrushes and such grass as they usually make their houses of and to dig around nuts. The white people have the right of highway and pasturage."

These land transfers made more trouble than almost any other thing. An Indian could not understand ownership in the same way that the white man did. Because he had sold his land seemed no reason to an Indian for giving it up. Property lines puzzled him, too, and he never could understand the need of fencing his cornfield although he was angry when the white man's cattle broke through and destroyed his corn.

About the year 1653, Pogattacut died and Wyandanch became Grand Sachem in his place.

Wyandanch was the strongest and wisest ruler the Long Island Indians ever had. He was the last of the really Grand Sachems.

He lived with his tribe on Montauk Point and with him was his wife, Wichikittawbut and his son Wyancombone and a daughter, Quashawam also called Momone or Heather Flower.

The first white man to settle within what is now the town of Easthampton was an Englishman, Lion Gardiner. He was an engineer and a soldier and came from Saybrook, Connecticut where he had built a fort.

In 1639, he bought the island we now know as Gardiner's Island from the Indians.

Lion Gardiner named his island the Isle of Wight. Later its name was changed to Gardiner's Island. Here on the 14th of September, 1641, his daughter, Elizabeth, was born. She was the first English child to be born in this part of the country.

Before settling on his island Lion Gardiner made friends with the Montauk Chief, Wyandanch. It was a friendship that lasted all their lifetime and kept peace between the natives and the white men.

The early settlers had much to thank Lion Gardiner for.

So great was the faith of Wyandanch in his friend that when he died he appointed Lion Gardiner guardian of his son, Wyancombone, until he should come of age.

Remember Lion Gardiner as a fine gentleman and a brave soldier and when you go to East Hampton pay your respect to his monument in the old burying ground between the windmill and the pond.

In the early days the Montauk Indians were allied with the Pequot Indians of Connecticut. This tribe was often in trouble with the other tribes on the mainland, especially the Narragansets. When this happened they promptly called on the Montauks for help.

In 1653, Ninnigrate, chief of the Narragansets, waged a war with the Long Island tribes which lasted off and on for several years. During this time had it not been for the wisdom of Wyandanch and the help of the people of East Hampton the Montauk Indians would probably have all been wiped out.

In one of these raids led by Ninnigrate, the Narraganset Indians surprised Wyandanch and his family in the midst of a marriage feast for his daughter. Their wigwam was set on fire, their food was stolen and destroyed

A BEACHED WHALE

Roasted whale fins were the best sacrifice that
could be made to the gods. Finding a beached
whale was a time for great rejoicing.

and many young Indians killed. Among them was the bridegroom. Worst of all the bride was captured and carried away.

Once again Lion Gardiner proved himself a true friend for he arranged to ransom the daughter of Wyandanch and had her brought back to her people.

In gratitude for this Wyandanch later gave to Lion Gardiner all the land we now know as Smithtowm.

On April 10, 1655, Wyandanch gave the people of East Hampton the right to pasture their cattle on Montauk Point for seven years. He also said should the Montauk Indians ever want to sell their precious land they might sell it to East Hampton. This was about 9000 acres, mostly thick woods of white and black oaks with fine springs and fresh ponds.

During the years 1658-59 many Indians died of plague. Wyandanch died at this time, too. It is said he was poisoned. With him went the glory of his tribe. No one knows where Wyandanch lies buried.

His son, Wyancombone, was then nineteen, not old enough to succeed his father as Grand Sachem, so he and his mother, Wichikittawbut, ruled together and she was known as the Sunq Squaw. Lion Gardiner was his guardian and advisor.

In 1662 another and worse plague came among the Indians. The people of East Hampton feared the disease might spread among them so for a time all Indians were forbidden to enter the town and any white man who went among them was whipped and fined.

In this plague Wyancombone died.   He was then 22.

His mother and sister, Quashawam, lived after him. Later Quashawam married a Pequot Chief and had a son whom she named Wyandanch.   Shortly after this the old enemy of the Montauks, the Narragansets, began making trouble again.   Knowing how weak they had become, the Montauks put themselves under the protection of the people of East Hampton, as they had done more than once since Wyandanch's death and finally sold them their land. The land was dear to them, so dear that it was sold with the agreement that they might one day buy it back.

Long before the white men came, Indians had gone after whales off the South Shore beaches in their dug-out canoes with huge wooden harpoons so they were able to show the newcomers many things about whaling.

At first the white settlers were afraid to trust them with whaling tools.

We read in 1643, Robert Bond, who was a blacksmith in Southampton, was ordered "not to make for Indians any harping irons (harpoons) or fishing irons which are known to be dangerous," however, the white people got bravely over that and the Indians were part of almost every group of whalers and were very skillful.

Later when men from Long Island began going to sea for whales Indians made up part of the crew. Young Montauk and Shinnecock Indians shipped on voyages to the South Seas for whales.

In 1670, two Indians, Towsacum and Phillip, hired themselves to Josias Laughton to whale off Mecox for each season. Their pay was "3 Indian coats, 1 pair of shoes (or a buck neck to make them) 1 pair of stockings, 3 pounds of shot, ½ pound of powder and a bushel of Indian corn."

As the years went by, the Indians who stayed among the English and Dutch, gradually fell more and more into their ways of living. They learned to speak their language and many of the younger ones became household servants or farm hands.

In those days a servant was usually apprenticed to a master. That is, he belonged to him or served him without pay for a certain number of years and in return was taught a trade.

There were many like the Indian boy, named Toby, who came from Southold. He was apprenticed to a man in Brookhaven for three years to learn the trade of carpenter.

During the time his master promised to give him "enough meat, drink, washing, lodging and proper clothing." At the end of two years Toby was to have a present of "two new suits of clothes from head to foot, one suit to be for working days and the other for holy days. Also one broad axe, one hand saw, one square, one pair of compasses, one broad chisel, one narrow chisel, one gage, one augur and the sum of forty shillings."

But during the three years, Toby, like all other bound servants, must obey his master. He might not go away night or day without his master's permission He must do his master no harm, nor allow others to do him harm by stealing from him or otherwise. More than that, Toby might not play cards nor dice nor marry while he was in his master's employ.

At the end of three years Toby was free to set out and earn a living for himself.

Jophat, another Indian, "engaged to live and work truly and faithfully with Richard Siede from this time, June 28, 1670, until the 29th day of September and in return Richard promises to give him a coat and a pair of Indian breeches and a peck of corn and a shirt."

The older Indians lived out their lives as peaceable, quiet people who would not beg but would steal when pinched by hunger. They lived on small patches of ground which they tilled. They fished and picked berries in the summer and trapped in winter and made baskets and fish-nets for the fishermen.

Small quarrels of course occurred between Indians and early white settlers and townfolk banded together for protection but we also read that in the days of hardship for the white people the Indians often came to their rescue when food was scarce.

Troubles seem to have been many between the first white settlers of Southampton and the Shinnecock Indians, from whom they bought their land in 1640.

The deed for the sale of Southampton was signed on December 13, 1640. In it, for "16 coats and three score bushels of Indian Corn, to be paid upon the last of September 1641, the new settlers were granted eight square miles of land from sea to sea—beginning at the place where the Indians hayle (haul) over their canoes from North Bay to the South." This was the Indian portage at Niamuck which the white settlers called Canoe Place.

Perhaps some of the trouble came from the Englishmen forbidding the Indians to do many things. For example, they might not dig for ground nuts, one of their main foods.

Indians were at first forbidden to enter the town at all. No one might sell food to them. Their dogs were ordered to be killed. No wonder they rebelled and once in revenge burned several Southampton houses. Later Indian women and "ancient men" were permitted to enter the town but they must obtain tickets.

As the years went by, however, one by one of these restrictions were lifted so that by 1675 the feeling between the Englishman and the Indian had grown quite friendly.

As white settlements increased on Long Island laws were passed to protect the Indians. It was against the law to sell them either firearms or strong liquor since both brought great trouble to them. Also land must not be taken from them without consent of the Governor and the Sachems.

CHAPTER 12

SOME FAMOUS INDIANS

On the South Shore of Long Island at Woodmere, there is a monument to an Indian. His name was Cull-u-loo and he was one of the Rockaway tribe.

Where Broadway and Linden Streets now meet in Woodmere was the house in which Culluloo lived and died as a very old man. Few of his tribe were left.

Culluloo hunted and fished for a living but the boys in the neighborhood remembered him best for the stories he told. One of these boys, Abraham Hewlett, never forgot him and many years after had a monument erected to Culluloo over the place where the Indian had lived.

When Broadway was widened the monument was taken to Willow Road where you may find it now and read the tribute placed there by his friend

HERE LIVED AND DIED
CULLULOO TELEWANA
A. D. 1818

The last of the Rockaway Iroquois Indians Culluloo who was personally known to me in my boyhood, I owning the land have erected this monument to him and to his tribe.—ABRAHAM HEWLETT, 1888.

Many white preachers tried to teach the Indians the white men's belief in God.

The first minister in East Hampton, the Rev. Thomas James, translated some chapters of the bible into the Montauk tongue and preached to them in their own language.

Azariah Horton of Southold, Long Island was a missionary among the Long Island Indians from 1741-1750 and lived for some time among the Montauks.

One of the most famous preachers to the Indians on Long Island was one of their own people. His name was Samson Occom and he came from Connecticut about 1755. He was the first Indian preacher to go to England to preach and brought back a considerable sum of money for the establishment of schools for the American Indians.

Samson Occom was a teacher as well as a minister and he started a school for the Montauk Indians.

His first winter at Montauk he had about thirty scholars in his day school and gave lessons at night to those who could not come during the day.

He had a way of his own of teaching the alphabet by sight as well as sound. He cut the letters out of paper and pasted them on cedar shingles. Then he would pile the shingles one on another and the child must find a chosen letter from the pile.

At other times he played a kind of game. The cedar shingles were stood up in the ground in a row. Then a child's name and a letter was called and he must run and get the letter and bring it to the teacher.

On Sundays Samson Occom preached three times. He visited the sick, wrote letters for them and was called upon for all manner of help.

Samson lived on Montauk with very few household articles to bother him—just a few cooking pots, his tools and a suit of clothes that he only wore when he went among the white men. Besides this he had a library of a dozen or more books that he used to carry in a saddle bag.

Poor Samson seems to have had bad luck with all his horses.

He bought a mare on which to ride to and fro among his people but she was lost in the quick sands. He bought another but she was stolen. The third horse died of distemper and the fourth had a colt and then broke her leg and the colt died. After that Samson Occom gave up trying to own a horse and went about his business on foot instead.

He later married Mary Fowler, one of his pupils in the Montauk school and from that time on Samson seems to have lived in a better state.

Besides teaching and preaching and writing hymns and poems, Occum turned his hand to all manner of things to support his family He worked in wood, making spoons, gun-stocks, pails and churns.   He also learned how to bind books and bound them for the English people in Easthampton and other places.

When Sir William Johnson of Johnson Hall, west of Albany, Commissioner of Indian affairs in America, visited East Hampton, Amagansett and Montauk in the summer of 1773, he and his party stayed for some time, at Samson Occom's house.

Another Indian preacher was Peter John, born at Hay Ground, Bridgehampton. He gathered little churches together at Wading River, Poosepatuck, Islip and Canoe Place, He was buried at Poosepatuck.

His grandson, Paul Cuffee, born in 1757, preached and worked among the Indians of Montauk and Canoe Place.

You may see the grave of Paul Cuffee today to the left of the main highway as you cross the bridge over the railroad after leaving Hampton Bays. On the grave stone you may read these words.

"Erected by the New York Missionary Society in memory of Rev. Paul Cuffee, and Indian in the Shinnecock Tribe, who was employed by the Society for the last thirteen years of his life on the eastern part of Long Island where he labored with fidelity and success. Humble, Pious, indefatigable in testifying to the Gospel of the Grace of God, he finished his course with joy on the

7th day of March, 1812, aged 55 years and three days.''

The story is told that for many years after Paul Cuffee died his people used to come to his grave and pray for help in trouble and help often came if they were honest.

In September 1773, a Boston minister, Rev. David McClure, visited the English minister of East Hampton Mr. Buell. He was taken out to visit the Indians on Montauk Point and he wrote in his diary.

''A number of their young men were out on a fishing voyage. Their houses made a curious appearance—conical in shape with an opening at the top to let out the smoke and let in the light. The Indians were glad to see us and treated us kindly. The next morning I preached to them. They understood English and all but the aged speak well . . .

In Fowler's wigwam we wrapped ourselves in our cloaks . . . and lay down on a mattress or spreading of dry flaggs and slept comfortably.

Some young men went out early on the water and brought in a fine bass which we had for breakfast with a tolerable dish of tea. The Indians expressed great thankfulness for our visit.''

During the Revolutionary War Shinnecock Indians were in Capt. John Hulbert's Company which marched with a flag to the Continental Congress in Philadelphia in 1775. Long Island Indians also went as guides and scouts with the troops that were marching to the northern part of the state.

The so-called Queen of the Poosepatuck Indians, who lived near Mastic, was called Betty. The chief was a half-breed named William Cooper. Sometimes he worked for General Smith but, being lazy and a rover by nature, he often roamed away.

Just before the War of 1812 when British Naval officers were capturing Americans to serve on their ships, William Cooper was taken up one day at the port of Sag Harbor and pressed into service aboard a British ship.

While this ship lay in the English Channel, the American ship Constitution was also there and Cooper escaped by swimming and was taken aboard the Constitution. Later, on December 29, 1812, when the Constitution was engaged in a battle with the Java Cooper was killed.

In later years two large families, the Fowlers and the Pharohs, remained of all the Indians on Montauk Point. Mrs. Maria Banks called the "last Queen of the Montauks" died in 1936.

In 1819 their "King" called Stephen died and David Pharoh stood in his place as head of the family. David lived until the year 1878. He was called the last King of the Montauks. One of David's sons was named Wyandanch after the famous Sachem and old settlers still tell about this boy who often came to East Hampton selling berries.

Stephen Pharoh, another member of the family, was commonly called Talkhouse. He was born in a wigwam on the side of a little hill where the old and the new Fireplace roads meet. He lived with his mother, Mary (or Molly) until as a lad he was sold to Col. Parsons of Fireplace for $40.

Molly's wigwam was burned and for a long time afterwards bones and stones and Molly's broken cooking pots showed where the wigwam had been. When the road was cut through all traces of the place were lost, though people to this day call the section Molly's Hill.

Stephen, or Talkhouse, was a great walker. It is said he walked from Brooklyn to Montauk in a day and often stepped from Montauk to Bridgehampton and from there to Sag Harbor for dinner and back.

When an Indian walked from one place to another he seldom followed an open road but cut straight across country "as the crow flies," travelling at a good pace.

Talkhouse lived to be sixty years old and was buried on Montauk on a hill east of Lake Montauk not far from the old willows and stones that mark the last Indian dwelling places. If you have sharp eyes you may find his grave marked with a stone and a faded flag. The flag is there because Talkhouse served with the Union Army in the Civil War.

Most graves in the Indian Field Cemetery are marked only by rough field stones set in deep circles in the tangled grass. The earliest burial places were not marked but were carefully levelled off lest enemies come and rob the graves for scalps. These graves on Montauk would have been lost but for a fence put up by the town long ago.

On December 11, 1876, a number of the finest young men of the Shinnecock tribe were lost in a wreck off Mecox Point.

A sailing ship, called the Circassian, was stranded on a sand bar in the midst of a blinding storm of snow and sleet. The Coast Guard went out and rescued the crew. All but the officers and the ship's carpenter were sent back to New York. They stayed behind until the wreckers could get the ship off the reef.

Among the wreckers were a big group of Shinnecock Indians. In the midst of their work another big storm came up. The ship was broken in two and all but a very few of the young Shinnecocks were drowned. Thus perished the best of what was left of the true Long Island Indians.

From that time on their numbers grew less and less because so few men were left.

Many people in Southampton today remember Mary Rebecca Kellis, or Aunt Becky as she was called, who died at Shinnecock in April 1936.

Aunt Becky was the last of the full-blooded Shinnecock Indians and lived to be over a hundred years old.

She was born on the Shinnecock Reservation and was the daughter of David Bunn, a whaler.

More than a hundred years ago, Aunt Becky became a servant in the household of David Thompson, a direct descendant of Lion Gardiner, the Indian's friend in the old days. She stayed with the Thompson family as a faithful member of the household for many years.

During her long life Mrs. Kellis taught school at Shinnecock Reservation. At one time she was a servant in the family of the former President Theodore Roosevelt. Aunt Becky remembered him as a little boy and said he was a "weak little fellow."

Aunt Becky had reason to remember the wreck of the sailing ship Circassian that I have told you about, because her brother, Frank Bunn, was one of the young Indians who was drowned.

In 1703, the Shinnecock Hill region had been leased back to Indians by the settlers who had bought the land from that tribe. They held it until 1859 when a large section of the Hills once more was sold and just a small part left to the Indians as a reservation.

This they still hold. The land belongs alike to the few that are left. They have their church and a little schoolhouse. They pay no taxes.

For many years there has been a reservation on Mastic Neck. It belongs to the Poosepatuck Indians. They have 170 acres, a church and a schoolhouse.

This tract of land was deeded to these Indians and their chief, Tabacus, by William Smith, the Lord of the Manor of Saint George "to be lived upon and planted forever."

When their crops were gathered in they were to give William Smith and his family who should come after him, "two yellow ears of Indian corn."

From that time until a few years ago the two ears of yellow corn were carried to the Manor House every year.

Every June the Indians at Shinnecock gather together all that is left of their people for a meeting or a picnic according to the old custom of holding a powwow.

Indian barns are still hidden away under woody growth. Fragments of shell heaps may still be discoveed along the shore and the plow and the spade still turn up arrow heads, stone knives or paint cups in Long Island fields if you have eyes sharp enough to see them.

These and their names and their few descendants living about the Island are all we have left of the Long Island Indians today.

INDEX

For the sake of discussion, it is convenient to divide prenatal development into three periods: the predifferentiation period, the period of the embryo, and the period of the fetus. The distinction, however, is only conceptual. The conceptus, throughout gestation, is in a continual state of orderly biochemical and structural transition during which new constituents are being formed and spatially rearranged. At any time in the total span of development, these ongoing processes can be subtly deflected, severely perturbated, or abruptly halted, resulting in various embryopathic consequences.

A. Predifferentiation Period

The interval between the fertilization of the oocyte and its implantation in the endometrium is approximately 6 days in both rat and man; it is referred to as the preimplantation or predifferentiation period. During this time, the ovum, while remaining relatively undifferentiated, undergoes a series of mitotic divisions changing from a one-cell zygote to a multicellular blastocyst. The blastocyst, suspended in uterine fluid, is actively transported through the fallopian tube to the uterine cavity. Drugs contained in the fluid readily pass into the intercellular spaces of the embryo. Agents that produce malformations later in development, however, are generally thought to be without teratogenic effect during this early period. It appears that exogenous substances are either toxic to the entire embryo resulting in its death, or if toxic to a limited number of cells, the "regulative" potentialities of the embryo result in repair with no apparent damage (Langman, 1963).

Behavioral effects have nonetheless been reported following the administration of drugs during the predifferentiation period in rats (e.g., Werboff & Havlena, 1962). While such early treatment might produce effects by acting directly on the blastocyst, other mechanisms could account for these observations. For example, it has been shown that administration of either phenothiazines (Gauron & Rowley, 1969) or morphine (Friedler & Cochin, 1972) prior to conception subsequently alters the growth and behavior of the offspring. Even though the drug has presumably cleared from maternal plasma, preconceptual drug exposure alters the maternal environment in some as yet unknown way to modify offspring development. Another possibility is afforded by the so-called "ambush effect;" agents with a relatively long half-life may be cleared slowly from maternal and/or embryonic fluid. If, for example, such agents are administered during predifferentiation, just prior to organogenesis, they may persist long enough to produce effects at later susceptible periods. Thus, most workers agree that the predifferentiation period is not a susceptible period for teratogenesis. Whether it is similarly refractory for producing behavioral effects awaits further evidence.

B. Period of the Embryo

The interval between early germ-layer differentiation and the completion of major organ formation (organogenesis) is referred to as the period of the embryo. This phase of development, characterized by the formation of complex, multicellular tissues and organs of diverse origins and functions, begins soon after implantation and, in man, continues through approximately the eighth week of gestation. The comparable period in the laboratory rat extends from about Day 8 through Day 14 of gestation. (The laboratory rat is born around Day 22.) During organogenesis, the embryo is maximally susceptible to gross structural malformation if exposed to teratogenic agents. The nature of the defect will depend both on the effect of the agent on embryonic cells and the gestational age at the time of exposure.

Although it is beyond the scope of this chapter to discuss embryopathic mechanisms extensively (for a discussion of irradiation effects, see the chapter by Hicks and D'Amato, in this volume), an appreciation of how these agents produce structural and, ultimately, behavioral effects derives from a fundamental understanding of such mechanisms. For our purpose here, we might say that to understand the effect of a teratogenic agent is to understand first, what the agent does to embryonic cells (usually, populations of proliferating cells), and second, what developmental processes the cells are carrying out at the time of exposure.

J. G. Wilson (1973) has formulated a paradigm of teratogenic action presented in Table I which describes how teratogenic drugs initiate a sequence of pathogenic effects beginning at the cellular level. Interference with some fundamental aspect of cellular physiology, such as protein synthesis or enzyme activity leads, for example, to cell death or a failure of cellular interactions. J. G. Wilson (1973) suggests that "... these initially different types of pathogenesis may converge into a relatively narrow channel of abnormal development, for example, one that would lead ultimately to insufficient cells or cell products to carry out morphogenesis or to carry on function at the site of the final defect" (p. 25).

In other words, an agent may have a very specific toxic action at the cellular level. It might, for example, kill actively proliferating cells while sparing those in the resting phase or only those cells in a particular phase of the cell cycle. In either case, however, populations of cells are killed, and are therefore not available to participate in the developmental process. The result is a structurally defective embryo.

The nature of the defect will depend on the gestational age of the embryo at the time of exposure, or more specifically, the embryological processes or events that are correlated with the gestational age of the conceptus. "Critical periods" are recognized for various organs and systems for a given species

TABLE I

SCHEMATIC SUMMARY OF INITIAL CELLULAR REACTIONS AND DIFFERENT TYPES OF PATHOGENESIS INTO A FINAL COMMON PATHWAY.[a]

Mechanisms	Pathogenesis	
Initial cellular reaction(s) within germ cells, embryos, or fetuses:	Abnormal developmental sequence	
Mitotic interference	Early pathogenesis initiated as one or more of the following:	Final common pathway
Altered nucleic acid functions	Cell death	
Mutation	Failed cellular interaction (induction)	Insufficient cells or cell products to carry out morphogenesis or to carry on function
Chromosomal nondisjunction	Reduced biosynthesis	
Lack of substrates, precursors, etc.	Impaired morphogenic movement	
Lack of energy sources	Mechanical disruption	
Enzyme inhibition	Tissue disruption	Resulting in final defect(s) expressed as one or more of the following:
Changed membrane characteristics	Altered differentiation schedules	Intrauterine death
Osmolar imbalance		Malformation
		Growth retardation
		Functional deficit:
		Neurobehavioral
		Hormonal

[a] After J. G. Wilson (1973).

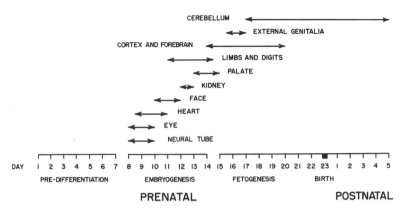

FIG. 1.   Critical periods in the pre- and postnatal development of the laboratory rat (*Rattus norvegicus*).

and refer to the fact that, in general, "particular organs and parts are chemically and morphologically developing at their own paces and according to their own timetables, and each therefore has its characteristic temporal shifts in proneness to damage. . . ." (Kalter, 1968, p. 5). Critical periods for the laboratory rat are shown in Fig. 1. This describes a continuum of differential susceptibility that extends from Day 8 of gestation through the first several days of postnatal life. A teratogenic agent administered about Day 9, for example, will generally give rise to a pattern of gross structural malformations of the brain, spinal cord, eye, and heart. The same treatment administered a few days later, about Day 14, will usually produce a very different pattern that includes cleft palate, limb and digit defects, but none of the defects noted earlier.[1]

With increasing gestational age, there is a corresponding decrease in susceptibility to teratogenesis; agents administered after Day 15 or so, as organogenesis becomes complete, do not produce gross defects. They can, however, produce subtle damage in the central nervous system by interfering with histogenesis in those areas of the brain indicated in Fig. 1.

In summary then, the processes of cell division, differentiation, and migra-

---

[1]Contrary to older conceptions suggesting a precise correlation between developmental events at the time of exposure and the specific nature of the malformation, it is now recognized that the critical period for producing a given malformation does not necessarily correspond to the time of rapid organogenesis of its anlage, i.e., the earliest discernible precursor of the structure. Within limits, different agents may produce the same malformation at different gestational ages, sometimes before the appearance of recognizable anlage (e.g., see Shenefelt, 1972). As J. G. Wilson (1973, p. 123) points out, the notion of critical periods is useful as an approximation of the time of inception of abnormal development but should not be taken as a definitive scientific principle.

tion are of fundamental importance during the pre- and early postnatal period. And, at different times in development, the dividing cell is carrying out a beautifully integrated and exquisitely timed sequence of events— initially, the creation of specialized cells and tissue underlying organogenesis and later, as these processes continue, the building of the cerebral cortex and cerebellum, and the "wiring" of their interconnections with other regions of the brain. Until these processes reach their conclusion, they will remain vulnerable to damage caused by drugs.

1. LETHALITY, MALFORMATION, AND BEHAVIORAL EFFECTS AS A FUNCTION OF DOSE LEVEL

Because studies of drug teratogenesis involve two or more mutually interacting biological systems—the mother and offspring—dose-response relationships are highly complex. The effects produced can include death, malformation, growth retardation, and functional impairment, and these can occur either alone or in various combinations. Moreover, the nature of the effects will depend on a multitude of variables including the agent, gestational age, genotype, species, diet, season, and so on.

J. G. Wilson (1973) has formulated a dose-level relationship commonly observed in experimental studies of teratogenic agents that is shown in Fig. 2. Just above the dose level for producing embryotoxic effects, there is a relatively narrow teratogenic range with a relatively steep slope. As the dose is increased through this zone, the frequency of malformations, growth retardation, and embryonic death increase. Further increases produce a high frequency of embryonic death while teratogenicity appears to decrease. Fewer malformations are seen, however, because many defective embryos die before term. The higher doses eventually reach levels that are lethal to the mother.

An obvious constraint in studying behavioral effects produced by teratogenic agents administered during the period of the embryo is that many of

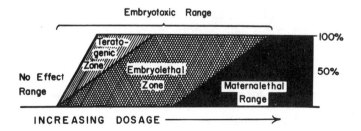

FIG. 2. Diagram of the toxic manifestations shown by embryos and maternal organisms as dosage of a teratogenic agent increases. From J. G. Wilson (1973).

the central nervous system malformations typically induced (e.g., exencephaly, spina bifida) are lethal postnatally. Butcher and his colleagues, however, have studied the behavioral effects of two agents teratogenic to the central nervous system by administering what he called "subteratogenic" doses; that is, dose levels at or just below the teratogenic threshold (that area in Fig. 2 immediately to the left of the "teratogenic zone" designated "no effect").

In one study, Butcher, Brunner, Roth, and Kimmel (1972a) administered 100,000 IU/kg of vitamin A on Days 9, 10, and 11 of gestation in rats.[2] Learning ability was tested beginning at 50 days of age by requiring the offspring to learn the escape route from a water-filled multiple T-maze. During five escape trials on each of two successive days, drug-treated offspring made significantly more errors than the control animals. By the third and last test day, however, there appeared to be no difference in the number of errors made by either group. Thus, the vitamin-A-treated offspring appeared to be impaired in learning the escape task, but with continued training their error rate diminished to the control level.

In a similarly designed study, Butcher, Vorhees, and Kimmel (1972b) administered 250 mg/kg of salicylate on Days 9, 10, and 11 of gestation. Offspring were tested as in the first study except that they were given two additional days of testing during which they were required to learn the backward path through the maze. As in the experiment with vitamin A, the salicylate-treated offspring made significantly more errors than the control animals over the 5 test days. However, unlike the first experiment, in this study acquisition data (i.e., error frequency as a function of training) were not provided. Thus, except for the overall finding of more errors, the specific nature of the impairment produced by the salicylate is not clear.

In another study, Butcher, Scott, Kazmaier, and Ritter (1973) investigated the behavioral effects of prenatally administered hydroxyurea. The concern here, however, was not with subteratogenic dose levels, but rather with the specific action of the agent. Hydroxyurea is a potent inhibitor of deoxyribonucleic acid (DNA) synthesis, and when administered during organogenesis in rats, results in cell death in limb buds and the neural tube. At term, however, gross limb malformations are common while those of the central nervous system are not. The authors suggested that despite the absence of gross central nervous system defects, behavioral impairments might be evident postnatally.

Hydroxyurea in doses of either 375 or 500 mg/kg was administered on

[2]The day of finding sperm is called either Day 0 or Day 1 of gestation in different studies. So that gestation days refer to the same conceptual age, gestation days have been calculated by designating the day of finding sperm Day 1 for all of the studies cited in this chapter.

Day 13 of gestation. Beginning at 30 to 40 days of age, offspring were tested for differences in exploratory and locomotor behavior in an "open-field" test followed by escape training as described earlier. Although there were no differences in exploratory behavior among any treated or control group, more than 20% of both dose-level groups displayed an abnormal gait characterized by an outward splaying of the hind limbs. Compared with the control group, drug-treated offspring made significantly more errors over all training trials on both the forward and the backward path of the maze. There was, however, no clear dose-level effect and acquisition data were not provided.

Acetazolamide, an inhibitor of the enzyme carbonic anhydrase, has an unusual specificity in that the malformation it produces in rats is confined largely to the distal, postaxial parts of the right forelimb and rarely, if ever, includes the central nervous system. Because of this apparent lack of effect on developing nervous tissue, Butcher, Hawver, Burbacher, and Scott (1975) investigated whether such an agent could produce behavioral effects. A dose of 500 mg/kg was administered on Days 11 and 12 of gestation and offspring tested as described in the open-field and swimming maze. Despite a limp produced by the forelimb defect, drug-treated offspring were no different from control animals in exploratory activity. Similarly, their performance on the maze problem revealed no impairment.

Although confirming studies are needed, these findings suggest the following tentative conclusions: (1) teratogenic agents (such as acetazolamide) that do not produce early central nervous system pathogenesis or gross central nervous system malformations do not appear to produce postnatal behavioral effects; (2) agents that produce gross malformations of the central nervous system, such as vitamin A and salicylate, appear to produce behavioral effects when administered at dose levels near or just below the threshold for producing malformations; (3) teratogenic agents (such as hydroxyurea) that produce early pathogenesis in the developing central nervous system (i.e., cell death) but not gross central nervous system malformations, may produce a residual functional impairment evident in postnatal behavior. As to the nature of these behavioral effects, the swimming maze used in these studies provides only a preliminary screening technique indicating either the presence or absence of behavioral differences. Whether these differences are the result of sensory, motivational, or perceptual-cognitive deficits awaits a more thorough behavioral analysis.

2. BEHAVIORAL EFFECTS OF TERATOGENIC DRUGS IN MAN

Estimates place the incidence of birth defects at around 2–4%. (For a complete review of human teratogens, including environmental contaminants, see Tuchmann-Duplessis, 1975; J. G. Wilson, 1973.) But since most malformations occur spontaneously, individual occurrences are rarely attributable with any confidence to a particular agent. Thalidomide and alcohol are the exceptions; each produces a syndrome of malformations that rarely occurs spontaneously—a condition that helps to identify their teratogenicity—and these substances have yielded a unique population of individuals that can be studied behaviorally with virtual certainty of the etiologic agent.

Thalidomide. When the teratogenicity of thalidomide was first discovered, the syndrome of malformations was thought to affect limbs, ears, eyes, and viscera, but not the central nervous system. But, as the children matured, it became increasingly apparent that thalidomide did not spare nervous tissue (Stephenson, 1976).

A review of several studies of intellectual functioning in thalidomide children by McFie and Robertson (1973) indicates that most test within the normal range. However, the authors cite one study of 1.5- to 3.5-year-old affected children that yielded developmental quotients that were below average, with one-third of the subjects scoring in the borderline and mentally defective categories. In their own study of 56 thalidomide children 7 to 10 years old, McFie and Robertson (1973) found the mean IQ to fall within or above the normal range. Four subjects, however, were of subnormal or severely subnormal intelligence which is a much higher proportion than is expected to occur in the general population.

Stephenson (1976) reviewed the medical files of a group of 408 thalidomide children and found nine ranging in age from 13 to 16 who had histories suggestive of epilepsy. Further study confirmed seven with definite epilepsy, yielding a prevalence of 17.2 per 1000 compared with 2.42 per 1000 for a comparable age group in the general population. In addition, Stephenson found the varieties of epilepsy in these children to be unusual. Two had a relatively rare type of severe refractory epilepsy suggesting widespread brain abnormality. Three had unlocalized or generalized seizures that included episodes of unconsciousness possibly related to brain stem abnormality.

Mental impairment and epilepsy do not occur with the same high frequency as limb reduction among thalidomide-damaged children. Their significantly increased prevalence, however, confirms central nervous system involvement as an additional component of thalidomide embryopathy in man.

Alcohol. In 1973, Jones, Smith, Ulleland, and Streissguth described a syndrome of malformation among 11 infants born to chronically alcoholic women. The pattern of defects, which the authors termed the "fetal alcohol syndrome" included pre- and postnatal growth retardation, developmental delay, craniofacial anomalies, and limb defects. A later study indicated a perinatal mortality rate of 17% (Jones, Smith, Streissguth, & Myriantho-poulos, 1974). A study of 30 additional cases (Hanson, Jones, & Smith, 1976) has verified the initial diagnosis and provided additional evidence of severe central nervous system damage with related deficits.

During the neonatal period, tremulousness, hyperactivity, and irritability have been observed but their frequency is not reported. While possibly resulting from alcohol withdrawal, Hanson points out that the tremulous-ness frequently persists for months to years, while fine motor dysfunction may be permanent. Jones (1975) reported that 44% of the affected children had an IQ of 79 or below at 7 years of age compared with 9% of matched control children. Mental retardation is regarded as the most serious clinical consequence of the disorder.

Jones and Smith (1975) described brain findings of an infant with the syndrome that died at 5 days of age. In addition to agenesis of the corpus callosum, there was incomplete development of the cerebral cortex and an abnormal external appearance of the brain due to sheets of neuronal and glial cells that had abnormally migrated over the surface of the cerebral hemispheres. Extensive developmental abnormalities resulted from aberra-tion of neuronal migration and in multiple heterotopias throughout the leptomeninges and cerebral mantle and subependymal regions. The authors suggest that the joint (skeletal) anomalies may be related secondarily to diminished fetal movement associated with the neurological impairment of the fetus.

Whether the fetal alcohol syndrome is produced by ethanol directly, one of its metabolites such as acetaldeyde, or maternal dietary deficiencies is not yet known. It is clear, however, that heavy alcohol consumption during pregnancy produces, among other defects, widespread nervous system embryopathies with severe and chronic behavioral impairments.

Hydantoin. Recently, Hanson (1976) and Hanson and Smith (1976) have reported a relationship between maternal treatment with hydantoin anti-convulsants and a pattern of structural and behavioral defects in their infants. The syndrome consists of abnormalities of growth, dysmorphic craniofacial features, and behavioral deficits that include developmental delays and intellectual impairment ranging from dull mentality to frank retardation.

C. Period of the Fetus

Because the embryo becomes increasingly refractory to gross structural malformation as gestational age increases, studies of drug teratogenicity were initially devoted almost exclusively to agents administered during organogenesis. But in 1967, Langman and Welch (1967) initiated studies of the early fetal period and their findings had provocative implications for those concerned with behavioral impairments. They administered an excess of vitamin A, a well-known teratogenic treatment, to mice on 2 or 3 successive days during the early fetal period and examined the fetal and neonatal brains at regular intervals up until 10 days of postnatal life. They found that the treatment inhibited DNA synthesis in the neuroepithelial cells of the cerebral cortex. This acted to prolong the cell cycle by approximately 40%, thus interfering with the differentiation of existing neuroblasts, which resulted in a cerebral cortex with reduced cell density. These findings provided convincing evidence that teratogenic drugs administered later in pregnancy could indeed produce nonlethal brain damage and encouraged our laboratory to investigate the behavioral correlates.

In our first study (Hutchings, Gibbon, & Kaufman, 1973), we administered 60,000 units of vitamin A (approximately 230,000 IU/kg) to rats on Days 14 and 15 of gestation. Compared with control animals, the vitamin-treated offspring showed a generalized retardation in growth as evidenced by a delayed onset of fur growth and eye-opening and reduced body weight. In adulthood, animals were tested on various operant conditioning tasks in order to assess learning ability. No differences were observed on continuous water reinforcement and on an intermittent reinforcement schedule. However, differences emerged during the subsequent acquisition of an auditory discrimination. In the presence of the positive cue, S+, in which responding is reinforced, normal subjects typically show elevated rates, while gradually extinguishing their responding to the negative cue, S−, in which responding is never reinforced. Both treated and control animals acquired the discrimination during 80 daily training sessions, but the treated group learned more slowly to inhibit their responses to the S− cue. Direct observation suggested a "perseverative" quality, as though treated subjects were not attending as carefully to the onset of the S− signal.

Brain sections from half the treated animals were not obviously different from the control animals, while the remainder showed a diffuse reduction in overall size. However, the amount of brain reduction did not correlate with the discrimination impairment. An inhibitory impairment in an operant discrimination, similar to that found here, has been reported by other workers following irradiation in rats at approximately the same gestational age that vitamin A was administered here (Fowler, Hicks, D'Amato, & Beach, 1962; Persinger, 1971), which suggests a critical period for producing the effect.

In a second study, we investigated the effects of 90,000 units of vitamin A (approximately 280,000 IU/kg) on Days 17 and 18 of gestation (Hutchings & Gaston, 1974). At this time, the cerebellum is beginning active differentiation and accordingly we expected motor impairment along with or independent of cognitive deficits. The same control and testing procedures were used as in the previous study.

Unlike animals treated on Days 14 and 15, there was no retardation in growth and development. On the operant measures we found that the treated animals had significantly slower rates of response throughout testing compared with the control group. On the S +, S − discrimination task, they extinguished responding to S − as rapidly as the control animals and showed no impairment in learning. Although histological examination showed no reduction in brain size or any obvious abnormality of cellular elements of structure, Vacca and Hutchings (1977) reported in a separate study that the vitamin A treatment interfered with cell proliferation in the developing cerebellum. The major behavioral finding was that the animals treated on Days 17 and 18 of gestation failed to acquire a rate of response comparable to that of the control group. The lower rates of the treated animals might have been due to a minor motor disturbance, and, we did observe that some of the 17- to 18-day animals walked with a peculiar gait. Furthermore, Fowler et al. (1962), and Hicks and D'Amato (1966), found that rats irradiated on the same days that vitamin A was administered in our study were more sluggish in their placing reactions, more awkward in their general movements, and did not respond as rapidly as controls in a lever box—observations that nicely parallel our findings. Our study further demonstrates, however, that such an impairment need not be associated with a learning deficit.

The results of the vitamin A work and similar studies using irradiation indicate that there are critical periods during fetogenesis when exposure to teratogenic agents produces a specific kind of behavioral effect. This notion is further corroborated by the more recent work of Rodier, Webster, and Langman (1975) and Langman, Webster, and Rodier (1975) with mice. These authors administered 5-azacytidine on either Day 15 or Day 19 of gestation or on the third postnatal day. Although its mechanism is unknown, 5-azacytidine interferes with cell proliferation primarily by killing dividing cells. Treated animals differed from control animals but, a more important finding was that each treated group differed from the other. Animals treated on Day 15 had normal locomotor ability the first week of life but persisted in "pivoting," an immature locomotor pattern in which the animal rests on a limp hind limb and paddles with its forelimbs, thereby producing a spinning in place. Both the Day 19 and postnatally treated animals had pronounced intention tremors which disappeared by the third week of

life. Day-19 animals displayed normal, if not precocious, motor development, pivoted rarely, and had a well-coordinated gait. By contrast, the
postnatal treatment produced animals with an abnormal gait characterized
by splaying hind limbs and a tendency to pivot. During adulthood, Day-15
animals were hyperactive, Day-19 animals hypoactive, while the postnatally
treated animals were normally active.

In a separate study, Langman et al. (1975) investigated the morphological
effects produced by azacytidine in mice. Treatment on Day 15 resulted in
an extreme reduction in brain size, particularly in the cerebral cortex. In
addition, there was an abnormal layering of the pyramidal cells in the hippocampus and a reduced corpus striatum. Treatment on Day 19 produced
damage in more restricted brain areas with dead cells seen mainly in the
subependymal layer and external granular layer of the cerebellum. The
postnatal treatment killed many proliferating microneurons and microglia
in the cerebellum but did not result in obvious cell deficits in the adult brain.
Although they could not explain all of the motor effects in detail, the authors
concluded that the deficits produced were quite predictable on the basis
of the lesion sites.

The finding of hippocampal damage produced on Day 15 and adult
hyperactivity is consistent with the inhibitory deficit (given that the hyperactivity attenuates inhibitory control) we observed in rats for vitamin A
administered on Days 14 and 15 (Hutchings et al., 1973) and with a similar
impairment associated with hippocampal lesions in the adult (Isaacson,
1974). Furthermore, the observation of histological damage in the cerebellum and adult hypoactivity parallels the cytochemical damage we observed
in the same area (Vacca & Hutchings, 1977) and the sluggish rates of
response for vitamin A administered on Days 17 and 18 in rats (Hutchings &
Gaston, 1974).

These studies indicate that the fetus and neonate, although refractory to
gross structural defect, remain vulnerable to more subtle damage particularly in those areas of the brain that are actively proliferating. Exposure to
teratogenic agents either kills the dividing cells outright or slows the rate of
proliferation, thereby disrupting subsequent differentiation and migration.
Those areas of the brain sustaining cell loss apparently fail to function
normally with resulting behavioral impairment. Although more precise
knowledge of the behavioral correlates of the damage awaits further study,
the nature of the impairments appears to correspond to the known function
of the damaged areas. Whether such effects are produced in humans is not
known but some of the behavioral effects observed (e.g., inhibitory impairment, fine motor dysfunction) in animals bear a striking resemblance to
those frequently described for children with so-called minimal brain dysfunction.

IV. Toxic Nonteratogenic Drugs in Animals and Humans

Several classes of drugs such as tranquilizers, stimulants, hypnotics, and analgesics, while generally not teratogenic in animals or humans can nevertheless produce intrauterine death, growth retardation, and behavioral deficits. Although developmentally toxic, these drugs, unlike teratogens, probably do not selectively kill embryonic cells but appear rather to produce functional effects by interfering with neurochemical mechanisms in the developing brain. Their action is poorly understood, but some may act on specific embryonic sites (e.g., synapses) or interfere with the elaboration of neural systems utilizing particular neurotransmitters (e.g., catecholamines) to initiate a sequence of abnormal development following the scheme in Fig. 1. As compared with the action of teratogens, however, early pathogenesis and the final pathway involve biochemical rather than gross morphological effects.

For example, the prenatal administration of reserpine produces a relatively permanent change in brain catecholamine disposition during a critical period in prenatal development in both rat (Bartolome, Seidler, Anderson, & Slotkin, 1976) and chick (Lydiard & Sparber, 1974). In the latter species the biochemical effect is correlated with a behavioral impairment (Sparber & Shideman, 1968). The relationship of behavioral effect to gestational age at the time of treatment has yet to be determined for the agents discussed in the following sections. It would appear likely, however, that such a relationship exists and will be demonstrated in future work.

A. Amphetamine

Clark, Gorman, and Vernadakis (1970) administered 1 mg/kg of d-amphetamine sulfate on Days 12 through 15 of gestation in pregnant rats. Compared with a saline control group, the drug-treated offspring showed a significant reduction in locomotor activity at 21 days of age. However, they were not different when tested at younger ages or as late as 60 days of age. Beginning at 33 days of age, offspring were deprived of water and trained to run a T-maze for water reinforcement. Although they did not differ from controls in number of errors, their latency to reach reinforcement was significantly shorter suggesting heightened activity induced by deprivation.

Because amphetamine affects catecholamine systems in the adult brain, Middaugh, Blackwell, Santos, and Zemp (1974) investigated its prenatal administration on brain catecholamines and locomotor activity in the offspring. d-Amphetamine sulfate (5 mg/kg) was administered daily during the last week of gestation in mice. Some animals were sacrificed at regular intervals beginning on the day of birth for determination of brain norepinephrine and dopamine; others were tested behaviorally for activity differences (locomotion, rearing, and grooming) between 13 and 31 days of age, and at 75 days of age. Norepinephrine concentrations in the drug-treated offspring were depressed at birth, rose to control values by Day 3, and were elevated at 21 and 30 days of age. Dopamine levels were elevated at 30 days of age; by 75 days of age, both norepinephrine and dopamine were not different from control concentrations. Significant differences in activity did not clearly emerge until 75 days of age. Not only were the drug-treated offspring more active on total activity scores but they differed qualitatively as well; their activity was characterized either by increased nondirected locomotion or by greatly reduced locomotion often coupled with a high frequency of grooming. The relationship of the behavioral differences to the altered catecholamine levels was not clear but considering that some 570,000 American women of childbearing age are estimated to be using amphetamine-containing diet pills (Chambers & Griffey, 1975), additional studies of this agent are certainly indicated.

B. Tranquilizers

Animal studies of the behavioral effects of prenatal administration of tranquilizers such as chlorpromazine, reserpine, and meprobamate have yielded the most confusing, conflicting, and contradictory findings in the behavioral teratology literature. The earlier studies were critically reviewed by Joffe (1969) and Kornetsky (1970); Coyle, Wayner, and Singer (1976) have reviewed these as well as other studies that have appeared since 1970.

Well-controlled clinical studies, however, generally suggest that prenatal exposure to tranquilizers does not produce any obvious developmental effects in humans. Kris (1962) reported on 31 children of mothers treated with chlorpromazine throughout pregnancy and found no differences in development compared with sibs or peers of the same social class. Ayd (1964) studied 27 children from mothers who took chlorpromazine either throughout or during the last two trimesters of pregnancy. The children were observed from 1 to 6 years of age and found to develop physically and mentally within normal limits and were no different from sibs or peers.

C. Barbiturates

Middaugh, Santos, and Zemp (1975a) have emphasized the frequent use of phenobarbital among pregnant women. Some 25% or more use some kind of sedative, often phenobarbital, during the last trimester, many with epilepsy use it throughout pregnancy as an anticonvulsant, and it is sometimes used during late pregnancy as a prophylaxis for neonatal hyperbili-rubinemia. Moreover, it is commonly abused among the addict population. A paucity of animal studies of the behavioral effects of prenatal exposure led these authors to carry out the following study.

Three groups of mice were administered either 20, 40, or 80 mg/kg of phenobarbital sodium daily during the last week of gestation. The two higher doses have been shown to significantly increase neonatal mortality and de-crease body weight of surviving offspring (Zemp & Middaugh, 1975). In adulthood, the offspring were placed on a food deprivation schedule and self-trained to lever-press for food reinforcement in operant conditioning chambers. Following this, animals were trained on several fixed-ratio schedules of reinforcement which required an increasing number of responses per reinforcement across days.

There was no difference in the ability of the treated offspring to acquire the lever-press compared with saline-injected control animals. On the fixed-ratio schedules, control animals showed the expected increase in response rates with increasingly higher ratio schedules. The treated offspring, how-ever, responded less than controls and their response decrement became even more pronounced as the schedule demands were increased. The 80 mg/kg dose was less effective in producing the behavioral effect compared with the two lower doses. The authors suggest that this may have been the result of a selection factor due to high neonatal mortality produced by the highest dose. A previous study indicated that phenobarbital offspring were less responsive to aversive stimuli (Middaugh, Santos, & Zemp, 1975b). The present study suggested a similar unresponsiveness to appetitive stimuli, leading the authors to postulate that the primary behavioral effect of pre-natal phenobarbital exposure is a decreased responsiveness to environ-mental stimuli.

For years it has been recognized that maternal use of narcotics during pregnancy produces withdrawal symptoms in the neonate. Only recently, however, has a similar effect been described for barbiturates. Desmond, Schwanecke, Wilson, Yasunaga, and Burgdorff (1972) reported on 15 infants whose mothers were taking between 60 and 120 mg of barbiturates daily, either alone or in combination with anticonvulsants for the treatment of epilepsy throughout pregnancy or only during the last trimester. All of the infants were full-term by weight, had good 1-minute Apgar scores but ex-hibited a withdrawal syndrome characterized by overactivity, restless-ness, disturbed sleep, excessive crying, tremors, hyperreflexia, hyper-tonicity, sneezing, hiccuping, yawning, mouthing movements, hyperacusis, vasomotor instability, hyperphagia, vomiting, and diarrhea. The age of onset of the syndrome was later than that typically seen for heroin and the symptoms in some infants persisted for as long as 6 months. For reasons not clear, symptoms tended to be less severe when the medication included other anticonvulsants. Shapiro, Hartz, Siskind, Mitchell, Slone, Rosenberg, Monson, Heinonen, Idanpaan-Heikkila, Haro, and Saxen (1976) reported mental and motor test results at 8 months and 4 years of age of children whose mothers took barbiturates during pregnancy. They found no differences compared with a matched control group. Children of epileptic mothers who took barbiturates were also not different. The animal work found behavioral effects of prenatal barbiturate exposure that persisted well into adulthood. Whether long-term effects are similarly produced in humans awaits follow-up studies.

D. Opiates

Of the estimated 150,000 narcotic-dependent persons in the New York City metropolitan area, approximately 34,000 are women of childbearing age which include some 10,000 to 12,000 enrolled in methadone maintenance programs. A conservative estimate of the current birth rate of this total population is about 3000 per year in New York City alone (Carr, 1975).

Both heroin and methadone produce a neonatal withdrawal syndrome similar to that described for barbiturates. Some workers have suggested, however, that the methadone syndrome is more severe, prolonged, and difficult to control chemotherapeutically than is the heroin syndrome (Zelson, Lee, & Casalino, 1973). Although it had been generally assumed that these symptoms subside or disappear within several days or weeks, more recent observations suggest that at least some components of the syndrome—disturbed sleep patterns and hyperactivity—persist until 2 years of age (M. M. Davis, Brown, & Glendinning, 1973; Ting, Keller, Berman, & Finnegan, 1974; G. Wilson, Desmond, & Verniaud, 1973).

Given the widespread use of opiates, these reports are indeed disturbing, yet all are difficult to interpret because of a host of confounding variables inherent in the population studied. Most of the women have poor diets, are heavy smokers, and are concurrently abusing amphetamines, barbiturates, tranquilizers, or alcohol. In addition, the addicted neonate is typically administered barbiturates, phenothiazines, or hypnotics for several days or weeks depending on the severity, type, and duration of withdrawal symptoms. Clearly, one cannot attribute effects seen among these infants to opiates alone, and animal studies are needed to determine the behavioral effects independent of these confounding variables.

W. Davis and Ling (1972) administered to rats an initial dose of 15 mg/kg of morphine on Day 6 of gestation followed by 5 mg increments every 2 days, achieving a final dose of 45 mg/kg by late pregnancy. Litter size was not reduced but the offspring in the morphine group weighed less at birth and their perinatal mortality was greater than saline-injected control animals.

At 30–35 and 70–75 days of age, the treated offspring were significantly more active than control animals.

Hutchings, Hunt, Towey, Rosen, and Gorinson (1976) administered methadone orally to four groups of pregnant rats on Days 8 through 22 of gestation. Each group initially received 5 mg/kg for 4 days. One group was maintained at this level and the remaining groups were increased to maintenance doses of 10, 15, or 20 mg/kg with 5-mg increments at 4-day intervals. Increased doses of methadone produced a reduction in maternal weight gain and an increase in maternal mortality, resorptions, and stillbirths. Birth weight covaried with dose level and litter size. The 5-, 10-, and 15-mg doses yielded litter sizes that were comparable to, or somewhat smaller than nontreated and intubation control groups, but with lower birth weights. The 20-mg doses yielded the smallest litter sizes with birth weights heavier than any other treated or control group. Beyond Day 1 of life, there was no difference in mortality between treated and control offspring, and at weaning, the lower weights seen at birth were no longer evident. The heavier weights of the offspring receiving doses of 20 mg/kg persisted to weaning.

Finally, Lodge, Marcus, and Ramer (1975), using both behavioral and electrophysiological measures, investigated over a 2-year period the development of infants born to mothers who received methadone maintenance treatment for heroin addiction during pregnancy. During the neonatal withdrawal period, the methadone-dependent infants were characterized behaviorally by lower overall alertness accompanied by greater irritability, activity, motor tone, and an increased lability of state compared with normal infants. Although the addicted infants also displayed marked auditory responsivity and orientation, visual attention and following were difficult to elicit. Visual evoked response data indicated a diminished vertex response which appeared to reflect the lower arousal value of visual stimulation for addicted neonates. Rapid developmental gains were generally observed during the second and third months after the initial withdrawal symptoms subsided. By 1 year of age there appeared to be some leveling off of the rate of sensorimotor development, and performance tended to remain within the average range during the first 2 years. The authors suggested that with the provision of adequate prenatal care and facilitating environmental conditions, relatively normal development may be fostered in infants who experience perinatal drug addiction.

V. Summary

The major concern with drugs administered prenatally has been the risk of structural malformation. It has become increasingly evident, however, that a wide variety of pharmacological agents can produce a range of effects that include intrauterine death, growth retardation, and behavioral effects. Several agents that are teratogenic to the developing central nervous system in animals have been shown to produce learning impairments when administered during embryogenesis at subteratogenic doses; agents not specifically toxic to the central nervous system appear to be without effect. Further evidence indicates that there are critical periods in fetal development when agents produce histological and cytochemical damage in specific brain areas. These are associated with behavioral effects, such as inhibitory and motor impairments, which appear to correspond to the known function of the damaged areas. Of the agents known to be teratogenic in man, alcohol produces the most serious postnatal behavioral consequences. These include delayed development, hyperactivity, fine motor dysfunction, and mental retardation.

Other agents are discussed that are not teratogenic but are nevertheless developmentally toxic. Unlike teratogens, these drugs probably do not selectively kill embryonic cells but appear to produce behavioral effects by interfering with neurochemical mechanisms in the developing brain. For example, barbiturates and opiates, both addictive agents, produce a severe withdrawal syndrome in the human neonate, with hyperactivity and sleep disorders persisting up to 2 years of age. Animal studies of morphine report hyperactivity that persists into adulthood.

The actions of both teratogenic and nonteratogenic toxic agents are viewed within the conceptual framework of teratology. It is suggested that these agents, through a variety of embryopathic mechanisms, act on populations of embryonic cells and disrupt their normal pattern of development. An abnormal developmental sequence is initiated leading to a final common pathway that may include neurobehavioral deficits.

Acknowledgments

The author wishes to express his gratitude to Gilbert Gottlieb and his editorial board for their most constructive and critical review of the chapter. I am further indebted to my friends and colleagues, Dick Butcher, Larry Middaugh, and Pat Rodier for their support and many helpful comments. I am particularly grateful for the very able and dedicated assistance of Howard Gorinson who contributed to every facet of the preparation of this chapter. Finally, this would appear to be a particularly appropriate place to express my continuing gratitude to the staff of the 1966 Teratology Workshop held at the University of Colorado in Boulder, who provided the primordium out of which my subsequent work developed. The preparation of the chapter was supported by Grant DA-00449 from the National Institute of Mental Health.

References

Agar, M. H., & Stephens, R. C. The methadone street scene: The addict's view. *Psychiatry*, 1975, **38**, 381–387.

Ayd, F. J. Children born to mothers treated with chlorpromazine during pregnancy. *Clinical Medicine*, 1964, **71**, 1758–1763.

Barrow, M. A brief history of teratology to the early 20th century. *Teratology*, 1971, **4**, 119–129.

Bartolome, J., Seidler, F. J., Anderson, T. R., & Slotkin, T. A. Effects of prenatal reserpine administration on development of rat adrenal medulla and central nervous system. *Journal of Pharmacology and Experimental Therapeutics*, 1976, **197**, 293–302.

Butcher, R. E., Brunner, R. L., Roth, T., & Kimmel, C. A. A learning impairment associated with maternal hypervitaminosis-A in rats. *Life Sciences*, 1972, **11**, 141–145.(a)

Butcher, R. E., Hawver, K., Burbacher, T., & Scott, W. Behavioral effects from antenatal exposure to teratogens. In N. R. Ellis (Ed.), *Aberrant development in infancy: Human and animal studies*. Hillside, N.J.: Lawrence Erlbaum Associates, 1975. Pp. 161–167.

Butcher, R. E., Scott, W. J., Kazmaier, K., & Ritter, E. J. Postnatal effects in rats of prenatal treatment with hydroxyurea. *Teratology*, 1973, **7**, 161–165.

Butcher, R. E., Vorhees, C. V., & Kimmel, C. Learning impairment from maternal salicylate treatment in rats. *Nature (London), New Biology*, 1972, **236**, 211–212.(b)

Carr, J. N. Drug patterns among drug-addicted mothers: Incidence in use, and effects on children. *Pediatric Annals*, 1975, **4**, 65–77.

Chambers, C. D., & Griffey, M. S. Use of legal substances within the general population: The sex and age variables. In R. D. Harbison (Ed.), *Perinatal addiction*. Holliswood, N.Y.: Spectrum Publ., 1975. Pp. 7–19.

Clark, V. H., Gorman, D., & Vernadakis, A. Effects of prenatal administration of psychotropic drugs on behavior of developing rats. *Developmental Psychobiology*, 1970, **3**, 225–235.

Coyle, I., Wayner, M. J., & Singer, G. Behavioral teratogenesis: A critical evaluation. *Pharmacology, Biochemistry and Behavior*, 1976, **4**, 191–200.

Davis, M. M., Brown, B., & Glendinning, S. Neonatal effects of heroin addiction and methadone-treated pregnancies. *Proceedings of the Fifth National Conference on Methadone Treatment, National Association for the Prevention of Addiction to Narcotics*, 1973, pp. 1153–1164.

Davis, W., & Ling, C. Prenatal morphine effects on survival and behavior of rat offspring. *Research Communications in Chemical Pathology and Pharmacology*, 1972, **3**, 205–214.

Desmond, M. M., Schwanecke, R. P., Wilson, G. S., Yasunaga, S., & Burgdorff, I. Maternal barbiturate utilization and neonatal withdrawal symptomatology. *Journal of Pediatrics*, 1972, **80**, 190–197.

Forfar, J., & Nelson, M. M. Epidemiology of drugs taken by pregnant women: Drugs that may affect the fetus adversely. *Clinical Pharmacology and Therapeutics*, 1973, **14**, 632–642.

Fowler, H., Hicks, S. P., D'Amato, C. J., & Beach, F. A. Effects of fetal irradiation on behavior in the albino rat. *Journal of Comparative and Physiological Psychology*, 1962, **55**, 309–314.

Friedler, G., & Cochin, J. Growth retardation in offspring of female rats treated with morphine prior to conception. *Science* 1972, **175**, 654–656.

Gauron, E. F., & Rowley, V. N. Effects on offspring behavior of mothers' early chronic drug experience. *Psychopharmacologia*, 1969, **16**, 5–15.

Gilman, J., Gilbert, C., Gilman, T., & Spence, I. A preliminary report on hydrocephalus, spina bifida, and other congenital anomalies in the rat produced by trypan blue. *South African Journal of Medical Science*, 1948, **13**, 47–90.

Goodfriend, W. J., Shey, I. A., & Klein, M. D. The effects of maternal narcotics addiction in the newborn. *American Journal of Obstetrics and Gynecology*, 1956, **71**, 29–36.

Hanson, J. W. Fetal hydantoin syndrome. *Teratology*, 1976, **13**, 185–187.

Hanson, J. W., Jones, K. L., & Smith, D. W. Fetal alcohol syndrome: Experience with 41 patients. *Journal of the American Medical Association*, 1976, **235**, 1458–1460.

Hanson, J. W., & Smith, D. W. Fetal hydantoin syndrome. *Lancet*, 1976, **1**, 692.

Haskin, D. Some effects of nitrogen mustard on the development of external body form in the fetal rat. *Anatomical Record*, 1948, **102**, 493–512.

Hicks, S. P., & D'Amato, C. J. Effects of ionizing radiation on mammalian development. In D. H. M. Woollam (Ed.), *Advances in teratology*. London: Logos Press, 1966. Pp. 195–250.

Hutchings, D. E., & Gaston, J. The effects of vitamin A excess administered during the mid-fetal period on learning and development in rat offspring. *Developmental Psychobiology*, 1974, **7**, 225–233.

Hutchings, D. E., Gibbon, J., & Kaufman, M. A. Maternal vitamin A excess during the early fetal period: Effects on learning and development in the offspring. *Developmental Psychobiology*, 1973, **6**, 445–457.

Hutchings, D. E., Hunt, H. F., Towey, J. P., Rosen, T. S., & Gorinson, H. S. Methadone during pregnancy in the rat: Dose level effects on maternal and perinatal mortality and growth in the offspring. *Journal of Pharmacology and Experimental Therapeutics*, 1976, **197**, 171–179.

Isaacson, R. L. *The limbic system*. New York: Plenum, 1974.

Jaffe, J. H. Drug addiction and drug abuse. In L. S. Goodman & A. Gilman (Eds.), *The pharmacological basis of therapeutics*. New York: Macmillan, 1975. Pp. 284–324.

Joffe, J. M. *Prenatal determinants of behaviour*. Oxford: Pergamon, 1969.

Jones, K. L. The fetal alcohol syndrome. In R. D. Harbison (Ed.), *Perinatal addiction*. Holliswood, N.Y.: Spectrum Publ., 1975. Pp. 79–88.

Jones, K. L., & Smith, D. W. The fetal alcohol syndrome. *Teratology*, 1975, **12**, 1–10.

Jones, K. L., Smith, D. W., Streissguth, A. P., & Myrianthopoulos, N. C. Outcome in offspring of chronic alcoholic women. *Lancet*, 1974, **1**, 1076–1078.

Jones, K. L., Smith, D. W., Ulleland, C. W., & Streissguth, A. P. Pattern of malformation in offspring of chronic alcoholic women. *Lancet*, 1973, **1**, 1267–1271.

Kalter, H. *Teratology of the central nervous system*. Chicago: University of Chicago Press, 1968.

Kornetsky, C. Psychoactive drugs in the immature organism. *Psychopharmacologia*, 1970, **17**, 105–136.

Kris, E. Children born to mothers maintained on pharmaco-therapy during pregnancy and postpartum. *Recent Advances in Biological Psychiatry*, 1962, **4**, 180–186.

Langman, J. *Medical embryology*. Baltimore: Williams & Wilkins, 1963.

Langman, J., Webster, W., & Rodier, P. Morphological and behavioral abnormalities caused by insults to the CNS in the perinatal period. In C. L. Berry & D. E. Poswillo (Eds.), *Teratology: Trends and applications*. Berlin and New York: Springer-Verlag, 1975. Pp. 182–200.

Langman, J., & Welch, G. W. Excess vitamin A and development of the cerebral cortex. *Journal of Comparative Neurology*, 1967, **131**, 15–26.

Lodge, A., Marcus, M. M., & Ramer, C. M. Behavioral and electrophysiological characteristics of the addicted neonate. *Addictive Diseases: An International Journal*, 1975, **2**, 235–255.

Lydiard, R. B., & Sparber, S. B. Evidence for a critical period for postnatal elevation of brain tyrosine hydroxylase activity resulting from reserpine administration during embryonic development. *Journal of Pharmacology and Experimental Therapeutics*, 1974, **189**, 370–379.

McFie, J., & Robertson, J. Psychological test results of children with thalidomide deformities. *Developmental Medicine and Child Neurology*, 1973, **15**, 719–727.

Middaugh, L. D., Blackwell, L. A., Santos, C. A., III, & Zemp, J. W. Effects of d-amphetamine sulfate given to pregnant mice on activity and on catecholamines in the brains of offspring. *Developmental Psychobiology*, 1974, **7**, 429–438.

Middaugh, L. D., Santos, C. A., III, & Zemp, J. W. Effects of phenobarbital given to pregnant mice on behavior of mature offspring. *Developmental Psychobiology*, 1975, **8**, 305–313. (a).

Middaugh, L. D., Santos, C. A., III, & Zemp, J. W. Phenobarbital during pregnancy alters operant behavior of offspring in C57BL/6J mice. *Pharmacology, Biochemistry and Behavior*, 1975, **3**, 1137–1139. (b)

Nora, J. J., Nora, A. H., Sommerville, R. J., Hill, R. N., & McNamara, D. G. Maternal exposure to potential teratogens. *Journal of the American Medical Association*, 1967, **202**, 1065–1069.

Peckham, C. H., & King, R. W. A study of intercurrent conditions observed during pregnancy. *American Journal of Obstetrics and Gynecology*, 1963, **87**, 609–624.

Persinger, M. A. *Pre- and neonatal exposure to $10^{19}Hz$ and 0.5 Hz electromagnetic fields and delayed conditioned approach behavior.* Unpublished doctoral dissertation, University of Manitoba, 1971.

Rodier, P. M., Webster, W., & Langman, J. Morphological and behavioral consequences of chemically induced lesions of the CNS. In N. R. Ellis (Ed.), *Aberrant development in infancy: Human and animal studies.* Hillsdale, N.J.: Lawrence Erlbaum Associates, 1975. Pp. 169–176.

Shapiro, S., Hartz, S. C., Siskind, V., Mitchell, A. A., Slone, D., Rosenberg, L., Monson, R. R., Heinonen, O. P., Idanpaan-Heikkila, J., Haro, S., & Saxen, L. Anticonvulsants and parental epilepsy in the development of birth defects. *Lancet*, 1976, **1**, 272–275.

Shenefelt, R. E. Morphogenesis of malformations in hamsters caused by retinoic acid: Relation to dose and stage at treatment. *Teratology*, 1972, **5**, 103–118.

Sparber, S. B., & Shideman, F. E. Prenatal administration of reserpine: Effect upon hatching, behavior, and brainstem catecholamines of the young chick. *Developmental Psychobiology*, 1968, **1**, 236–244.

Stephenson, J. B. P. Epilepsy: A neurological complication of thalidomide embryopathy. *Developmental Medicine and Child Neurology*, 1976, **18**, 189–197.

Ting, R., Keller, A., Berman, P., & Finnegan, L. Follow-up studies of infants born to methadone-dependent mothers. *Pediatric Research*, 1974, **8**, 346. (Abstract).

Tuchmann-Duplessis, H. *Monographs on drugs. Drug effects on the fetus* (Vol. 2). Sydney: ADIS Press, 1975.

Vacca, L., & Hutchings, D. E. Effect of maternal vitamin A excess on S-100 in neonatal rat cerebellum: A preliminary study. *Developmental Psychobiology*, 1977, **10**, 171–176.

Warkany, J. Development of experimental mammalian teratology. In J. G. Wilson & J. Warkany (Eds.), *Teratology: Principles and techniques.* Chicago: University of Chicago Press, 1965. Pp. 1–11.

Warkany, J., & Kalter, H. Congenital malformations. *New England Journal of Medicine*, 1961, **265**, 1046–1052.

Warkany, J., & Kalter, H. Etiology and prevention of congenital malformations. *Proceedings, Biregional Institute on Maternity Care-Primary Prevention*, 1964, pp. 102–121.

Warner, R. H., & Rosett, H. L. The effects of drinking on offspring: An historical survey of the American and British literature. *Journal of Studies on Alcohol*, 1975, **36**, 1395–1420.

Werboff, J., & Dembicki, E. L. Toxic effects of tranquilizers administered to gravid rats. *Journal of Neuropsychiatry*, 1962, **4**, 87–91.

Werboff, J., Gottlieb, J. S., Dembicki, E. L., & Havlena, J. Postnatal effect of antidepressant drugs administered during gestation. *Experimental Neurology*, 1961, **3**, 542–555. (a)

Werboff, J., Gottlieb, J. S., Havlena, J., & Word, T. J. Behavioral effects of prenatal drug administration in the white rat. *Pediatrics*, 1961, **27**, 318–324. (b)

Werboff, J., & Havlena, J. Postnatal behavioral effects of tranquilizers administered to the gravid rat. *Experimental Neurology*, 1962, **6**, 263–269.

Werboff, J., & Kesner, R. Learning deficits of offspring after administration of tranquilizing drugs to the mothers. *Nature (London)*, 1963, **197**, 106–107.

Wilson, G., Desmond, M., & Verniaud, W. Early Development of infants of heroin-addicted mothers. *American Journal of Diseases of Children*, 1973, **126**, 457–462.

Wilson, J. G. *Environment and birth defects*. New York: Academic Press, 1973.

Young, R. D. Developmental psychopharmacology: A beginning. *Psychological Bulletin*, 1967, **67**, 73–86.

Zelson, C., Lee, S. J., & Casalino, M. Neonatal narcotic addiction. Comparative effects of maternal intake of heroin and methadone. *New England Journal of Medicine*, 1973, **289**, 1216–1220.

Zemp, J. W., & Middaugh, L. D. Some effects of prenatal exposure to d-amphetamine sulfate and phenobarbital on developmental neurochemistry and on behavior. *Addictive Diseases: An International Journal*, 1975, **2**, 307–331.

EFFECTS OF IONIZING RADIATION ON DEVELOPING BRAIN AND BEHAVIOR

SAMUEL P. HICKS AND CONSTANCE J. D'AMATO

Department of Pathology
University of Michigan Medical Center
Ann Arbor, Michigan

I. Introduction

Roentgen discovered ionizing radiation in 1895 in the form of X-rays, and it was not long before it was realized that this intense form of energy had a wide range of biologic effects depending on the amount of radiation, what tissues were exposed, and the time elapsed after the exposure. Now, decades later, the public has become much aware, through the press, of the many sources of ionizing radiations and their multiple biological effects, especially in relation to atomic weapons, nuclear reactors, space exploration, and medical irradiation. Ionizing radiations can assure medical diagnosis, cure cancer, and advance science and technology, but in an overexposure or nuclear detonation, it can kill or produce lingering illness. Even small doses from any source may increase the risk of cancer in those exposed, and genetic diseases in their descendants. Historically, it is of interest that radiation's deleterious effects on growing tissues were observed very soon after Roentgen's discovery, yet it was years before the subject of our review— the effects of radiation on the developing nervous system—was recognized as a problem and an area for research. Largely through the pioneering studies of Goldstein and Murphy (1929), it was shown beyond doubt that medical exposure of human fetuses to therapeutic doses of radiation caused them to develop small brains and mental deficiency. A large body of observations on the effects of radiation on development, a substantial part of it dealing with the mammalian nervous system and behavior, has accumulated in the last three decades. Most of the latter has come from experiments with rats, but work with other mammals including man has contributed. Major objectives in this work have been (1) to describe radiation effects on developing mammals and analyze the mechanisms of malformation involved, (2) to use radiation as an experimental tool in mammalian development, (3) to use the malformed animals to find correlations between developing brain and behavior, and (4) to understand and prevent radiation hazards in humans.

Sources of this work are extensive and scattered. We have elected to describe some of the biologic effects of radiation on development, recount a variety of experiments seeking correlations between abnormally developing brains and behavior, and summarize certain studies on humans. The references given are intended to be representative—several other reviews and comprehensive studies will lead to the literature of the field. Furchtgott

(1975) has extensively reviewed a wide range of experiments and observations on animals and man especially relating to behavior and including work of scientists of the Soviet Union. Sikov and Mahlum (1969) have edited the largest collection of studies (a symposium) on the radiobiology of the fetal and juvenile mammal. Experiments from Altman's laboratories, emphasizing the morphological and behavioral effects of irradiation of the infant rat's cerebellum and hippocampus, comprise a most extensive study of abnormal and normal development (for reviews, see Altman, 1975, 1976, and additional references cited later). Earlier articles from our own laboratory stress cellular mechanisms in the morphogenesis of malformations of the nervous system and other organs (Hicks & D'Amato, 1961, 1966) and problems of correlating altered brain structure and function (Hicks, D'Amato, & Falk, 1962a).

Other sources of references and viewpoints are the reports of the United Nations Scientific Committee on the Effects of Atomic Radiation (UNSCEAR, 1969) and the National Academy of Sciences Committee on the Biological Effects of Atomic Radiation (Comar, 1972).

II. Radiosensitivity of Developing Cells and Malformative Processes

A. The Concept of "Radiosensitivity," or the Selective Vulnerability to Alteration by Radiation

When ionizing radiations (named for their ability to ionize atoms by ejecting their orbital electrons or by other means) traverse biological systems, they initiate innumerable physical and chemical interactions. Despite this, in a given set of biological circumstances, different forms of ionizing radiations produce very similar effects dose for dose. The diversity of biological effects lies in the different kinds of vulnerability to radiation injury, or radiosensitivity, that different organisms, tissues, cells, and cell constituents possess. Radiosensitivity in popular usage commonly connotes cell death, but cell death is only one of many expressions of sensitivity to radiation effects. Cell death is important in the initiation of developmental malformations, but radiation does other things to immature cells and the significance of some of them for subsequent development is poorly understood or controversial. A brief perspective of the range and complexity of radiosensitivity through examples will serve the point.

The mature nervous system is regarded as relatively resistant to radiation compared with the immature developing nervous system. This only holds in circumstances where tens to hundreds of rads or R (roentgen) are involved.[1] In an industrial or nuclear reactor accident when a man absorbs tens of thousands of rads, damage to cell membranes is immediately initiated throughout his body. The rapidly collapsing functions of his nervous system that lead to death are among the first to manifest themselves: in this framework, the nervous system is relatively radiosensitive. In contrast, the mitotic apparatus in prophase of proliferating cells, and the nucleus of many non-dividing primitive cells during early development are especially radiosensitive, and rapid cell death in these stages may occur after exposure to 30 R. A threshold dose for killing some gonadal cells is a few R, and in other frames of reference, the geneticist and biochemist see radiosensitivity in the ease with which DNA is altered by tiny doses to produce mutations. The gerontologist is impressed that a few R at any time of life can have a measurable, although small, life-shortening effect. Finally, a behavioral scientist may see radiosensitivity as a normal detection attribute of the mature nervous system, because some mammals find sweet water aversive after they drink it during an exposure to a few R.

B. Vulnerability to Lethal Effects of Radiation of Cells in Different Stages of Development in the Mammalian Nervous System

1. Proliferative, Migratory, and Differentiating Cells in Relation to Radiosensitivity

The nervous system begins as a plate of cells that becomes a tubular and ventricular structure. Through genetically programmed proliferation and differentiation of myriads of cells, and by interactions of these cells with their surroundings, the nervous system attains maturity and lives out a functional life span. Early cellular proliferation, migration, and differentiation is depicted in simplified form (based on the rat) in Fig. 1. Proliferative cells ("neuroepithelium," "matrix," "ependymal zone") form a pseudostratified layer lining the tube and ventricle. Nuclei of cells synthesizing DNA (S-phase in the mitotic cycle) are concentrated in the outer part of this layer.

---

[1]The rad is the unit of absorbed dose for all forms of ionizing radiations, whether electromagnetic radiations such as X-rays, or electrons, or neutrons. R (roentgen) is the unit of exposure dose, based on the ionization that X or gamma radiations produce in air. The exposure dose describes the amount of radiation being directed at the subject. The amount of this radiation that is actually absorbed depends on the characteristics of the radiation and the nature and quantity of the tissue that it passes through. In large subjects, the rads absorbed at some level deep in the body may be numerically substantially less than the value of R. In work with small animals, however, this difference is usually small and it may be inferred that the absorbed dose is not different numerically from the value of the R dose, which is usually what is given.

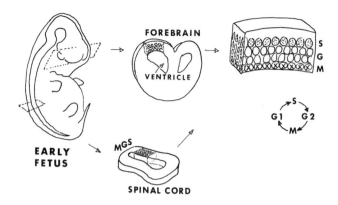

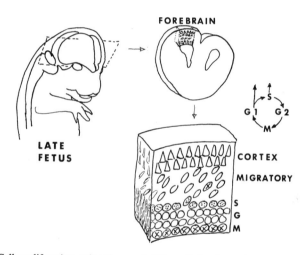

Fig. 1. Cell proliferation, migration, and differentiation in early and late rat fetuses. Cell cycles in the early cerebral vesicles and spinal cord are predominantly proliferative, most postmitotic G1 cells continuing in the cycle. In later cerebral vesicles, more and more G1 cells migrate and differentiate. Some S cells migrate and divide in transit. (Further description in text.) M = mitotic phase; G1, G2 = postmitotic and premitotic gap phases; S = DNA synthesis phase.

The inner ends of the cells are adjoined at the lining surface, and as S-phase nuclei enter prophase (G2), they move toward the ventricular surface to divide by mitosis (M). The daughter cells (G1) are incorporated into the proliferative cell colony to continue the in-out S-M-S movements, or they migrate and differentiate into neurons and glia as the developmental program dictates. In the earlier stages of various parts of the brain and spinal cord, the proliferative cell "in-out" mode of growth predominates.

Later, proportionately more and more of the postmitotic cells (G1 derivatives) migrate and differentiate instead of going into S-phase again, and this mode of growth predominates. Also, many S-phase cells now take off directly outward on migratory paths, dividing at the start and sometimes later en route.

Tritiated thymidine (H-3T) histologic autoradiography has been helpful in analyzing these proliferative and migratory activities in which the H-3T marker is taken up by cells preparing to divide (S-phase) so that they and their descendants can be traced. When fetal and newborn rats are exposed to 150 or 200 R, the most easily and rapidly killed cells are found to be late G2 and postmitotic primitive migratory cells, derivatives of the G1 phase. S-phase cells are relatively resistant. If radiation is administered shortly after H-3T uptake and the animal is studied histologically a few hours later to allow time for vulnerable cells to become visibly necrotic, there are very few labeled necrotic cells. If irradiation is done 4 or 5 hours after H-3T uptake to allow many of the S-cells to pass into late G2, examination a few hours later shows a high percentage of labeled dead cells, indicating that many G2 cells were killed. In the normal fetal and infant rat, the interval from S to M is commonly about 4 hours, but a substantial number of cells take 5, 6, or more hours. As a result, the initial appearance of synchrony in the mitotic cell population shortly after H-3T labeling is soon dissipated by the variable S-M interval itself. As each part of the nervous system progresses from a stage of predominantly proliferative activity to stages where there are more and more postmitotic primitive cells (G1 derivatives) accumulating along their migratory paths (Fig. 1), these migratory cells form a larger and larger proportion, and finally the majority, of all the cells killed in the fetus. The reason for the radiosensitivity (to 200 R) of these migratory cells is obscure, but they are actively differentiating and the metabolic processes associated with this are thought somehow to make them vulnerable.

Most of the cells killed by 200 R are visibly necrotic histologically in 4 to 6 hours, disintegration of a few nuclei appearing as early as an hour after irradiation. In the developing cerebellum, whose proliferative cells are gradually shifted from the periventricular region to the surface of the developing folia, similar mitotic cycles and rates of cell disintegration occur. How general this pattern is is not certain, but at least one major exception is known. The retina does not follow the pattern at some stages, and a brief description of some of its responses serves to illustrate that our understanding of mechanisms of radiosensitivity and malformative processes is still relatively descriptive and incomplete. From early embryonic stages to late fetal life, death of the rat's retinal proliferative cells after 150–200 R follows a pattern that parallels that in the cerebral hemispheres. From the 18th to 20th day of fetal life there is a marked decline in radiosensitivity expressed as cell death. This coincides with morphologic enlargement of the nuclei of the primitive cells and a decline in mitotic rate. This is not an end stage of differentiation, however, because in the next couple of days, just before birth, and extending into the first week of infancy, mitotic activity and radiosensitivity increase. The time pattern of cell death in this last period becomes strikingly delayed and most cells do not undergo necrosis until 18 to 24 hours after irradiation, comparatively few dying in 4 to 6 hours (Hicks & D'Amato, 1966; Hicks, D'Amato, & Joftes, 1962b).

There have been many elegant studies on radiosensitivity during different stages of the (mitotic) cell cycle, using isolated cell systems, which have demonstrated stage-specific susceptibility to different kinds of chromosome breaks, changes in DNA metabolism, repair of DNA damage, and rapid or delayed cell death (Fabrikant, 1972). It is extremely difficult to apply these findings to mammalian cell systems *in vivo*, especially developing ones, although we have indicated some. The radiosensitivity of the postmitotic migratory cells and the delayed necrosis in the retina stand out as especially puzzling, but the demonstration of their existence has been empirically useful in describing malformative processes.

Measuring radiosensitivity by cell death, then, depends on several variables. With exposure constant at 200 R, the populations of vulnerable cells are defined by the stage of development of the part of the nervous system under scrutiny, the balance between proliferative cell activity and accumulation of migratory and differentiating cells, and the time after irradiation. However, as will be seen, when these latter variables are held constant, different doses of radiation can be used to define very different populations of "radiosensitive" cells.

2. Dose of Radiation as a Determinant of Radiosensitivity

The newborn rat is a convenient subject in which to compare the effects of 100, 300, 400, and 500 R with those of 200 R, as seen about 6 hours after irradiation in identical regions of the mantle. After 100 R, noticeably fewer members of the periventricular and migratory primitive cell populations have been killed. Following 300 R, there are in addition to those cells killed by 200 R, a few young differentiating neurons recently arrived in the outer layers of the cortex. With 400 or 500 R exposures, larger and larger numbers of young neurons, and more and more of the primitive periventricular cells, including those in S-phase are destroyed. Figure 2, from Hicks and D'Amato (1963a), summarizes these findings. Comparable dose-response data are scant for the prenatal period, but increasing the radiation kills more and more of the differentiated cells.

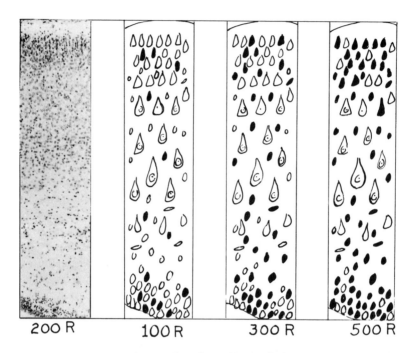

Fig. 2. Changing populations of "radiosensitive" cells in response to dose in the dorsal mantle of the newborn rat. Left, photomicrograph showing necrosis of periventricular cells, below, and migratory cells, above (black dots), 6 hours after 200 R (H & E, × 50). Right, corresponding diagrams show fewer necrotic cells after 100 R, and more necrotic cells, including young neurons after 300 and 500 R. (Further description in text.) From Hicks and D'Amato (1963a), by permission of the authors and publisher.

3. CHANGES IN RADIOSENSITIVITY WITH MATURATION

The responses in the forebrain of the rat to the same dose of radiation, say 400 R, change rapidly after birth. Less and less cell death occurs so that a week-old rat shows neither acute cell death (except the primitive proliferative cells), nor detectable alteration of cortical neuron differentiation. The spinal cord is more advanced in development than the cortex around the time of birth, and it is resistant to hundreds of R. Larger doses of radiation show that its responses are somewhat like those of the adult nervous system, especially as the irradiation continues into the juvenile period. Gilmore (1963, 1973) exposed a segment of the caudal part of the cord to 4430 R (100 kv, about 700 R per minute) in rats 1 to 15 days old. The youngest animals developed partial or complete paralysis of the hind limbs within a week and a half, while older animals showed less paralysis and it took longer to develop. Neuroglia were rapidly destroyed in rats a few days old and variable degrees of vascular necrosis followed. In survivors, myelination was severely impaired. After 2000 R many glial cells were rapidly destroyed, but later the glial cell population was reconstituted. After 1000 or 500 R, no changes were seen up to 2 months. A delayed radiation effect occurred a year after 2000 or 1000 R (50 kv, about 700 R per minute), manifested in the gray matter as proliferation of perivascular connective tissue cells, which laid down a dense meshwork of reticulum fibers.

Single exposures at these high rates to a localized part of the body are rarely encountered outside the experimental laboratory, but in therapy, fractionated daily doses totaling thousands of R in different circumstances are frequently directed to the human nervous system. The exaggerated effects of the single experimental dose have frequently been used in the laboratory to help explain the effects of therapy and overexposure. In fact it is hard to think of any well-conducted experiments as not contributing to knowledge in radiobiology. In the real world of accidents and nuclear warfare almost any kind of exposure that can be imagined may be realized.

C. Nonlethal Effects on Developing Cells as Evidence of Radiosensitivity

1. MORPHOLOGIC ALTERATIONS

As little as 10 to 40 R have been observed to change nerve-cell development in newborn and in fetal rats (D'Amato & Hicks, 1965). Within a few days after exposure of newborn rats, there is a lag in growth of the youngest neurons which occupy the outer part of the isocortex. As the animals reach maturity the apical dendrites of these cells are permanently stunted. Similarly, Purkinje cells in the cerebellum show permanently altered morphology of their dendrites. In late fetal life 30 R also permanently alters the arrangement and individual differentiation of cortical neurons. The functional significance of these changes is unknown. The dose range is that after which slight changes in developing behavior are first detectable in a number of studies with several species including man, but there are no direct correlations between the altered structure and function, as we shall discuss later.

After higher doses during fetal life quite striking changes in developing nerve cell morphology occur; 200 R in fetal life produces stage-specific alterations of particular cells. In late fetal life the dendrite growth of neurons in the outer cerebral cortex is severely affected, and neurons at all levels are affected when irradiation is done earlier (Fig. 3). Purkinje cells display an array of patterns of altered development depending on the time and exposures during prenatal or early postnatal development. The factors that may govern some of these changes have been the subject of much work by

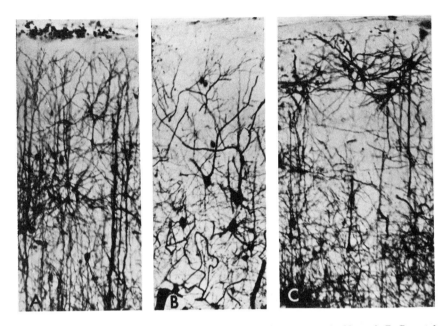

FIG. 3. Golgi stains of outer dorsal isocortex in mature rats. A. Normal. B. Prenatal irradiation with 200 R in the 16- to 17-day period, showing irregularly disposed neurons. C. Prenatal irradiation with 200 R in the 20- to 22-day period, showing branching of apical dendrites of outer neurons (X 200). From Hicks and D'Amato (1966), by permission of the authors and publisher.

Altman and his co-workers (Altman, 1976), which is discussed fully in Section IV.

2. BIOCHEMICAL CHANGES

De Vellis and Schjeide (1969) irradiated infant and juvenile rats and were able to demonstrate far-reaching biochemical changes in the maturing brain stem (excluding the cerebellum) and parts of the forebrain. These ranged from alterations in lipid and protein synthesis to failure of development of the normal complement of certain enzymes, which lasted at least into late juvenile life. Their interpretation of the results was that the most sensitive element was DNA and that it was probably damaged, whether infants or juveniles were irradiated. Because younger differentiating cells have ligher rates of transcription and shorter lived messenger RNAs, DNA damage was regarded as being the primary site of interference with normal transcription in protein synthesis. RNA metabolism did not appear to be primarily affected. A substantial part of de Vellis' and Schjeide's studies was done by exposing the heads of rats 2 days old to 750 R, a devastatingly

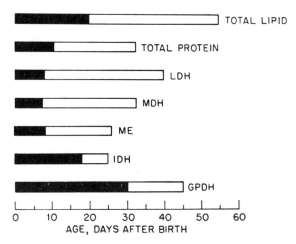

FIG. 4. Bar graphs representing the period of rapid developmental increase in the rat's brain stem, during the first 60 days, of lipid, protein, lactate dehydrogenase, malate dehydrogenase, malic enzyme, isocitrate dehydrogenase, and glycerophosphate dehydrogenase. The black portion is the period during which 750 R inhibits subsequent increases of these substances. From de Vellis and Schjeide (1969), by permission of the authors and publisher.

destructive dose for primitive cells and some younger differentiating cells, and a dose after which many chains of altered developmental events could be expected. Nonetheless, they were able to exclude DNA changes due to cell death as such. Of interest to the problem of influences on young differentiating neural cells was the finding that similar, less severe biochemical changes followed exposures as low as 100 R. Figure 4 shows the periods (black) during which 750 R would inhibit subsequent normal developmental increases in synthesis of lipid, protein, and five enzymes in the whole brain stem.

D. Radiosensitivity and Malformative Responses in the Developing Cerebral Cortex in the Rat. A Model for Mechanisms of Brain Malformation

1. INTRODUCTION

The human brain contains about a hundred billion neurons, and trying to understand what goes wrong in their assembly that leads to the often bizarre malformations seen in the profoundly mentally and neurologically retarded was for a long time a hopeless task. Radiation as a laboratory tool has provided many opportunities, that other teratogenic agents have not, to produce a series of highly reproducible brain malformations in mammals and to study their cellular morphogenesis. The reproducibility of the malformations and the use of certain anatomical methods have made it possible to model some of the rules and principles of abnormal mammalian nervous system development applicable to humans that were not previously available. In our laboratory we were able to work out many basic processes of abnormal development and also to show that many rules governing early embryonic development in lower vertebrates apply to mammals. By irradiating at a selected time in prenatal or postnatal life and then examining members of the exposed litters at a succession of intervals, we were able to reconstruct in a stepwise manner the developmental events from the initial injury to the final malformation, or in certain circumstances, the restitution of the injury. In experiments before birth, embryos and fetuses were removed surgically by a kind of "caesarean section." From a pregnant rat irradiated with 150 R on the 13th day of gestation, embryos might be removed 4 hours after exposure and again at 48 hours. The remainder might be sampled further during prenatal life, or allowed to be born, when samples just after birth and at maturity might be drawn. From several similarly irradiated litters, many steps in the sequence of developmental events could be observed (Hicks, 1954b, 1958; Hicks, Brown, & D'Amato, 1957; Hicks & D'Amato, 1961, 1966; Hicks, D'Amato, & Lowe, 1959).

When 150 to 200 R of X-rays are directed to rats at different stages of development a spectrum of malformations is elicited that involves virtually all parts of the body in varying combinations. Profound alterations of the basic form of the brain, spinal cord, skeleton, eye, and viscera result when irradiation occurs during early embryonic stages when organ systems are first forming. The brain (including the retina) continues to respond with patterns of malformative growth throughout the intrauterine period and in early infancy. These tend to involve cellular organization and differentiation. It is not possible to describe any of these in detail here, so we will sketch a few sequences of development altered by radiation that illustrate malformative and restitutive processes and which bear on the behavioral studies considered later.

2. MALFORMATIVE PROCESSES CHARACTERISTIC OF IRRADIATION IN THE 13- TO 14-, 16- TO 17-, OR 20- TO 22-DAY PERIODS OF PRENATAL LIFE IN RATS

Using Figs. 1 and 5 we can trace the essential processes that lead to the malformations initiated in these periods. In the 13- to 14-day rat fetus, the cerebral vesicles, which are the future hemispheres, are just beginning to develop; they are engaged in proliferation of cells and no cortex has yet formed by migration of the primitive cells toward the brain's surface. This stage is represented in the "early fetus" in Fig. 1 and in Fig. 5. When large numbers of the proliferative cells (shown as black ovals in Fig. 5) are killed by 150–200 R, the surviving primitive cells are thrown into chaos, and they

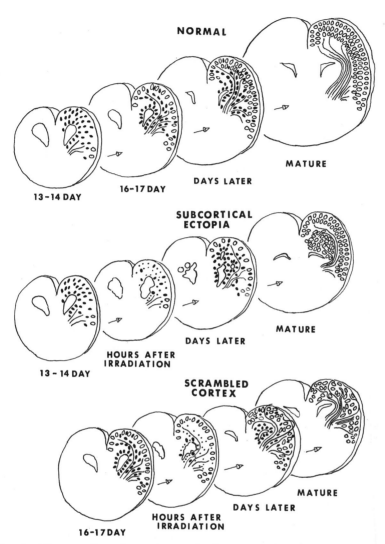

FIG. 5. Diagrams of morphogenetic events leading to normal cortical development, to the subcortical ectopia characteristic of prenatal irradiation in the 13- to 14-day period, and to the chaotic cortex of the 16- to 17-day period. Black ovals represent proliferative and migratory cell populations, dots are the killed cells in these populations, open ovals are young neurons, and lines are thalamocortical fibers. (Further description in text.)

form tiny neural tubes, called rosettes, because of their appearance in microscopic sections. They continue to proliferate cells, some of which migrate properly to form an abnormally thin cortex, but the majority move in all directions to form a large subcortical ectopia; that is, a huge sausage-like mass of displaced cortex. Animals with this defect have other abnormalities: basal structures of the forebrain and the diencephalon are small and their anterior and hippocampal commissures and corpus callosum fail to develop fully. Their spinal cords show abnormalities of the dorsal gray matter, but they have relatively minor skeletal defects.

When the radiation is given in the 16- to 17-day period, approximately represented in the "late fetus" of Fig. 1 and in Fig. 5, a cortex has just begun to form. Some thalamocortical fibers have developed in conjunction with the cortical growth. Destruction of many of the proliferative and migratory cells has an effect different from that at 13 or 14 days: the residual cells do not form rosettes, but the migratory cells they produce are unable to find their normal cortical destinations and a completely scrambled and very deficient cortex results. This is compounded by aberrant growth of thalamocortical fibers, which even find their way into the meninges. Like the 13- to 14-day-irradiated rats, these have basal forebrain and diencephalic deficiencies. Their forebrains are the smallest produced by the application of 150–200 R during the prenatal period.

By the time the fetal rat is approaching term (20–22 days), it has developed a substantial cortex, but many neurons are still to be added to it, some completing their migrations a week after birth. Figure 5 does not depict the malformative process, but the third figure in the normal sequence, which corresponds to the 20- to 22-day period, may be used to describe it. Many cells destined for the outer cortex—the rat cortex like that of most mammals is built from within outward—are killed by the radiation. Deficiencies especially of the outer layers result and, as already noted, the outer neurons that are present develop bizarre dendrites (Fig. 3).

3. RESTITUTIVE AND REGULATIVE CAPACITIES OF PRIMITIVE PROLIFERATIVE CELLS AFTER IRRADIATION

From the foregoing discussions it might be inferred that cell death always leads to malformation. It has long been known that experimental removal of substantial parts of the embryo in very early stages in chicks and amphibia could be followed by complete restoration. The primitive cells of the regions from which the parts were removed possessed a regulative capacity to change their original developmental programs and redress the injury. Removal of one neural fold—the earliest beginning of the brain—from the embryo is compensated by growth from the remaining fold and a normal brain and animal developed. We were able to duplicate certain aspects of this experiment in rats and mice. When irradiation with 150 R was done in rats at the stage when the body axis was being formed and induction processes were causing the neural plate to be elaborated, the animals that resulted had grossly deficient forebrains and associated skull parts were deformed. They were in some respects like human anencephalics. If the embryo was exposed at a slightly later stage, when the neural folds were rising to form the primitive brain, and the optic cups were just beginning to form, the outcome was an animal whose only apparent defect was a lack of eyeballs. By examining a series of stages after this schedule of irradiation by multiple "cesarean" operations, it was shown that several hours after irradiation vast numbers of primitive cells, including the neural folds, had been destroyed in the embryo. In many places more than half the cells were killed. After several more hours had passed, proliferation of the residual cells in the neural folds and beginning spinal cord was evident, and in a couple of days considerable replacement of the lost elements had occurred. By the time the stages of later fetal life had been attained, no residual abnormality could be recognized except that the eyes had not developed, or a few rudimentary structures related to them had grown. The inductive processes involving the beginning of the retina and other eye structures were vulnerable at the time of radiation and the regulative capacities of the residual cells could not surmount the damage.

Although this capacity for recovery in the very early mammalian embryo is striking, in our view a comparable ability of the rat to recover from extreme destructive injury from irradiation at a later stage is the most impressive. Irradiation with 150 R during the 11th intrauterine day (about 18 to 24 pairs of somites) results in a complex of malformations which in viable young (Fig. 6) includes hydrocephalus and skeletal and eye defects. Irradiation on the 13th day, the stage of about 40 pairs of somites, yields a brain malformation characterized by a large subcortical ectopia, as indicated earlier. In the period between, during the 12th day, the stage of about 26 to 36 pairs of somites when the fetus is a little younger than the "early fetus" in Fig. 1, 150 R produces devastating damage to the earliest cerebral hemispheres. The regulative power of residual cells throughout these fetuses is remarkable, and the adults that result have normal brains or the mantle may be only very slightly reduced when direct comparison is made microscopically with a normal control (Hicks *et al.*, 1957; Hicks & D'Amato, 1966). When 200 R is given in this same period, the regulative capacity of the residual surviving cells cannot surmount the damage, and such animals develop with severe brain defects which may include a ventriculocoele of the third ventricle and subcutaneous leakage of cerebrospinal fluid. There are skull and other skeletal defects, and the young at birth are not viable.

It must be emphasized that malformation is the rule after substantial cell

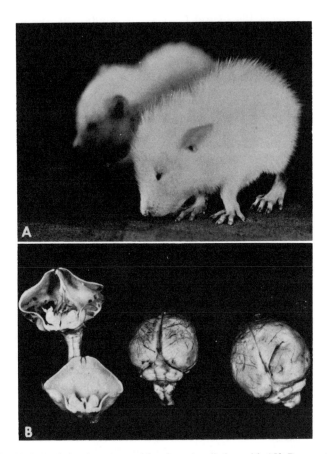

FIG. 6. Hydrocephalus in rats resulting from irradiation with 150 R prenatally on the 11th day. A. Live rats. B. Their brains and that of a littermate below. From Hicks and D'Amato (1963a), by permission of the authors and publisher.

destruction or interference with key inductive processes that seem to be extremely sensitive. The regulative capacity of primitive cell populations, which becomes more and more limited as growth proceeds, is at work through development countering the effects of destruction. Only rarely is it dramatically effective.

4. OTHER PATTERNS OF MALFORMATION

a. Cerebellum. Single exposures of 150 to 200 R in rats on one of the days from the 17th gestational day to a couple of weeks after birth provide a spectrum of gross and microscopic malformations of the cerebellum. These range from reduction in size after irradiation around the 17th prenatal day to irregularities of folial configuration and characteristic histological abnormalities. Jumbling of the cortical elements is an effect of radiation just after birth, and an ectopic or "lost" layer of granule cell neurons in the molecular layer is distinctive after irradiation on the last days of the week after birth. Exposure to 300 R, as far as it has been investigated, exaggerates the 200-R patterns. Figure 7 illustrates some gross and microscopic features (Hicks & D'Amato, 1961, 1966; Hicks, D'Amato, Klein, Austin, & French, 1969).

Altman (1973) has been able to show that the level at which the precursors of the ectopic or "lost" granule cell neurons settled in the molecular layer of the cerebellar cortex depended on how far the advancing afferent axons (mossy fibers) had grown to meet them. Normally, of course, they meet to form the granule cell layers of the cerebellar cortex, but by delaying the formation of the granule cell precursors, he could cause the meeting between the fibers and the precursors to occur at different levels in the molecular layer. Altman (Altman & Anderson, 1973) also examined the fine-structure relationships that developed in the course of radiation-induced malformations of the cerebellum. Many kinds of aberrant connections between cells were found, one of them being synapses between nerve cells and glia (Fig. 8).

b. Retina. The responses of the developing eye and retina to radiation from early embryonic stages to a week after birth in the rat, when cell proliferation in the retina stops, yields perhaps the longest spectrum of malformations produced in any region of the body. Anophthalmia or rudimentary eyes result from 150 to 200 R during the early somite stages and recur when irradiation is done at the stage of about 20 pairs of somites. An extensive series of malformations of varying severity—we noted the changing radiosensitivity of the fetal retina earlier—follows irradiation during the period of about the 16th prenatal day to a week after birth (Hicks & D'Amato, 1963b, 1966). The changing capacity of the proliferative cells, as retinal development progresses, to redress cell losses is similar to that of the proliferative cells elsewhere in the nervous system. From about 12 to 14 days, when the retina is rather comparable in maturity to the cerebral vesicles at the same stages, restitution of severe damage after 150 R is virtually complete. There is little malformation after irradiation around the 20th day of fetal life, but just before and after this, and during the first week after birth, malformation is the outcome. Higher doses, as far as they have been studied prenatally, probably do not allow restitution to normal in any period. Postnatally they produce more severe malformations, and some functional aspects of malformation initiated in this period are discussed later.

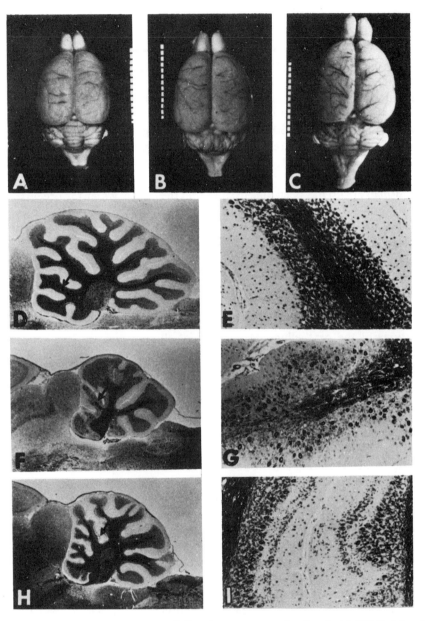

FIG. 7. Malformation of the cerebellum in mature rats irradiated with 300 R at 1 or 5 days of age, as seen grossly and microscopically. A. Normal. B. Irregular cerebellar folia, irradiation at 1 day. C. Slightly irregular folia, irradiation at 5 days. D, F, H. Sagittal sections, low magnification, of the cerebellar region from A, B, and C. E, G, I. Higher magnifications of regions denoted by arrows in D, F, and H. D, normal; G, intermixed Purkinje and granule cells; I, ectopic granule cell layer. (Further description in the text.) (Luxol fast blue and cresyl violet stain.) From Hicks *et al.* (1969), by permission of the authors and publisher.

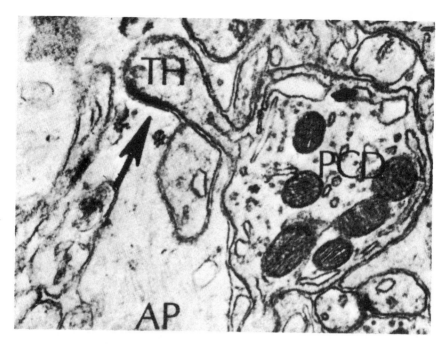

FIG. 8. Pseudosynapse (postsynaptic membrane thickening at arrow) between the thorn (TH) of a Purkinje cell dendrite and an astrocyte process (AP). Cerebellum of rat 30 days old, 7 exposures of 150–200 R from the 4th to 15th postnatal days. (Enlarged from X 25,080.) From Altman and Anderson (1973), by permission of the authors and publisher.

5. Comparison of Effects of Radiation with Those of Other Teratogenic Factors

Early in the history of experimental mammalian teratology it was sometimes suggested that if one teratogenic agent would produce a particular pattern of malformation when it was administered at a specific period in development, then any other deleterious agent given in the same period would produce the same malformation. There is some superficial truth in the notion, as illustrated by the gross similarities between the destructive effects of radiation and mechanical ablation on parts of the very early embryo. The resemblances between radiation effects and those of so-called radiomimetic drugs, certain hormones, and some other agents was shown to be quite limited (Hicks, 1954a). That it is an interaction of teratogenic factors, stage of development, and additional modifying circumstances that determines the course that abnormal development will follow is attested to in the chapters in this volume by Hutchings, by Zamenhof and van Marthens, and by Whitsett and Vandenbergh.

III. Behavioral Development in Rats Following Prenatal Irradiation: The Search for Correlations between Altered Structure and Function

A. Introduction

Many studies have been made of the behavior of rats irradiated *in utero*, most commonly with single exposures of 25 to 200 R and sometimes 300 R. Changes in various measures of emotionality, motor functions, certain reflexes, maze learning, sexual activities, visual functions, classical conditioning, and induction of convulsive seizures have been investigated. There were high expectations early in the history of such radiobiological experiments that with the extraordinarily high reproducibility of the malformative patterns, an unparalleled opportunity to correlate developing abnormal brain structure and function lay at hand. This has been only partly realized, because (1) radiation may alter development of many parts of the nervous system at once, (2) irradiation at certain stages of development does not result in malformation but still alters behavioral development, and (3) the nervous system is an integrated structure in which localization of function to a particular part is difficult to establish, except in the periphery such as sense organs and peripheral nerves. (One might say that the demonstration of blindness in the rat born without eyeballs provides a one-to-one correlation, but it is not the kind of relation investigators have been seeking.)

The exploratory experiments of Werboff, Havlena, and Sikov (1962) illustrate how developmental behavioral alterations in offspring may follow prenatal irradiation and show no definable correlation with brain malformations. They found that among rats irradiated with 25, 50, or 100 R on Day 5 (when malformation virtually never results), Day 10, Day 15, or Day 20 of gestation, facilitation of maze learning occurred in females, and both sexes showed deviations from normal in some aspects of motor performance and activity. Furchtgott and his co-workers (Furchtgott, 1975), however, found that certain kinds of behavior were associated with irradiation during specific periods of development, that they paralleled certain patterns of brain malformation, and there were some rational relationships between the parts of the brain predominantly affected and the functions that were disturbed. Generally, the severity of the abnormal behavior also increases with the dose. At the same time, there is a basic alteration of behavior common to most rats irradiated prenatally during any of the periods chosen: an increased reactivity to novel stimuli. This is expressed in a variety of forms ranging from changes in locomotor behavior including hyperactivity to increased emotionality including deviations in autonomic nervous system reactivity, such as increased heart rate (Furchtgott, Tacker, & Draper, 1968).

B. *Some Effects of Varying Doses of Radiation at Different Prenatal Stages on Development of Behavior*

Furchtgott and co-workers (Furchtgott & Echols, 1958; Furchtgott, Echols, & Openshaw, 1958) irradiated rats pregnant 14, 16, or 18 days, with 50, 100, 200, or 300 R and studied locomotion, maze learning, and certain aspects of emotionality and activity in the offspring. Similar experiments (except with 50 R) were done with neonatal rats. Locomotion was tested by having the animals traverse two parallel horizontal rods, the distance between them being increased by increments to make locomotion more difficult. Failures on these rods were scored. Maze learning was tested in a Lashley III maze. Both locomotion and learning were affected in some degree after 300 R at any of the stages studied, but learning was most easily affected at 14 days, 100 R being deleterious. As little as 50 R altered locomotor development in the 18-day irradiated rats. It will be recalled that malformation resulting from irradiation around 14 days especially involves the forebrain and to some extent the diencephalon, while these parts are less seriously affected as development proceeds. The cerebellum is affected increasingly during late fetal life and early infancy. Learning would reasonably be expected to be impaired with the forebrain and diencephalic alterations, and motor dysfunction would be associated with cerebellar abnormalities. These correlations are quite general, however. Emotionality was most easily increased at 14 days; 50 R had some effect and larger doses had more. The affected animals were hyperactive and more easily aroused than normals, and they approached and explored novel objects less than normals. They were reluctant, or fearful, to emerge from a home cage. Even animals irradiated in the newborn period showed some of this fearfulness, the expression being a tendency to freeze in a novel situation rather than to move around a great deal. Thus, it appears that irradiation during any of the periods studied can alter the development of emotionality, but the mechanisms are unknown.

Furchtgott and co-workers also examined aversive conditioning and the acquisition, extinction, and discrimination of a classically conditioned response in prenatally irradiated rats (Furchtgott, Jones, Tacker, & Deagle, 1970; Walker & Furchtgott, 1970). In respect to the aversive conditioning, adult rats prenatally exposed to 100 or 200 R on the 16th day were tested in four experiments: shuttle box shock avoidance, a Sidman avoidance conditioning paradigm, escape conditioning in an electrified T-maze, and escape conditioning in an electrified Lashley III maze. The animals irradiated with 200 R showed more rapid conditioning to avoid shock in the first two situations than normals or those irradiated with 100 R. In the two maze experiments, which required discriminative learning, they performed more poorly.

In the classically conditioned response experiments, adult rats exposed to 50, 100, or 200 R on the 16th day *in utero* were used. The 200-R-irradiated rats took longer to acquire and extinguish a response conditioned to a 400-Hz tone than normals, but discriminated 400 from 1000 Hz normally. The response studied was pushing a door open to a food compartment. The rats exposed to 100 R, but not those exposed to 50 R, acquired the response more slowly than did the controls. The most noticeable difference occurred during the beginning of the acquisitions, final performance levels being about the same in irradiated and normal animals.

In a study which also included conditioning, Fowler, Hicks, D'Amato, and Beach (1962) tested rats irradiated with 150 R in the 13- to 14-day period on performance in a modified Hebb-Williams maze, for emotionality in an open field, for alternation tendency in a T-maze, and in a visual discrimination learning situation with food reward in which they were conditioned to a light stimulus. (The rats were studied in detail morphologically, their brains showing the characteristic abnormalities described earlier.) As in Furchtgott's experiments, they were more "emotional" and made more errors in the maze than normals. They were less adaptable than normals in the alternation experiment and less able to stop responding during periods when the light stimulus was turned off.

In respect to all these experiments, Furchtgott (1975) points out that while precise correlations between altered brain structure and function are not possible, the development of the cerebral cortex is especially severely interfered with by irradiation in the 13th- to 18th-day period of prenatal life in rats. The view has been expressed by some that the cortex is concerned with handling complex discriminations and competing responses as it directs the organism's explorations toward goals. A disordered cerebral cortex might therefore be expected to interfere in performances involving these functions, but not in responses such as shock avoidance that did not involve discrimination. Hyperactivity and emotionality have also been attributed to diminished cortical control. Whether this view of the cortex as governor is supportable or not, it must be reemphasized that these animals' cortices were not the only parts altered; they also had deficiencies of development of their corpora striata, other basal forebrain regions, and their diencephalons including the hypothalamus and subthalamus. Also, although emotionality was increased by irradiation during almost any period of development, it was most marked after exposure in the 13th- to 16th-day period when these deep regions were most severely affected.

The specificity or nonspecificity of hyperactivity in brain-injured animals, whether it is related to different doses of prenatal radiation or other causes, has received much attention. Norton, Mullenix, and Culver (1976) measured attributes of hyperactivity in rats irradiated prenatally on Day 14, or exposed to carbon monoxide at 5 days of age, or with bilateral lesions of the globus pallidus made during adulthood. One group of activity levels was measured with photocells in a residential maze at night and included locomotion such as walking and running. In another group, the duration, frequency, and sequencing of behavior components were analyzed with the help of computer programs from successive frames of film taken of the animals for a period after being introduced into a plain cage. These components included five body positions such as rearing or lying down, and 10 acts, such as sniffing, scratching, grooming, and looking. With such an analysis, the behavior of naive normal rats upon being introduced to a cage was found to be distinctly structured. A common characteristic of the abnormal animals, all of which were hyperactive in varying degrees, was less structured behavior, with a shortened duration of many behavioral acts, and a tendency to increase exploratory behaviors at the expense of grooming behaviors. What was particularly interesting to the authors was that there was no difference in behavior structure which related uniquely to any of the hyperactivities from different kinds of brain damage.

Altogether, then, hyperactivity and emotionality seem to be consequences of a variety of circumstances in which the integrity and stability of the normally adaptive nervous system failed to mature or were broken after they were attained.

C. How Much Malformation Can Parts of the Developing Nervous System Tolerate and Still Function?

It is a common belief that successful function of the nervous system depends on extraordinarily precise development of its elements and circuits within close tolerances. Yet observations on humans and laboratory animals show that virtually normal function, or much less impairment than would be expected on the basis of this belief, can develop in the presence of gross structural defects. Virtually absent cerebellum, hippocampal-fornix system, or corpus callosum, and extreme underdevelopment of one cerebral hemisphere are among the remarkable examples in humans. Falk and his coworkers (Falk & D'Amato, 1962; Hicks & D'Amato, 1975; Hicks et al., 1962a; Falk, cited in Hicks et al., 1959; Lipton, 1966) sought qualitative measures of spared function in the presence of varying degrees of malformation. Functions usually believed to depend for their integrity on the intactness of specific regions of the central nervous system were explored: pattern vision, skilled locomotor function, positioning reflexes of the limbs, and taste. Rats bearing the malformations characteristic of irradiation with 150 or 200 R on the 13th, 15th, 17th, or 19th day of gestation were usually able visually to discriminate vertical from horizontal stripes as well, or nearly as well, as normals, but their rate of acquisition was slower than normals. The 17th-day-irradiated rats' average level of correct responses was the lowest (Hicks *et al.*, 1962a). All of these animals placed tactually with forefeet, and displayed essentially normal hopping reactions. This may have less significance now than it seemed to at the time of the experiments, because in rats with motor-sensory cortex bilaterally removed at birth, these reflexes develop essentially normally (Hicks & D'Amato, 1975). The reflexes may have been spared in the presence of malformed cortices, but skilled locomotion was not; 17th-day-irradiated rats are severely handicapped in traversing two parallel horizontal rods (Lipton, 1966). The 17th-day-irradiated rats were also tested for preference between salt water and drinking water, and between a series of dilute solutions of quinine sulfate and drinking water. In this test there was no difference between normals and irradiated animals in the quinine tests, although irradiated animals did not show as great a preference for salt water as did normal animals (Falk, cited in Hicks *et al.*, 1959).

In the foregoing studies of visual function in the prenatally irradiated rats, the possible contributions of retinal abnormalities could not be assessed. In newborn rats, radiation could be limited to the eyes and immediately adjacent tissues by shielding, providing an opportunity to observe how severely malformed a retina would have to be before it could no longer mediate pattern and other detail vision. Rats with retinas malformed by 200, 300, or 400 R at birth were able to jump variable distances in any direction to stationary or moving platforms, or a platform dimly lighted in the dark. They performed as well as normals in discriminating horizontal from vertical stripes, and upright from inverted triangles on a Lashley visual pattern discrimination apparatus. When 600 R was given, the rate of acquisition to criterion (20 out of 20 consecutive errorless trials in one session) in the pattern discrimination tests was sometimes slower than that of normals, and jumping to a moving platform was sometimes less accurate. Exposure to 600 R is devastating to the newborn rat's retina, and the malformation resulting from this exposure was characterized by extreme deficiency of the cellular elements, and profound morphologic disorder of their arrangement. Photoreceptors, elements of the bipolar-amacrine cell layer, and ganglion cells were recognizable, and differentiation of individual cells, as inferred from Golgi stains, seemed relatively normal. Rats blinded at birth could not accomplish these tasks, nor could the experimental subjects when their eyelids were closed. When 700 or 900 R was administered, the retinas were reduced to rudiments, and the animals behaved like those that were blinded (Hicks & D'Amato, 1975).

In other experiments, the test was made to find out whether patterns learned through a retina malformed by 600 R would be recognized by the brain when seen through a normal retina. One eye only was irradiated and the animals were taught to discriminate horizontal from vertical stripes with that eye alone. Then with the irradiated eye closed, they were tested with the normal eye alone. They recognized the patterns (i.e., made the interocular transfer) as rapidly as normal rats. The conclusion was that coding for the brain by the malformed retina was qualitatively the same as the normal (Hicks & D'Amato, 1975).

These experiments on sparing of function in the presence of malformation only demonstrate that deficient and malformed neural tissue can function. An obvious "explanation" is that enough organization developed to subserve function, but we have no details yet to define what is enough. These experiments with animal models should however be pursued, because it may be possible to describe empirically some of the degrees and kinds of disorder, say of the cerebral cortex, that will or will not subserve some useful function. Such models would be of interest in our own examinations of the brains from autopsies of the profoundly and mildly mentally and neurologically retarded people in our state institutions. We are in the same dilemma here as in the animal work: the correlations are presently poor.

D. Further Attempts to Correlate Brain and Behavioral Abnormalities Initiated by Prenatal Irradiation

1. LOCOMOTOR BEHAVIOR AND COMMISSURAL SYSTEMS

Rats irradiated on the 13th, 14th, or 15th day of gestation often hop rather than walk, moving the hind limbs in phase. Mullenix, Norton, and Culver (1975) studied this characteristic in rats exposed prenatally to 50 or 125 R on the 14th, 15th, 16th, or 17th day, attempting to relate the gait to incomplete development of brain commissural systems. The peculiar gait was rare or absent in those rats irradiated on Days 16 or 17. One might think of hopping as an all-or-none mode of travel, but these authors analyzed the gait of the animals by inking their feet with different colors and letting them make footprints on paper as they moved. Lines drawn between two succeeding prints of the same hind foot and between both hind feet formed a triangle which allowed measurements of width and length of stride, and of the angle drawn between the two hind footprints. In hopping animals this angle was almost 90°; in the nonhopping rats irradiated on Days 15 or 16, the angle was still greater than normals, and the width of the stride was also greater. In the rats irradiated on the 14th or 15th day the temporal, transverse, and anterior parts of the anterior commissure were reduced or absent, and in the 14th-day-irradiated rats the ventral part of the hippocampal commissure

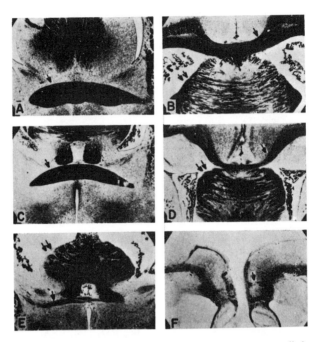

FIG. 9.   Maldevelopment of rostral brain commissures in mature prenatally irradiated rats.
Frontal sections. A, B. Normal anterior commissure, corpus callosum, and dorsal and ventral
hippocampal commissures (arrows). C, D. Nearly normal anterior commissure and deficient
corpus callosum, and dorsal hippocampal commissure resulting from 125 R on day 17. E, F.
Deficient anterior commissure, corpus callosum, and dorsal hippocampal commissures
resulting from 125 R on day 14. (Further description in text.) (Luxol fast blue and toluidine
blue, reduced from X 11.55.) From Mullenix *et al.* (1975), by permission of the authors and
publisher.

was deficient. These structures were little affected in 16th- or 17th-day-
irradiated rats, while all of the irradiated animals developed virtually no
corpus callosum (Fig. 9). The authors postulated that afferent feedback from
positioning and placing the feet in locomotion is an important component in
maintaining the integrated rhythm of normal locomotion, whatever its style.
The deficiencies of the interhemispheric commissures, most fully expressed
in the 14th- and 15th-day-irradiated rats, might affect the integrity of rhyth-
mic locomotion in two ways. In one, normal integrated governance of
locomotion through contralateral placing and positioning responses might
be disrupted. In another, perhaps not much different from the first, a
bilaterally integrated mechanism in the forebrain for initiating alternate or
hopping gaits would be out of order without the commissures.
    The spinal cord is malformed in animals irradiated with 150 or 200 R

on any day from 11 to 16; proliferation of cells in the cord is essentially completed by Day 16 (Hicks *et al.*, 1957, 1959). Whether the spinal abnormalities contribute to the hopping gait has not been determined.

2. PRENATAL IRRADIATION AND REPRODUCTIVE BEHAVIOR

Irradiation during early life can affect reproductive functions and behavior in a number of ways. Oocytes in the femals rat are easily destroyed by radiation around the 15th prenatal day or the 5th day after birth. Irradiation with 200 R in the period from the 18th prenatal to the 2nd postnatal day in males prevents the formation of spermatogenic tissue. Irradiation with 150 R on prenatal Day 11 may prevent the formation of gonads. Behaviorally, male rats irradiated at several stages prenatally were slower to initiate mating in novel surroundings than normal animals, in part an expression of the disturbed reactivity of such animals (Furchtgott, 1975).

Mullenix and Norton have examined the hypothalmic regions of the brain and reproductive behavior in rats exposed to 50 or 125 R on gestational Days 14, 15, 16, or 17. Among their findings, females irradiated with 125 R on any of the days showed persistent vaginal estrus (epithelial cornification) and their ovaries generally showed corpora lutea with few follicles. Females irradiated with 125 R on Day 14 did not respond to mating advances of normal males, although they were sometimes impregnated by persistent males (but did not carry their litters to term). Males so irradiated showed no sexual interest in normal females. Males irradiated on Days 15 or 16 evinced interest in females but did not attempt to mate. Some females irradiated on these days displayed estrus behavior, others did not. Mating and reproductive behavior were essentially unimpaired in animals of both sexes irradiated on Day 17. Golgi stains of the central hypothalmic region were made in some of the rats in each group, which revealed that neurons in the 15th and 16th day-irradiated rats (both sexes) had distorted perikarya with fewer dendrites arising from the perikaryon and supporting less secondary branching. The dendrites showed beading close to the soma and lacked spines. Corresponding neurons in normals had spine-covered primary dendrites that supported extensive secondary branching.

The study emphasizes the complexity of factors that are involved in analyzing abnormal reproductive behavior. It opens the way for further studies of radiation effects on the hypothalmus in relation to reproduction, for as we noted earlier, defects of development in this region characterize irradiation from the 13th through the 17th or the 18th day of gestation in rats.

IV. Effects of Radiation on Infant Rats

A. *Effects of Schedules of Multiple Doses of Radiation on the Development of the Cerebellum in the Rat*

1. EFFECTS OF RADIATION ON DIFFERENT CELL TYPES AND ON CIRCUIT FORMATION

The sequential formation of granule, basket, and stellate interneurons is known empirically to influence the growth and differentiation of Purkinje cells and the organization of their circuits, but the nature of these influences has been poorly understood. To analyze these interactions in normal and in abnormal circumstances induced by radiation, Altman and co-workers (reviewed in Altman, 1975, 1976) devised schedules of repeated daily doses of radiation, to the infant rat's cerebellum to halt completely, or interrupt briefly, the proliferation of the primitive precursors of the various interneurons. The idea was to see what would happen to the development of Purkinje cells when any one type, or all of the interneurons were prevented from forming. Schedules usually ranged from 2 to 8 exposures of 150 to 200 R given at daily or greater intervals in the first 2 weeks of postnatal life. Shorter schedules allowed some reconstitution of the external germinal layer of proliferating cells.

Figure 10 depicts a summary of normal postnatal cerebellar development, schedules of radiation, and the various effects of the irradiations in Altman's studies. They are the results of extensive experiments based on cerebellar lobules that had the same timescale of development. Some stages shown are extrapolations from data from other stages observed experimentally. Normal events relevant to the experimental outcomes are indicated in the first row. The heavy black line represents the external germinal layer (egl), among whose products are the interneurons: granule cells (gc), basket cells (bc), and stellate cells (sc). Purkinje cells (Pc) become aligned in rows, as seen in microscopic sections, in the first few postnatal days, then form their apical dendrites in the first week, secondary dendritic branches in the next few days, and spiny branchlets in the latter half of the second week. Synaptogenesis between Pc dendrites and parallel fibers (pf) occurs with branchlet formation, progressing from the proximal to the distal parts of the Pc dendrite arbor. By 30 days, Pc are relatively mature. Granule cell neurons, which are formed continuously until about 21 days after birth, send their parallel fibers into the deeper part of the molecular zone first, during the early postnatal period, and in the superficial part later. Basket cells are principally produced from about the 5th to 9th days, and stellate cells during the next several days. The consequences of various radiation schedules are shown in succeeding rows: in the left-hand column a designa-

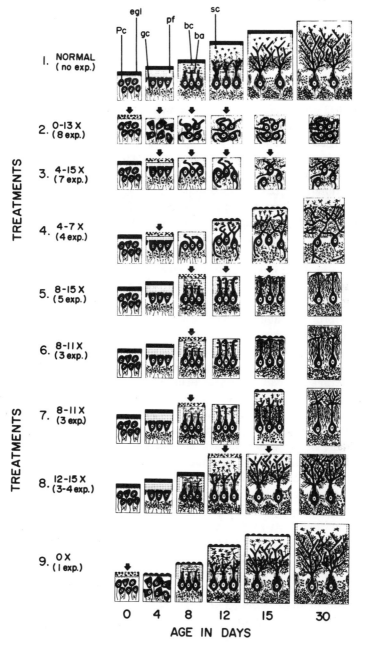

FIG. 10. Summary of experiments in which the infant rat's cerebellum was irradiated according to certain schedules that would prevent the formation of various interneurons. The purpose was to observe the effects of eliminating these cells on the development of Purkinje cells and the formation of their circuits. (Further description in text.) From Altman (1976), by permission of the author and publisher.

tion of 0–13 × (8 exp) means 8 exposures of 150–200 R between birth and 13 days, 8–11 × (3 exp) means 3 exposures between 8 and 11 days. In the far right column, the final picture at 30 days is shown. Permanent eradication of the egl resulting from irradiation beginning soon after birth led to production of virtually no gc, bc, or sc, as shown in rows 2 and 3. Pc polarity and dendrite differentiation was considerably aborted and distorted. However, electronmiscroscopic studies showed that postsynaptic membrane specializations formed in these haphazardly developed Pc processes. If the radiation was controlled, as in row 4, to allow some recovery of the egl (indicated by the undulating black line on surface), gc and sc were formed, but not bc. The result was failure of the normal perpendicular growth of the single stem dendrite of the Pc, and sometimes there were several stems. However, smooth branches and spiny branchlets differentiated. It was postulated that the bc were necessary for the perpendicular phase of growth. When the radiation was given later than 8 days after birth, which allowed bc to form, but interrupted sc and late gc formation, a long single-stem dendrite developed.

If late-forming sc and especially late gc were prevented from forming, as in row 5, the development of smooth branches and spiny branchlets of the distal part of the dendrite arbor was inhibited, and the Pc became truncated. It is presumed that lack of an opportunity to complete synaptogenesis with these interneurons causes the growth inhibition. With less and less radiation, as in rows 6 to 9, more late-forming interneurons were permitted to develop and the truncation diminished. Some variation in the response was found in the experiments with 3 exposures between 8 and 11 days; in row 7, more sc formed and the Pc arbor was less stunted distally, presumably because of the stimulating effect of sc on smooth branch development.

The conclusions in these experiments are that bc, whose axons (ba) formed a basket around Pc, exert a governing influence on the formation of a straight, single-stem Pc dendrite, and sc and gc control smooth branches and spiny branchlets of the dendritic arbor. Primary irradiation effects on the Purkinje cells are not considered to be a substantial factor.

When the rats were irradiated, they were immobilized in plastic tubing, and placed in holes in Lucite blocks to facilitate shielding, direction of the radiation, and monitoring. The radiation was directed in a beam 5 or 6 mm wide front to back, through the part of the head containing the growing cerebellum (Altman, Anderson, & Wright, 1968), or the whole head was irradiated. Some of the accumulated exposures were quite large, in excess of 1000 R. The effects on other parts of the brain and other tissues in the head and neck region including endocrines, and the possible contributions of changes in them to abnormal cerebellar growth are unknown. The consistencies within the whole set of results, however, make it seem unlikely that influences other than the altered developmental relations between Purkinje cells and interneurons were significant.

2. EFFECTS ON MOTOR DEVELOPMENT

Altman and co-workers (Altman, 1975; Brunner & Altman, 1973) made extensive qualitative and quantitative observations on motor functions in animals irradiated on some of the schedules previously described. They were observed during locomotion on flat surfaces or ascending inclines and as they traversed horizontal rods with different diameters and surface textures. A particularly difficult test was for the animals to traverse one of these rods while it was being slowly rotated. Other performances included ascending a rod to escape shock, behavior in activity wheels, locomotion while pulling weights, swimming, and jumping. Changes in the pattern of descending a rope as the irradiated rats developed was compared with that of normals.

Irradiated rats were least affected in ordinary locomotion on flat surfaces and swimming, and greatly affected in performances requiring finer motor control, as traversing a rotating rod. The impairment was generally more severe in animals receiving the larger doses, but there were essentially no stage-specific syndromes. The hind limbs frequently seemed to be the most affected members. During infancy and early juvenile life, rats abandon pivoting in locomotion and substitute a head-down position for a tail-first posture in descending a rope. This maturation was delayed in the irradiated animals. Rats that received multiple exposures exhibited tremor and incoordination during locomotion as they matured. The tremor was worst in the juvenile period, subsiding later unless the dose of radiation was very large, in which case it persisted.

B. Comparison of Cerebellar Irradiation with Cerebellectomy in Infant Rats

Single doses of 200 R produce a spectrum of cerebellar malformation when given during periods from late fetal to infant life in rats, as noted earlier. Functionally, rats irradiated with 200 R on the 1st or 5th postnatal day showed distinctive but mild disorders of gait as they matured. If the dose was raised to 300 or 400 R, incoordination of movement became severe and persisted. A coarse tremor, evident during movement or standing, developed late in the third week, but largely disappeared a couple of weeks later. When 400 R was directed to narrow longitudinal bands in the sagittal plane of the cerebellum at 1 or 5 days after birth, incoordination greater than that seen after 200 R to the whole cerebellum developed. In none of the irradiated animals was there any interference with maintaining an upright position.

When the developing cerebellum was surgically ablated partially or virtually completely at the age of 1 or 5 days, a wholly different neurological syndrome appeared. The animals whose ablations were virtually complete, including the deep cerebellar nuclei, were never able to stand or walk in an upright position for more than a moment or two. As they matured, they crawled about on their bellies or sides. This did not prevent them from attempting to romp with normal litter mates as juveniles, and in a couple of instances an affected female and male mated successfully and the female reared her litter. Beginning about 3 weeks of age, these rats with virtually completely ablated cerebella showed frequent episodes of tonic, spastic episodes of the whole body lasting about 10 to 20 seconds. Partial cerebellectomy that did not include the midline deep nuclei had relatively little effect on locomotion. (Adult rats subjected to complete cerebellectomy were severely incapacitated, unable to stand or move in an upright position. After several weeks, they showed some recovery, enough to walk a few steps before toppling over.)

The essential features of radiation-induced malformation and ablation of the cerebellum in infancy are as follows. Malformation affected the organization of cerebellar cortex but spared the deep midline nuclei concerned with maintaining an upright position, and incoordination of movement resulted. Ablation destroyed the midline deep nuclei, removing essential mechanisms for maintaining the upright position (Hicks *et al.*, 1969).

C. Effects of Radiation Directed Locally to the Developing Hippocampal Formation in Infant Rats

Altman and co-workers (Bayer, Brunner, Hine, & Altman, 1973) focally irradiated the hippocampal region in infant rats on schedules of cumulative single doses of 150 or 200 R similar to those employed in the cerebellar work. From a long series of studies of normal development of the hippocampus, these workers were able to estimate quantitatively the deficits of neurons in the hippocampus, particularly the granule cells of the fascia dentata which develop relatively late. Reduction of the number of these cells ranged from 59% after 2 exposures to 84% after 8 exposures totaling 1300 R. At maturity, these animals functionally resembled rats whose hippocampal regions had been surgically ablated. They showed less than normal spontaneous alternation in a T-maze and poorer than normal acquisition and retention of a passive avoidance response. They were more than normally emotional and active in an open field. However, they were able to avoid shock more often than normals in a two-way (shuttle) conditioned shock avoidance experiment.

V. Effects of Radiation on Humans

There have been very few autopsies reported on humans exposed prenatally to radiation, but the available material and clinical experience
indicate that the basic cellular responses and kinds of malformative effects
from doses of hundreds of rads are similar to those in laboratory mammals.
Driscoll, Hicks, Copenhaver, and Easterday (1963) studied two human
fetuses exposed to radiation from radium at 4 and 5 months gestation. The
mothers of the fetuses were being treated for cancer of the cervix. One
fetus was irradiated for a period of about 1 day, the other for about 4 days.
The dose in various parts of the head in the first case was in the range of low
hundreds of R, and in the second case in the high hundreds to more than
1000 R near the surface of one part of the head. The circumstances of
irradiation were different from those in most of the experimental work
described: the irradiation was protracted, and the source was close to the
fetus, creating steep gradients of radiation fall-off as the distance from the
source increased. Nonetheless, the pathological effects in the brain were
quite comparable to those in animal experiments. The fetus with the lower
dose showed destruction of proliferative and migratory cells in the forebrain and cerebellum very similar to that seen in rats exposed in the range
of 100 to 300 R. In the other fetus, the damage was somewhat more extensive, comparable to that which we described earlier after correspondingly
higher doses.

Our knowledge of the epidemiological aspects of human irradiation was
extended considerably by studies of the Japanese exposed to the atomic
bombs in Nagasaki and Hiroshima in 1945 during World War II. Those
irradiated *in utero* have been followed carefully and compared with control
subjects who were not irradiated. A report by Wood, Johnson, and Omori
(1967) shows that the consequences of prenatal irradiation in humans are in
accord with findings in laboratory mammals. There were 183 individuals
exposed *in utero* to the bomb at Hiroshima, of whom 78 were fetuses of
15 weeks or less gestation at the time of exposure, and 105 were more than
15 weeks. Of the 78 exposed early, 25 showed head circumferences more
than 2 standard deviations below the mean for their age and sex ("microcephalic"), and 11 of these were mentally retarded (but 2 had Down's
syndrome); of the 105 exposed later in gestation, 7 were microcephalic as
defined, and 4 of these were retarded. Twenty-four were exposed less than
1200 meters (m) from the hypocenter of the bomb, 11 of these (including
the two cases of Down's syndrome), all less than 16 weeks gestation at the
time of exposure, were retarded. Except for the 2 cases of Down's syndrome,
which were not likely to have been caused by the bomb, there were no other
factors except substantial irradiation that could account for the other 9 cases

of mental deficiency. According to a 1965 estimate, the maximum doses of radiation for mothers were 1300 rads at 800 m, 447 rads at 1000 m, and 154 rads at 1200 m. Two of the other 4 retarded children were older fetuses when they were exposed and in the 1200- to 1500-m range, in which the estimated maternal doses dropped from 154 to 32 rads. The remaining two were exposed between 1500 and 1800 m, and one of them had had encephalitis in infancy. Mental retardation was diagnosed in the study only if the person was unable to perform simple calculations, carry on a simple conversation, care for himself, or if he or she was completely unmanageable or had been institutionalized. This study was made in 1965 when the subjects were about 20 years old. The same subjects had been examined in 1954, and there were usually psychometric studies available from the earlier periods, which were in good agreement with the diagnosis of mental retardation.

Children's heads have often been exposed to radiation in the treatment of fungus infections of the scalp ("ringworm"). Albert, Omram, Brauer, Dove, Cohen, Schmidt, Baumring, Morrill Schultz, and Baer (1966) made a follow-up study of 1548 cases of such radiation therapy compared with 1363 control cases without radiation therapy. Careful dosimetry established the radiation doses: the scalp received 500 to 800 rads while the surface of the brain received 140 rads. The children averaged 7 years of age when treated, and the report was made 12 years after those irradiated were treated, and 15 years after the control population received an alternative form of therapy. There were 5 cases of malignant neoplasm (leukemia, glioma, sarcoma) among the irradiated children, considerably in excess of what would be expected in the general population, and no neoplasms in the nonirradiated group. There were 45 cases of psychosis and personality or psychoneurotic disorders among the treated children, and only 13 among the controls. These diagnoses are so difficult to define and interpret that their significance is in doubt, but certainly more research on effects of low hundreds of rads in the juvenile period is needed.

Therapeutic abortion has often been considered when a fetus is known to be at risk for a serious form of developmental disorder, including that which could result from radiation. The evidence to be weighed in this regard for prenatal exposure includes: (1) observations in animals that as little as 20 rads may permanently change the development of nerve cell structure, (2) the threshold for alterations in the development of behavior in animals and humans lies between 25 and 50 rads, and (3) in children who are exposed *in utero* to a few rads in the latter part of gestation, there is a very slightly increased risk of developing certain tumors including those of the brain (Comar, 1972).

VI. Summary and Conclusions

Ionizing radiations produce a wide range of effects in mammals depending on the dose of radiation and the nature and stage of development of the cells and tissues exposed. Changes in differentiation, biochemical characteristics and function, delayed growth, mutations, and cell death are among the effects. Advantage has been taken of one effect, selective cell death in the developing nervous system after a specific dose, to bring about a series of reproducible malformations, especially in rats. Study of the morphogenetic sequences in the development of these malformations have helped to explain how the mammalian brain, including the human, develops abnormally. Experimental mammals with malformed brains have been used extensively in behavioral studies. For the most part, these have provided only very general correlations between abnormally developed parts of the brain and altered behavior, such as impairment of some discriminative functions in forebrain malformations, and motor disturbances in the presence of cerebellar abnormalities. Many experiments have shown sparing of functions in the presence of malformation of parts of the brain that would have been expected to be deleterious. Such observations are potentially valuable as models for determining how early brain injuries in humans disturb behavior in some cases but not in others.

There have been few precise studies of the pathologic effects of radiation on the developing human brain, but clinical follow-up studies, such as those of the Japanese exposed *in utero* to the atom bombs in 1945, provide evidence that radiation effects on humans are similar to those in experimental mammals.

Acknowledgments

The authors' work described here was supported by USPHS grant NS10531, and AEC contract AT(11–1)–1201.

References

Albert, R. E., Omram, A. R., Brauer, E. W., Dove, D. C., Cohen, N. C., Schmidt, H., Baumring, R., Morrill, S., Schultz, R., & Baer, R. L. Follow-up study of patients treated by X-ray for tinea capitis. *American Journal of Public Health*, 1966, **56**, 2114–2120.

Altman, J. Experimental reorganization of the cerebellar cortex. III. Regeneration of the external germinal layer and granule cell ectopia. *Journal of Comparative Neurology*, 1973, **149**, 153–180.

Altman, J. Effects of interference with cerebellar maturation on the development of locomotion. An experimental model of neurobehavioral retardation. In N. A. Buchwald &

M. A. B. Brazier (Eds.), *Brain mechanisms in mental retardation.* New York: Academic Press, 1975. Pp. 41–91.

Altman, J. Experimental reorganization of the cerebellar cortex. VII. Effects of late X-irradiation schedules that interfere with cell acquisition after stellate cells are formed. *Journal of Comparative Neurology*, 1976, **165**, 65–75.

Altman, J., & Anderson, W. J. Experimental reorganization of the cerebellar cortex. II. Effects of elimination of most microneurons with prolonged X-irradiation started at four days. *Journal of Comparative Neurology*, 1973, **149**, 123–131.

Altman, J., Anderson, W. J., & Wright, K. A. Gross morphological consequences of irradiation of the cerebellum in infant rats with repeated doses of low-level X-ray. *Experimental Neurology*, 1968, **21**, 69–91.

Bayer, S. A., Brunner, R. L., Hine, R., & Altman, J. Behavioral effects of interference with the postnatal acquisition of hippocampal granule cells. *Nature (London), New Biology*, 1973, **242**, 222–224.

Brunner, B. L., & Altman, J. Locomotor deficits in adult rats with moderate to massive retardation of cerebellar development during infancy. *Behavioral Biology*, 1973, **9**, 169–188.

Comar, C. L. (Chair) *Report of the advisory committee on the biological effects of ionizing radiations. The effects on populations of exposure to low levels of ionizing radiation.* Chap. 6. S. P. Hicks (Chair), J. I. Fabrikant, E. Furchtgott, R. W. Miller, J. J. Mulvihill, & M. R. Sikov, *Report of the subcommittee on effects on growth and development.* Washington, D.C.: Natl. Acad. Sci., 1972. Pp. 73–82.

D'Amato, C. J., & Hicks, S. P. Effects of low levels of ionizing radiation on the developing cerebral cortex of the rat. *Neurology*, 1965, **15**, 1104–1116.

de Vellis, J., & Schjeide, O. A. Effects of ionizing radiation on the biochemical differentiation of the rat brain. In M. R. Sikov & D. D. Mahlum (Eds.), *Radiation biology of the fetal and juvenile mammal. Proceedings of the ninth annual Hanford Biology Symposium.* Oak Ridge, Tenn.: US AEC, Div. Tech. Inf. Ext., 1969. Pp. 857–875.

Driscoll, S. G., Hicks, S. P., Copenhaver, E. H., & Easterday, C. L. Acute radiation injury in two human fetuses. *Archives of Pathology*, 1963, **76**, 113–119.

Fabrikant, J. I. *Radiobiology.* Chicago: Year Book Medical Publ., 1972. Pp. 154–186.

Falk, J. L., & D'Amato, C. J. Automation of pattern discrimination in the rat. *Psychological Reports*, 1962, **10**, 24.

Fowler, H., Hicks, S. P., D'Amato, C. J., & Beach, F. A. Effects of fetal irradiation on behavior in the albino rat. *Journal of Comparative and Physiological Psychology*, 1962, **55**, 309–314.

Furchtgott, E. Ionizing radiations and the nervous system. In G. E. Gaull (Ed.), *Biology of brain dysfunction.* New York: Plenum, 1975. Pp. 343–379.

Furchtgott, E., & Echols, M. Locomotor coordination following pre- and neonatal X-irradiation. *Journal of Comparative and Physiological Psychology*, 1958, **51**, 292–294.

Furchtgott, E., Echols, M., & Openshaw, J. W. Maze learning in pre- and neonatally X-irradiated rats. *Journal of Comparative and Physiological Psychology*, 1958, **51**, 178–180.

Furchtgott, E., Jones, J. R., Tacker, R. S., & Deagle, J. Aversive conditioning in prenatally X-irradiated rats. *Physiology and Behavior*, 1970, **5**, 571–576.

Furchtgott, E., Tacker, R. S., & Draper, D. O. Open-field behavior and heart rate in prenatally X-irradiated rats. *Teratology*, 1968, **16**, 441–452.

Gilmore, S. A. The effects of X-irradiation on the spinal cords of neonatal rats. I. Neurological observations. II. Histological observations. *Journal of Neuropathology and Experimental Neurology*, 1963, **22**, 285–301.

Gilmore, S. A. Long-term effects of ionizing radiation on the rat spinal cord: intramedullary connective tissue formation. *American Journal of Anatomy*, 1973, **137**, 1–18.

Goldstein, L., & Murphy, D. P. Etiology of ill-health of children born after maternal pelvic irradiation. II. Defective children born after postconception pelvic irradiation. *American Journal of Roentgenology and Radium Therapy*, 1929, **22**, 322–331.

Hicks, S. P. The effects of ionizing radiation, certain hormones, and radiomimetic drugs on the developing nervous system. *Journal of Cellular and Comparative Physiology*, 1954, **43** (Suppl. 1), 151–178. (a)

Hicks, S. P. Mechanism of radiation anencephaly, anophthalmia, and pituitary anomalies. *Archives of Pathology*, 1954, **57**, 363–378. (b)

Hicks, S. P. Radiation as an experimental tool in mammalian developmental neurology. *Physiological Reviews*, 1958, **38**, 337–356.

Hicks, S. P., Brown, B. L., & D'Amato, C. J. Regeneration and malformation in the nervous system, eye, and mesenchyme of the mammalian embryo after radiation injury. *American Journal of Pathology*, 1957, **33**, 459–481.

Hicks, S. P., & D'Amato, C. J. How to design and build abnormal brains using radiation during development. In W. S. Fields & M. M. Desmond (Eds.), *Disorders of the developing nervous system*. Springfield, Ill.: Thomas, 1961. Pp. 60–97.

Hicks, S. P., & D'Amato, C. J. Effects of radiation on the developing embryo and fetus. In J. V. Meigs & S. H. Sturgis (Eds.), *Progress in gynecology* (Vol. 4). New York: Grune & Stratton, 1963. Pp. 58–74. (a)

Hicks, S. P., & D'Amato, C. J. Malformation and regeneration of the mammalian retina following experimental radiation. In L. Michaux & M. Feld (Eds.), *Les phakomatoses cerebrales, deuxieme colloque international, malformations congenitales de l'encephale*. Paris: S.P.E.I., 1963. Pp. 45–51. (b)

Hicks, S. P., & D'Amato, C. J. Effects of ionizing radiations on mammalian development. In D. H. M. Woollam (Ed.), *Advances in teratology*. London: Logos Press, 1966. Pp. 195–250.

Hicks, S. P., & D'Amato, C. J. Functional adaptation after brain injury and malformation in early life in rats. In N. R. Ellis (Ed.), *Aberrant development in infancy: Human and animal studies*. Hillsdale, N. J.: Lawrence Erlbaum Associates, 1975. Pp. 27–47

Hicks, S. P., D'Amato, C. J., & Falk, J. L. Some effects of radiation on structural and behavioral development. *International Journal of Neurology*, 1962, **3**, 535–548. (a)

Hicks, S. P., D'Amato, C. J., & Joftes, D. L. The nature of the radiosensitive cells in the developing nervous system studied with tritiated thymidine. In B. Gross & V. Zeleny (Eds.), *Effects of ionizing radiation on the nervous system*. Vienna: IAEA, 1962. Pp. 199–205. (b)

Hicks, S. P., D'Amato, C. J., Klein, S. J., Austin, L. L., & French, B. C. Effects of regional irradiation or ablation of the infant rat cerebellum on motor development. In M. R. Sikov & D. D. Mahlum (Eds.), *Radiation biology of the fetal and juvenile mammal. Proceedings of the ninth annual Hanford Biology Symposium*. Oak Ridge, Tenn.: US AEC, Div. Tech. Inf. Ext., 1969. Pp. 739–753.

Hicks, S. P., D'Amato, C. J., & Lowe, M. J. The development of the mammalian nervous system. *Journal of Comparative Neurology*, 1959, **113**, 435–469.

Lipton, J. M. Locomotor behavior and neuromorphological anomalies in prenatally and postnatally irradiated rats. *Radiation Research*, 1966, **28**, 822–829.

Mullenix, P., & Norton, S. Prenatal irradiation and reproductive functions. *Neuroendocrinology*, in press.

Mullenix, P., Norton, S., & Culver, B. Locomotor damage in rats after X-irradiation *in utero*. *Experimental Neurology*, 1975, **48**, 310–324.

Norton, S., Mullenix, P., & Culver, B. Comparison of the structure of hyperactive behavior in rats after brain damage from X-irradiation, carbon monoxide and pallidal lesions. *Brain Research*, 1976, **116**, 49–67.

Sikov, M. R., & Mahlum, D. D. (Eds.) *Radiation biology of the fetal and juvenile mammal.*

Proceedings of the ninth annual Hanford Biology Symposium. Oak Ridge, Tenn.: USAEC, Div. Tech. Inf. Ext., 1969.

United Nations Scientific Committee on the Effects of Atomic Radiation. *Report* 24th Session, Supplement No. 13 (A/7613). New York: General Assembly, Official Records, 1969.

Walker, S., & Furchtgott, E. Effects of prenatal X-irradiation on the acquisition, extinction, and discrimination of a classically conditioned response. *Radiation Research*, 1970, **42**, 120–128.

Werboff, J., Havlena, J., & Sikov, M. R. Effects of prenatal X-irradiation on activity, emotionality, and maze-learning ability in the rat. *Radiation Research*, 1962, **16**, 441–452.

Wood, J. W., Johnson, K. G., & Omori, Y. *In utero* exposure to the Hiroshima atomic bomb. An evaluation of head size and mental retardation: Twenty years later. *Pediatrics*, 1967, **39**, 385–392.

HORMONAL INFLUENCES ON BRAIN AND BEHAVIORAL DEVELOPMENT

J. MAL WHITSETT AND JOHN G. VANDENBERGH[1]

Department of Zoology
North Carolina State University
Raleigh, North Carolina

Division of Research
North Carolina Department of Mental Health
Raleigh, North Carolina

I. Introduction

Our purpose is to discuss the influence of hormones early in life upon sex differences in the behavior of adults. We shall label this developmental process, the *sexual differentiation of behavior or neurobehavioral sexual differentiation.* It should be clear, however, that these are shorthand terms

[1] Present address: Department of Zoology, North Carolina State University, Raleigh, North Carolina 27607.

73

referring to the anatomical and physiological changes during fetal and neonatal life that are responsible for sex differences observed in the behavior
of adults. While we intend to provide an introduction to the subject of the
sexual differentiation of behavior, we also present selected issues that we
believe to be of current interest to researchers in this field. Finally, we
discuss the applicability of concepts derived largely from studies of laboratory rodents to behavioral development in primates and birds.

II. Sexual Differentiation

A. Reproductive System

The current theory of the sexual differentiation of behavior did not arise
in a vacuum. Long before behavioral investigations began, experimental
embryologists had clarified many of the processes of morphological sexual
differentiation. Because the rationale of the behavioral studies is based on
the previous morphological work, we shall examine briefly some aspects of
morphological differentiation before we go on to consider neurobehavioral
sexual differentiation.

The first step in the determination of the sex of a mammal occurs at conception when the egg is fertilized by either an X-bearing or a Y-bearing
sperm to produce the female (XX) or male (XY) complement of sex chromosomes. Although knowledge of the chromosomal complement allows us to
predict whether the individual in question will function as a male or female
in adulthood, it yields little information about sexual differentiation, the
developmental process by which this end is achieved. The Y chromosome
contributes, in some as yet unknown manner, to the initial stage of sexual
differentiation in the male mammal. When the Y chromosome is present,
the "indifferent" gonad develops into a testis; in its absence, the gonad
becomes an ovary. The reader interested in this process may consult the
recent monograph by Mittwoch (1973).

The sex ducts, the next reproductive tissues to undergo sexual differentiation, exist as *discrete primordia*. A fetus of either sex has both Wolffian and
Müllerian ducts. In a male the Wolffian ducts become the vas deferens,
epididymes, and sex accessories, whereas the Müllerian ducts eventually
regress. In a female, the Müllerian ducts develop into uterus, oviducts, and a
portion of the vagina, and the Wolffian ducts disappear. Male differentiation
results from the influence of secretory products of the testis. An androgen,
probably testosterone, stimulates development of the Wolffian ducts, and
some other, as yet unidentified, substance causes the Müllerian ducts to
regress. Sex duct differentiation in the female proceeds in the absence of
any gonadal influence. The ovaries, which develop somewhat more slowly

than the testes, are inactive during the period of sexual differentiation. Removal of ovaries has no effect on differentiation in females, whereas castration of the developing male results in the female pattern of development (Jost, 1953).

In our examination of the differentiation of the sex ducts, a principle has emerged that applies to the differentiation of physiological and behavioral systems as well as to morphological characteristics. A female mammal develops in the absence of any influence by the gonads. A male is produced only when tissues differentiate in the presence of secretions from the testis.

The external genitalia differentiate somewhat later than the sex ducts, but still during the fetal period in most mammals. In a female the labioscrotal folds develop into the labia majora and the undifferentiated phallus into a clitoris. In a male these anlagen become the scrotum and penis, respectively. Again, female differentiation occurs in a sex-hormone-free environment, whereas male genitalia differentiate under the influence of testicular androgen. The differentiation of the external genitalia differs from that of the ducts in one respect, however. There are no separate, discrete primordia for male and female tissues. They develop from a *single bipotential primordium.* For example, a phallus becomes either a penis or a clitoris. It is not possible to produce, through experimental manipulation or accidents of nature, an individual with both a clitoris and a penis. They have their origin in a single organ.[2]

B. *Neuroendocrine System*

During the breeding season, or year-round in continually breeding species, males tend to be rather constant in their readiness to mate. Females, however, generally exhibit cycles of readiness. Cycles of ovulation and receptivity are the result of constantly changing hormonal secretions of the hypothalamus, pituitary, and ovary. Hypothalamic neurohormones regulate the secretion of the gonadotropins, luteinizing hormone, and follicle-stimulating hormone by the anterior pituitary. A surge in the secretion of the

[2] A comment on the rather confusing notion of *hermaphroditism* is appropriate at this time. The term *hermaphrodite* is derived from Hermaphroditos, the name of the mythical son of Hermes and Aphrodite, whose body was joined in physical union with that of his spurned admirer, the nymph Salmacis. To zoologists, a hermaphrodite is an organism that produces both male and female gametes. In medical terminology, a hermaphroditic individual possesses the external genitalia characteristic of both sexes. As just noted, such a person would not have both a penis and a clitoris, although the development of a penis along with labia and a patent vagina has been documented. Finally, some writers use the term hermaphrodite to refer to any alteration of the genitalia in the direction of the configuration typical of the opposite sex. We shall have occasion to discuss genetic females with enlarged clitorides (Section III) and shall refer to them as *pseudohermaphrodites*, following the usage of Young *et al.* (1964).

gonadotropins stimulates ovulation of the egg from the ovarian follicle, and ovarian sex steriods are responsible for the induction of behavioral receptivity.

There is a fundamental sex difference in the ability of adults of a species to exhibit ovarian cyclicity; ovaries transplanted into castrated males fail to cycle. The basis for this difference was first established for rats and later verified for other species as well. Pfeiffer (1936) conducted a series of experiments in which he discovered that male rats receiving ovarian transplants would undergo regular cycles of ovarian development if they had been castrated shortly after birth. Pfeiffer interpreted his results as indicating that testicular secretions during the neonatal period were responsible for suppressing the ability of the pituitary to operate in a cyclical manner in its regulation of the ovary. More than two decades elapsed before this seminal research was pursued further. The eventual discovery that the pituitary is itself controlled by secretions of the hypothalamus was followed by studies that led to the present view that the control of presence or absence of cyclical pituitary and ovarian function lies in the hypothalamus itself. Crucial experiments were the demonstration that a male pituitary transplanted into a female maintains normal ovarian cyclicity (Harris & Jacobson, 1952) and the report of Wagner, Erwin, and Critchlow (1966) that implantation of testosterone directly into the brain of neonatal female rats abolishes the ability of these animals to exhibit normal ovarian cyclicity in adulthood.

This research concerning the control of cyclicity is important for several reasons. It established that neural tissue undergoes sexual differentiation just as does the reproductive system *per se*. Furthermore, neural differentiation follows the same rules as the differentiation of other tissues. That is, the female characteristic (cyclicity) develops in the absence of gonadal hormones whereas maleness (acyclicity) requires the addition of testicular androgenic secretions. Third, the research demonstrates that the sensitive period for the sexual differentiation of neural tissue may occur later in development than that of some of the other tissues and even, in certain species, may extend into the early postnatal period.

C. Sexual Behavior

1. GENERAL PRINCIPLES

It is in the behavior of animals and humans that we see some of the most interesting differences between the sexes. In fact, even if a species is otherwise monomorphic, the sexes must differ in their copulatory behavior, at the very least. There are several possible explanations to account for sex differences in behavior. Perhaps an adult animal of one sex fails to display the behavior characteristic of the opposite sex because it lacks the gonads, and thus the sex hormones, found in the opposite sex. A second possibility is that social experiences have determined the type of behavior exhibited in adulthood. Little information exists concerning this possibility in animals, but it is an especially important consideration in humans (to be discussed later). A third possible explanation is that behavioral sex differences are the result of hormonal conditions early in life. It is this view that has received the strongest experimental support and that will be the subject of the remainder of this chapter.

Systematic study of the sexual differentiation of behavior began only recently despite the existence of early reports containing relevant information for several species (guinea pigs, Dantchakoff, 1938; chickens, Domm & Davis, 1941; rats, J. G. Wilson, Hamilton, & Young, 1941). The importance of these studies, like that of Pfeiffer, was not appreciated for many years.

Current interest in the problem of the sexual differentiation of behavior was triggered by a study of guinea pigs by Phoenix, Goy, Gerall, and Young (1959). These investigators demonstrated that female offspring born of mothers that had been injected with testosterone propionate (TP) during pregnancy had masculinized genitalia. Furthermore, when ovariectomized and injected with estrogen and progesterone as adults, they exhibited less feminine sexual behavior than did control females that had not received androgen prenatally. Similarly, upon treatment with TP in adulthood, the prenatally androgenized females displayed more masculine sexual behavior than did the control females. Males born of the TP-injected mothers exhibited no morphological or behavioral aberrations. This study demonstrated clearly that the addition of androgen to a genetic female shifts behavioral propensities in the male direction. It also established a phenomenon that was to recur in many later studies. The effect of early hormone treatment on behavior generally is to alter the probability or intensity of a given behavior, rather than to eliminate entirely one behavior and create another, *de novo*.

The guinea pig was not an ideal species with which to take the next logical step, the determination of the behavioral effects of the removal of gonads early in development. In this species, with its relatively long gestation period of 63 days, sexual differentiation occurs entirely during the prenatal period. As we mentioned previously, neural sexual differentiation is not complete at birth in the rat. Clearly, castration is performed more easily after birth than *in utero*. Grady, Phoenix, and Young (1965) reported that male rats castrated at 5 days of age or earlier resembled females in that they readily displayed the female receptive posture (lordosis) and associated feminine behaviors when treated with estradiol benzoate (EB) and progesterone and placed with a stimulus male in adulthood. Males castrated at later ages were like normal males in their reduced ability to display feminine sexual behavior. Also, the neonatal castrates exhibited less complete masculine sexual behavior (fewer intromissions, ejaculations) in response to adult TP treatment than did control males castrated after the neonatal period.

The preceding studies, along with others conducted in the 1960s, indicated clearly that copulatory behavior resembles the morphology of the reproductive system and the ability to exhibit ovarian cyclicity in being regulated by hormonal conditions early in life. The normal female tendency toward display of feminine rather than masculine sexual behavior differentiates in the absence of gonadal secretions. The addition of androgen, either endogenously through testicular secretion in males or exogenously by injection in females, results in the male tendency to display masculine rather than feminine sexual behavior. Additional studies during this period confirmed the original conclusion and examined such matters as the temporal aspects of the phenomenon, its applicability to other species, and dosage-response relationships. References to many of these articles can be found in the reviews by Beach (1971) and by Goy and Goldfoot (1973). Rather than discuss the ample confirmatory work, we now shall examine several problems that currently are important to investigators studying the sexual differentiation of behavior.

2. SITE OF DIFFERENTIATION

The basic division of opinion concerning the region of the body at which androgen induces the male pattern of behavioral differentiation is similar to that in other areas of behavioral physiology. That is, does the hormone act centrally or peripherally? By central effects, one usually means direct effects of the hormone upon the brain and spinal cord. Peripheral effects generally are envisioned as changes in effector organs or in sensory receptors, which might or might not be located in the effector organ.

Because the two major aspects of neurobehavioral sexual differentiation, *defeminization* (production of acyclicity and suppression of feminine sexual behavior) and *masculinization* (stimulation of ability to display masculine sexual behavior), are viewed somewhat differently, each will be discussed separately.

Defeminization can be produced experimentally by implantation of TP directly into the brain of the neonatal female rat. Females treated in this manner are acyclic as adults (Sutherland & Gorski, 1972; Wagner *et al.*, 1966) and display less feminine sexual behavior than do control females (Nadler, 1968, 1972). A problem in interpreting such experiments is the difficulty of proving that none of the hormone migrated from the site of implantation to other regions of the brain or to some other part of the body.

Such leakage was detected by Nadler (1968). A later study by Nadler (1972), although not including an examination of peripheral tissues, found androgen implants to be effective in certain regions of the basal brain, particularly in the ventromedial hypothalamus, but not in other nearby regions. Such a result suggests that the spread of hormone was probably not too great.

The site at which androgen masculinizes the perinatal male has been more subject to question than has the site of defeminization. One reason for this difference is the existence of a plausible peripheral site for masculinization. For sexual behavior, at least, changes in the structure of the penis might be sufficient to account for the increase in masculine compulatory behavior observed after androgen treatment of perinatal females and the decrease in such behavior as a result of castration of males during this period (Beach, 1971).

There can be no question that the complete expression of copulatory behavior to the stage of ejaculation is facilitated by a fully formed and functioning penis. Structural alteration or desensitization of the penis acts to reduce substantially the ability of the adult male to ejaculate (Adler & Bermant, 1966; Beach & Holz, 1946). Castration of the neonatal rat results in a structurally deficient penis. In comparison to a male castrated later in life, the neonatal castrate has, even after androgen treatment in adulthood, a penis that is smaller (Larsson, 1966) and lacking in the epidermal spines or papillae that may offer sensory stimulation to the male during intromission (Beach, Noble, & Orndoff, 1969).

Such extensive structural deficiencies in the neonatally castrated rat lend plausibility to the view that masculinization of behavior is largely dependent upon masculinization of the phallus. However, several lines of research argue against this view. (1) Phallic and behavioral development can be dissociated experimentally. Treatment of castrated neonates with the androgen fluoxymesterone (Hart, 1972) stimulates penile development without inducing the capacity for the complete copulatory response, including ejaculation. (2) Mounting is less likely to be dependent upon phallic condition than are the subsequent elements of the masculine copulatory pattern, intromission and ejaculation. Female hamsters, unlike female rats, rarely mount. Numerous recent studies have demonstrated unequivocally that the ability of adult hamsters to mount is determined by the presence of androgen during the early postnatal period. Mounting is reduced by castration of the male as a neonate (Eaton, 1970) and is induced in the genetic female by neonatal treatment with androgen (Swanson & Crossley, 1971). Such females mount receptive females, but usually without insertion of the modified clitoris into the vagina of the stimulus animal. At the present time there is no reason to invoke phallic modification as the explanation for the increased mounting behavior resulting from neonatal exposure of hamsters to androgen. (3) The

occurrence of sex differences in several behaviors having little direct relationship to copulatory behavior, and thus not dependent upon the copulatory
organ, provides additional evidence that behavioral masculinization involves more than phallic modification. Aggressive behavior is readily
influenced by neonatal hormone conditions in house mice (Bronson &
Desjardins, 1968) (Section II, D), as is ventral-marking behavior in gerbils
(Turner, 1975).

In summary, the acyclicity and low levels of feminine behavior typically
found in males appear to be the result of the influence of androgen upon
central neural structures early in life. Whether the increased display of
masculine behaviors is similarly mediated is unknown, but changes in
penile structure appear to provide an incomplete explanation for all aspects
of behavioral masculinization.

3. HORMONE ACTION

Although the theory that sexual differentiation is dependent upon the
androgenic status of the perinatal mammal assumes that the testes secrete
androgen during the appropriate stage of development, there is little direct
evidence to support that assumption. Testosterone is present in the blood of
neonatal male rats, then declines and remains low until the surge of puberty
(Resko, Feder, & Goy, 1968). The fetal testis of the rat can produce testosterone *in vitro* during the early stages of sexual differentiation, but surprisingly, this ability declines sharply around the time of parturition (Warren,
Haltmeyer, & Eik-Nes, 1973). Fetal testes of male guinea pigs (Price,
Zaaijer, Ortiz, & Brinkmann, 1975), rhesus monkeys, and humans (see
Section III) also are known to secrete androgen.

All available evidence indicates that testicular androgen, most likely
testosterone, is responsible for neurobehavioral sexual differentiation.
Recently, however, it has been demonstrated that testosterone is a rather
labile molecule and often produces its physiological effects only after first
being converted to another molecule (J. D. Wilson & Gloyna, 1970). In
neural tissue androgens are converted (aromatized) to estrogens at a low
rate. The possible role of aromatization in neurobehavioral sexual differentiation (Reddy, Naftolin, & Ryan, 1974) currently is the subject of intensive
investigation. The aromatization hypothesis helps to explain several puzzling
phenomena, including the finding that the administration of estrogen to a
neonatal rodent does not feminize the animal, but rather mimics the
influence of androgen in eliminating estrous cyclicity, suppressing the display of feminine behaviors, and enhancing the exhibition of masculine
behaviors (Mullins & Levine, 1968; Paup, Coniglio, & Clemens, 1972). Also,
treatment with nonaromatizable androgens typically is ineffective in pro-

ducing neurobehavioral masculinization and defeminization when administered to neonates (Luttge & Whalen, 1970; Paup et al., 1972).

Although critical evaluation of the aromatization hypothesis is beyond the scope of this chapter, we want to point out that it will be difficult to obtain conclusive evidence demonstrating that the neural cells in which aromatization occurs (Reddy et al., 1974) are the same ones that undergo sexual differentiation. Also, some recent studies of hamsters and guinea pigs have produced results apparently inconsistent with the hypothesis (Gerall, McMurray, & Farrell, 1975; Goldfoot & van der Werff ten Bosch, 1975). Given the difficulty of performing critical experiments and the likelihood of species differences, probably we should reserve judgment, for the moment, on the possible role of aromatization in neurobehavioral sexual differentiation in normal male mammals.

In order to investigate the manner in which androgen produces the anatomical–physiological changes responsible for sex differences in behavior, it obviously is necessary to know the locus of such events. As discussed earlier, the identity of such a locus is none too certain, although it seems likely that at least neurobehavioral defeminization (elimination of estrous cyclicity and suppression of feminine sexual behavior) occurs in the hypothalamus of the brain. Certainly most investigators seeking biochemical explanations have been willing to make this assumption. Despite the publication of more than two dozen studies in the last several years, a biochemical explanation of the defeminization process has yet to emerge. Although we do not intend to review these studies, we do wish to call attention to two lines of research.

Before launching large-scale neurochemical studies, it is necessary to determine whether blood-borne testosterone finds its way to the presumptive locus of neurobehavioral sexual differentiation. Studies of the uptake of radioactively labeled testosterone that have employed liquid scintillation counting techniques generally have not found higher concentrations of radioactivity in the hypothalamus than in other brain regions or in blood following administration of [3H]testosterone to neonatal rats or mice (Heffner & van Tienhoven, 1973; Whitsett, Bronson, Peters, & Hamilton, 1972). Furthermore, the failure of nonlabeled testosterone to reduce uptake of [3H]testosterone in the hypothalamus of the neonatal rat implies the lack of a limited capacity uptake mechanism in this region (Barnea, Weinstein, & Lindner, 1972).

A recent finding, however, is consistent with the existence of a high affinity–low capacity receptor for testosterone in the neonatal brain. Using autoradiographic analysis, Sheridan, Sar, and Stumpf (1974) have demonstrated that the distribution of labeled testosterone or its metabolites following the administration of [3H]testosterone to the neonatal rat is similar to that in an adult male treated in this manner. Radioactivity was concentrated most highly in the nuclei of cells in the basal hypothalamus, preoptic area, and amygdala. Pretreatment with either testosterone or estradiol-17β inhibited the nuclear concentration of radioactivity.

It is reasonable to assume that the process of sexual differentiation involves alterations in ribonucleic acid (RNA) and protein metabolism. Although a number of reports have dealt with this hypothesis by examining changes in the synthesis of these macromolecules as a function of neonatal hormone status, the results are inconclusive. One line of research seems particularly promising, however. Several studies have investigated the influence of drugs that inhibit macromolecular synthesis upon the androgen-induced inhibition of estrous cyclicity. Kobayashi and Gorski (1970) injected neonatal female rats with TP and either actinomycin D or puromycin, inhibitors of the synthesis of RNA and protein, respectively. Actinomycin-D-treated females were protected somewhat against the anticipated production of acyclicity by TP. In subsequent studies the metabolic inhibitors have been placed directly into the brain of TP-treated females. Certain inhibitors of DNA synthesis (hydroxyurea, Salaman & Birkett, 1974), RNA synthesis (α-amanitin, Salaman & Birkett, 1974), and protein synthesis (cycloheximide, Gorski & Shryne, 1972) have been reported to block the androgen-induced sterilization of these animals whereas others have been ineffective. Although these studies have ignored the behavioral aspects of defeminization, perhaps future research will correct this shortcoming.

4. ORGANIZATION HYPOTHESIS

W. C. Young and his associates used the term *organization* in their descriptions of the influence of perinatal hormone conditions upon later behavior. Beach (1971) and others have argued that such studies provide evidence of alterations in response thresholds to hormones in adulthood, but not of the occurrence of organization, a structural concept historically applied to the differentiation of new tissues or organs in response to various inducing substances. Two lines of recent evidence bear upon this controversy, as follows.

Female rhesus monkeys exposed to androgen *in utero* are masculinized in their play behavior as juveniles (Section III,A). Of major importance is the fact that this sexually dimorphic play is exhibited prior to the secretion of gonadal hormones at puberty. Thus, early androgen conditions can influence behavior through a direct alteration of neural mechanisms underlying behavior in the absence of activating sex hormones. Similarly, Beach (1975) has demonstrated that female dogs treated with androgen perinatally may develop the leg-lifting urinary posture characteristic of males even when they receive no additional hormone treatment. Clearly, the effect of the presence or absence of androgen in perinatal life is not limited merely to an alteration of response thresholds to hormones in adulthood.

Accepting the structural limitation of the organization concept for the moment, we might ask whether there are structural differences in the brain in response to hormone conditions early in life. Only a little evidence is available. Dörner and Staudt (1968, 1969) have found that the cell nuclei of the preoptic area and hypothalamus are larger in females than in males. Castration of neonatal males results in an increase in nuclear volume unless accompanied by TP treatment. Raisman and Field (1971) have reported that male and female rats differ in synaptic connections in the preoptic. In males synapses involving axons that are not of amygdaloid origin terminate on the shafts of dendrites primarily, whereas in females, a significant number terminate on dendritic "spines." Castration of males as neonates increases the number of spine synapses, whereas neonatal androgen treatment of females reduces their number (Raisman & Field, 1973). The possibility that androgen during perinatal life alters neural connections in a region of the brain highly involved in sexual physiology and behavior would be consistent with an organizational influence of such androgen. Particularly promising as a system in which structural responses to hormones may be studied is the sexual dimorphism in size of brain regions involved in vocalization in canaries and zebra finches (Nottebohm & Arnold, 1976).

In terms of the present argument concerning the term organization, there appears to be sufficient evidence to stay its removal from the lexicon of the behavioral endocrinologist. However, a more fundamental matter is at issue as well. It no longer seems appropriate to limit the concept of organization to gross structural changes. As a result of more than a decade of revolutionary advance in molecular biology, structure–function distinctions, once so appealing to anatomists and physiologists, have lost most of their meaning at the level of interacting molecules. Even the membrane of a cell, so clearly a structural entity, now is viewed as being highly organized, yet fluid and constantly changing. If reduced sensitivity of a behavioral mechanism to hormone stimulation accurately describes one influence of perinatal androgen, its biochemical basis may lie in a reduced number or altered configuration of receptor proteins. However, such *structural* changes may, in turn, result from altered rates of metabolism of other molecules involved in the regulation of the abundance and configuration of the receptors. Attempts to delineate the structural aspects of such interactions are unlikely to be rewarding. There may be good reasons for being reluctant to apply the concept of organization to the influence of perinatal hormone conditions upon later behavior. Its use to describe the elimination of a behavior or physiological process seems incongruous, for example. Yet to reject organization for its structural connotations may be to insist upon etymological purity at the cost of losing a useful explanatory construct.

5. BISEXUALITY OF BEHAVIOR

The ideal species for the study of the sexual differentiation of behavior has not yet been discovered. In such a species, christened the "ramstergig" by Beach (1971), males would behave only in a masculine manner and females would be entirely feminine. Thus, members of each sex in this species would be entirely *heterosexual* and would direct their mating behavior only toward members of the opposite sex. Considerable confusion in the study of neurobehavioral sexual differentiation arises from the fact that in every species yet examined, *bisexual* behavior has been observed; that is, a member of one sex of the species can perform the copulatory behavior that is considered to be appropriate for the opposite sex, and will direct that behavior toward members of its own sex. Often when such behavior is observed in nature or in zoos, it is labeled as *homosexual* behavior. However, this is generally a misnomer because the same animal also will exhibit behavior normal for its sex. Needless to say, there is strong natural selective pressure against purely homosexual behavior.

Another distinction is required. Bisexual behavior may be either *manifest* (exhibited under relatively natural conditions) or *latent* (exhibited only under highly contrived conditions). While manifest bisexuality is dramatic and worthy of explanation, latent bisexuality perhaps poses the greater obstacle to the generality of the theory of behavioral sexual differentiation. An example of latent bisexuality is seen in the male hamster which rarely displays the feminine lordotic posture under normal conditions. Treatment of the male hamster with estrogen and progesterone, however, readily elicits such feminine behavior (Tiefer, 1970).

All species observed thus far are *partially* bisexual, in the sense that bisexuality, manifest or latent, is found predominantly or exclusively in only one sex of the species. In rats, the female is more bisexual than the male in that females frequently mount, whereas males exhibit lordosis only occasionally (Pfaff, 1970). The reverse is true of the hamster; the male displays the lordotic posture under the proper hormonal and stimulus conditions, but the normal adult female almost never mounts even when administered androgen prior to testing. The mouse resembles the rat, and the rhesus monkey appears analogous to the hamster in that males "present" but females exhibit little mounting.

The regular occurrence in a species of individuals that are capable of exhibiting both masculine or feminine sexual behavior raises doubts concerning the thesis that the anatomical–physiological substrate of behavior undergoes a developmental process of sexual differentiation analogous to that occurring in the tissues of the reproductive system. In fact, the widespread acceptance of the thesis owes much to a careful selection of species and problems. Rats generally are used in studies of defeminization whereas hamsters furnish the most convincing data on masculinization. In other words, one usually studies the influence of perinatal hormone conditions upon the more sexually dimorphic copulatory pattern of a species. Now we shall consider whether the existence of bisexuality constitutes evidence against neurobehavioral sexual differentiation or whether it is explicable within the confines of this theory.

Two models of the sexual differentiation of behavior, both based on the sexual differentiation of the reproductive system, have been proposed by Goy (1970). One of these models is not easily reconciled with the occurrence of normal bisexuality of behavior, whereas the other one may be.

The *first* model is based on the mode of sexual differentiation of the external genitalia. As we mentioned earlier (Section II,A), a bipotential primordium differentiates into either a male or a female organ; the phallus, for example, becomes either a penis or a clitoris. It cannot become both of these. As Goy (1970) has discussed, data on behavioral differentiation in guinea pigs appear consistent with this model. The administration of androgen prenatally both augments masculine sexual behavior and suppresses feminine sexual behavior (Goy, Bridson, & Young, 1964). Furthermore, Phoenix, Goy, and Young (1967) found a correlation between masculinization and defeminization in individual androgenized females. The bipotential primordium model of neurobehavioral sexual differentiation, with its implication that masculinization necessarily implies defeminization, appears to be inconsistent with the existence of individuals capable of exhibiting both masculine and feminine sexual behavior.

The *second* model of sexual differentiation postulates the existence of discrete male and female primordia, one of which develops while the other regresses. We have seen this situation in the differentiation of the sex ducts. According to this model, it is at least theoretically possible, if difficult in practice, to maintain both masculine and feminine systems into adulthood. Experimental preservation of both the Wolffian and Müllerian sex ducts beyond the stage of sexual differentiation has been accomplished (Jost, 1953). Similarly, the maintenance of both masculine and feminine behavioral systems into adulthood has been achieved by experimental manipulation in two species. (1) Male rats castrated neonatally and injected with androstenedione at this time exhibit, under the proper hormonal conditions in adulthood, both lordosis and complete masculine copulatory behavior, including intromission and ejaculation (Goldfoot, Feder, & Goy, 1969; Stern, 1969). (2) Treatment of neonatal female hamsters with low dosages of

TP induces the ability to mount in response to androgen treatment in adulthood, without suppressing lordotic behavior in response to the administration of estrogen and progesterone (Debold & Whalen, 1975; Whitsett & Vandenbergh, 1975) or reducing the ability of intact females to cycle, mate, bear and rear young (Whitsett & Vandenbergh, 1975).

The coexistence of masculine and feminine mating patterns after experimental manipulation indicates that the discrete primordial model is applicable to neurobehavioral sexual differentiation in at least two species. In addition, it raises the possibility that the natural occurrence of bisexuality may not be contrary to the theory that sexual behavior undergoes a process of sexual differentiation in response to the hormonal milieu during perinatal development. Unfortunately, little evidence is available concerning the basis of normal bisexuality. Clemens and Coniglio (1971) observed a positive correlation between the mounting behavior of female rats and the number of males present *in utero*. Ward and Renz (1972) demonstrated that prenatal treatment with the antiandrogen, cyproterone acetate, blocks the development of mounting in female rats. These results suggest that the bisexuality of the female rat may be a result of exposure to androgen sufficient to masculinize but not defeminize genetic females. The ability of male hamsters to exhibit lordosis may result from the exposure, during neonatal life, to an amount of endogenous androgen that is sufficient to induce the ability to mount and to eliminate the capability for estrous cyclicity (demonstrated by ovarian implantation, Swanson, 1970), but not to eliminate entirely the ability to display lordosis under the right hormonal conditions (Swanson & Crossley, 1971). Thus, normal bisexuality found in one sex of a species may reflect the androgenicity of the perinatal environment of the members of that sex.

Because bisexuality is found exclusively or predominantly in only one sex of a species, Goy (1974, p. 3) has called attention to the "inverse relation between the sexes with respect to bisexuality; thus the greater the bisexuality of the male, the less the bisexuality of the female, and vice versa." We suggest that it may be useful to expand upon this idea by regarding entire species as lying on a sexuality continuum extending from complete maleness to complete femaleness. Because the adjectives *masculine* and *feminine* have been used in a specific and limited sense in this chapter as well as in other recent writings, we have chosen to characterize species on the female side of the continuum (Fig. 1) as being *gynecomorphous*[3] and those on the male side as *andromorphous*.

The criterion being used for assignment of species to a position on the continuum is the sex in which bisexuality of behavior predominantly occurs.

---

[3] "Having the form, appearance, or attributes of a female"—Random House Dictionary of the English Language, Unabridged Edition, 1966.

Thus the greater bisexuality found in female than in male rats and mice results in these species being characterized as relatively andromorphous. Masculine behavioral traits are found in both sexes, whereas feminine behavior is seen primarily in the female. Male bisexuality is seen in hamsters and rhesus monkeys. As a result, they may be viewed as occupying a position on the gynecomorphic side of the continuum. Although one hesitates to place humans on this continuum, the apparently greater incidence of manifest bisexuality (including adolescent "homosexual" experience) in males than in females of the population examined by Kinsey, Pomeroy, Martin, and Gebhard (1953) raises the possibility that we are a relatively gynecomorphous species.

No species can move too far toward either end of the continuum and retain its capability for sexual reproduction. Of course, some species have become exclusively female, reproducing by means of parthenogenesis. Even with the restriction on sexual reproduction, there remains considerable opportunity for interspecific variation. The distribution of species along the sexuality continuum is unknown. Three hypothetical distributions are shown in Fig. 1. First, it is possible that species are normally distributed around the midpoint represented by the purely heterosexual species. The second distribution assumes that, within the limits defining sexually reproducing species, position is of no particular consequence. As a

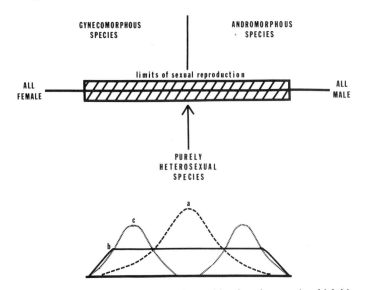

FIG. 1. Species sexuality continuum. Species position based on sex in which bisexuality of behavior predominantly occurs. Lower section of figure represents three hypothetical distributions of species along continuum: a, normal distribution around mean occupied by purely heterosexual species; b, random distribution of species within limits of sexual reproduction; c, bimodal distribution with purely heterosexual species at trough.

result, no position would be considered any more likely to occur, *a priori*, than another. The third distribution assumes that there may be significance in the failure to identify any purely heterosexual species as yet, and thus it is bimodal in nature. Certainly one of the peaks in this bimodal distribution may be higher than the other. The frequent observation of mounting by females in many species raises the possibility that the andromorphous peak would be the higher of the two. As existing laboratory species form a regrettably small sample of mammalian species, the empirical demonstration of the nature of the distribution of species along the continuum cannot be anticipated in the near future.

It is not clear why a particular position on the continuum is occupied by a given species. Perhaps bisexuality (particularly the latent form) is neither advantageous nor disadvantageous in some species. Thus the position of such a species would be essentially a pleiotropic result of natural selection of other, more important, traits. In other species bisexual behavior is of social consequence. In the rhesus monkey, for example, the ostensibly anomalous feminine "presenting" posture exhibited by males is part and parcel of social dominance interactions.

Finally, we wish to suggest that interspecific variation in position along the sexuality continuum is a reflection of interspecific variation in perinatal physiology. In the simplest form, this hypothesis implies that *both* males and females of andromorphous species are exposed to greater quantities of androgen perinatally than are their counterparts in gynecomorphous species. In the purely heterosexual species, the female would be exposed to too little androgen to induce the ability for mounting and the male would be exposed to a large quantity of androgen, sufficient not only for masculinization, but also for complete defeminization. Because this outcome would require the greatest difference between the sexes in the androgenicity of the perinatal environment to be found in any species represented by a position on the continuum, the purely heterosexual species may be the most difficult of all species to create. The existence of both andromorphous and gynecomorphous strains within a single domestic species (guinea pigs, Goy, 1974) is both remarkable and indicative of a developmental tendency to avoid the midpoint of the continuum.

D. Aggressive Behavior

Copulatory behavior is the most dramatic, but not the sole, behavior that is different in males and females. Typically the sex differences in other behaviors are quantitative rather than qualitative, and as a result, it is often misleading to speak of such behaviors as being either masculine or feminine. Nonetheless, hormone conditions during the perinatal period influence the development of sex differences in these noncopulatory behaviors. In order to illustrate the applicability of the concepts discussed earlier to behaviors other than copulation, we now shall examine briefly the aggressive behavior of laboratory house mice.

For some time it has been known that male mice fight more readily than females, and that fighting in males is reduced by castration and enhanced by exogenous androgen treatment (Beeman, 1947; Tollman & King, 1956). Bronson and Desjardins (1968) and Edwards (1968) demonstrated that the sex difference was attributable to hormone conditions in early life. Female mice injected with either TP or EB neonatally were more aggressive than were control females. The aggressiveness of females in adulthood is maximized by the administration of large amounts of TP soon after birth (Bronson & Desjardins, 1970; Whitsett et al., 1972). The demonstration that massive amounts of TP are effective when administered later in development (Edwards, 1970) indicates the existence of a maximally sensitive period rather than a critical period for the androgen-induced enhancement of aggression.

Castration of neonatal male mice reduces the level of fighting exhibited in adulthood unless the males also receive TP during the neonatal period (Bronson & Desjardins, 1969). Peters, Bronson, and Whitsett (1972) have shown that castration is most effective in reducing the aggressive responsiveness of adults to exogenous androgen if the operation is performed prior to Day 6 of postnatal life. Using a more sensitive assay system, Owen, Peters, and Bronson (1973) found that Day 10 castrates were retarded in their response to a single injection of TP in adulthood in comparison to males castrated at 50 days of age, a finding that again illustrates that the delineation of a sensitive period in developmental studies is greatly influenced by the methodology of a given experiment.

Despite the clear-cut nature of many of the experiments on the influence of neonatal hormone conditions upon aggression in the adult mouse, it must be understood that fighting by adult female mice is not unknown (Anderson & Hill, 1965; Crowcroft & Rowe, 1963). Such fighting is enhanced by the physiological events associated with lactation (Gandelman, 1972), the use of a juvenile mouse as an opponent (White, Mayo, & Edwards, 1969), and the rearing of females in groups rather than in isolation (Gray, 1976). It now appears that studies of the sexual differentiation of aggression have been conducted under conditions that maximized the aggressiveness of male mice but minimized that of females. That is, the animals were reared in isolation and generally fought against an adult opponent. As a result, the sex difference is extreme, and support for a differentiating role of androgen is strong. Nonetheless, when such modifying factors are taken into account, males still appear to exhibit more aggression than females (Gray, 1976).

Androgen in neonatal life does influence aggressive behavior in mice, but the effect is subtle and quantitative, rather than all-or-none as was implied in the initial studies.

III. Sexual Differentiation in Primates

A. Monkeys

The rhesus monkey is the only nonhuman primate in which the sexual differentiation of behavior has been studied. This species was chosen purposely (Phoenix, 1974) because pseudohermaphroditic rhesus monkeys have been produced and the anatomy of their reproductive tract was described (Wells & van Wagenen, 1954). These animals were females with ovaries but masculine genitalia and perhaps some modification of the Müllerian duct system. Furthermore, behavioral studies by Rosenblum (1961) had revealed a striking sex difference in play behavior that might be subject to hormonal conditions in early life.

A number of investigations of the anatomical and behavioral consequences of prenatal hormones have been reviewed in detail elsewhere (Phoenix, 1974; Young, Goy, & Phoenix, 1964). Here only certain aspects of these studies will be summarized. Phoenix (1974) presents a particularly lucid summary of the experimental results and much of the material reviewed in the following paragraphs stems from his review.

A considerable sex difference exists in the levels of testosterone in the blood of fetal monkeys (Resko, 1970, 1975; Resko, Malley, Begley, & Hess, 1973). Umbilical arterial blood from male fetuses contains approximately three times the concentration of testosterone as that from female fetuses (Fig. 2). There is, however, great variability in the blood level of testosterone in male fetuses with some males having a concentration equal to or less than the mean of that seen in females (Resko, 1975). The testosterone level in the systemic circulation of pregnant female monkeys also varies with the sex of the fetus. Pregnant females at 100–150 days of gestation carrying a male fetus have a mean testosterone level twice that of those carrying female fetuses.

In view of the elevated level of testosterone in maternal circulation resulting from the presence of a male fetus, a preliminary report of research on pigtail macaques (*Macaca nemestrina*) may be very interesting. Erwin and Anderson (1975) observed the aggressive behavior of 15 pregnant females in social groups of 10–20 animals and found that females carrying male fetuses displayed higher levels of aggression and were more socially dominant than females carrying female fetuses. This finding is not conclusive because of the small sample tested but should stimulate a more detailed examination of the influence of fetal sex on maternal behavior.

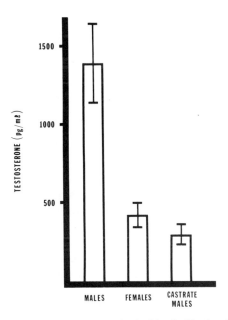

FIG. 2. The concentration of testosterone in the blood of fetal male, female, and castrated male monkeys. Drawn from data in Resko *et al.* (1973).

Fetal progesterone concentration in monkeys also differs between the sexes, with females having approximately double the male levels (Resko, 1975). The importance of this difference is not known but Resko has suggested that since progesterone can protect the female against the masculinizing and defeminizing effects of testosterone in rodents, it may act similarly in the monkey fetus to protect it against the action of the small amounts of testosterone that are present in the female (Resko, 1974, 1975). The absolute levels of the hormones may not be important but rather the ratio between fetal testosterone and progesterone may determine the direction of sexual differentiation. The ratio of testosterone to progesterone in male monkey fetuses is approximately 10-fold higher than in females.

How the absolute level of testosterone or the higher ratio of testosterone to progesterone acts upon neural tissue to influence later behavior is unknown. No sex differences in brain structures have been reported in monkeys as have been noted in birds and rodents (Nottebohm & Arnold, 1976; Raisman & Field, 1971). Nevertheless, differences in behavior between males and females are observed and some of these sexually dimorphic behaviors can be influenced by prenatal hormone manipulations.

In the behavioral studies, the results obtained from eight pseudohermaphroditic female monkeys were compared with a larger number of untreated

male and female monkeys. The pseudohermaphrodites were produced by
injecting pregnant females with different dosages of TP at varying times
during gestation. Although the pregnant females received varying regimens of TP, the effects on the female offspring were sufficiently similar
that they were regarded as belonging to a single treatment group. All of the
genetic female offspring were born with a well-developed scrotum and a
small but normally formed penis. After weaning at 3 months of age the offspring were caged individually except during short intervals daily when
they were housed in small groups with peers of both sexes. Observations of
these monkeys over a 4-year period revealed that five behaviors were
exhibited more frequently by males than females: rough-and-tumble play,
threat, play initiation, chasing play, and mounting. The pseudohermaphroditic females displayed frequencies of these behaviors intermediate
between those of the untreated males and females. A sample of these data
showing the mean frequency of rough-and-tumble play is illustrated in
Fig. 3. In addition to the difference in the frequency of behaviors shown
between the sexes there were also qualitative differences in some of the
behaviors such as mounting.

The differences between males and females and the intermediate status

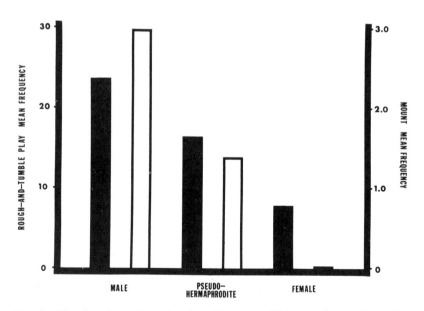

Fig. 3. The frequency of rough-and-tumble play (solid bar) and mounting behavior
(open bar) of male, female, and pseudohermaphroditic monkeys 12–15 months of age. Redrawn from Phoenix (1974).

of the pseudohermaphrodites seem to be a consequence of prenatal exposure to testosterone which does not require "activation" by artificial hormone manipulation later in life (Section II,C,4). The possible role of androgens "activating" sexual behavior has been tested in a small number of the pseudohermaphroditic females (Eaton, Goy, & Phoenix, 1973). When ovariectomized and treated with different dosages of TP for 30 weeks, the pseudohermaphroditic females showed increased sex-related behaviors with some exhibiting mounting. One individual achieved intromission and ejaculation. It would thus seem that some sexually dimorphic behaviors do not require an "activating" exposure to androgens for expression but that the expression of some sex-related behaviors can be potentiated by the presence of androgens later in life.

In addition to changes in behavior, pseudohermaphroditic females attain puberty 7.6 months later than control females (Goy, 1966). They menstruate through a penis rather than a vagina and, once established, the ovarian cycles are comparable to those of control females. This result may be analogous to the recent finding that female hamsters treated neonatally with dosages of TP too low to abolish estrous cyclicity begin cycling at a later age than do normal females (Whitsett & Vandenbergh, 1975). In both species males mature sexually later than females. Perhaps the timing of pubertal development is another sexually dimorphic characteristic regulated by hormone conditions in perinatal life. Blood levels of ovarian hormones monitored during a single cycle in the pseudohermaphroditic female monkeys were normal, showing both the preovulatory estrogen surge and the postovulatory rise in progesterone (Goy & Resko, 1972). This apparently normal ovarian cyclicity in the rhesus monkey after prenatal androgen exposure contrasts directly with the marked disruption of ovarian cycles generally produced by androgen treatment of female rats and may be due to differences in the doses of androgen given or to basic differences in ovarian function between these species.

B. Human Gender Orientation

The human fetal testis also contains a significant amount of testosterone at the time of genital differentiation, whereas the ovary and adrenal in both sexes remain relatively quiescent (Reyes, Winter, & Faiman, 1973). More recently, Reyes, Boroditsky, Winter, and Faiman (1974) reported that testosterone concentration in fetal blood was higher in male than in female human fetuses and peaked between 14 and 18 weeks of fetal age. Although there is a significant difference between androgen levels in male and female fetuses, there is a great deal of individual variability within a sex in humans as well as in monkeys. More than half of the 33 human female fetuses had blood levels of testosterone equal to or greater than the lowest values in males, suggesting that some differences in later behavior may be due to variations in prenatal hormone levels.

Prompted by the experiments conducted on rodents and nonhuman primates, studies have been undertaken to determine whether the sex differences in gonadal hormones during the prenatal period in humans could underlie sexual differences shown in later behavior. These studies have been reviewed (Ehrhardt & Baker, 1974; Money & Ehrhardt, 1971, 1972) and more recently have been critically examined by Quadagno, Briscoe, and Quadagno (1977). Data from two sources provide information bearing on the question of whether prenatal hormones influence human behavior: (1) endocrine imbalances during the prenatal period resulting from spontaneous genetic anomalies or other pathological conditions and (2) the treatment of certain disorders, such as threatened miscarriage, with hormones.

The best studied of the spontaneous anomalies is the adrenogenital syndrome. This is a genetically recessive, autosomal condition, which, in the homozygous state, results in an excessive production of adrenal androgens beginning in the fetal period and continuing throughout life. After birth, the condition can be controlled by cortisone therapy and the afflicted girls are thus protected against the masculinizing effects of adrenocortical hormones. This syndrome results in the production of both male and female offspring that have been exposed prenatally to a complex of adrenocortical hormones having androgenic properties.

In addition to the spontaneously occurring adrenogenital syndrome, clinical treatment over the past two decades for pregnancy-maintenance involving the use of artificial progestins has resulted in the exposure of fetuses to androgenic compounds. The progestins used in this treatment are similar in structure to androgens and had androgenic effects on fetal tissues (Ehrhardt & Money, 1967; Wilkins, Jones, Holman, & Stempfel, 1958). Exposure to such progestins resulted in a variable amount of genital masculinization of female babies in which the phallus is enlarged and labioscrotal folds may be fused. Surgical feminization of the genitalia is necessary if the degree of masculinization is great.

These conditions, resulting from anomalies of development or endocrine therapy during pregnancy, mirror to a considerable extent those produced experimentally in rodents and monkeys. Female individuals with adrenogenital syndrome or those born to mothers treated with progestins have been exposed, as fetuses, to abnormally high levels of androgens. Although there are marked similarities between the human clinical conditions and the experimentally induced conditions in animals, comparisons must be drawn with caution not only because of known and unknown species differences but also because of the nature of the data. The animal data have been obtained mainly by controlled experiments, whereas the human material is based upon observant researchers taking advantage of opportunities afforded by the clinic.

Much of what is known about the influence of prenatal androgens on sexual differentiation and development in females derives from a series of studies on 10 girls with progestin-induced pseudohermaphroditism and 15 girls with the adrenogenital syndrome (Money & Ehrhardt, 1972). The studies indicated that the behavioral traits of these girls tended more to masculinity than to femininity. One characteristic possessed by many of the girls was increased involvement in activities requiring a high level of physical energy expenditure. For example, 9 out of 10 girls born to mothers treated with progestins expressed an interest in outdoor activities and preferred to compete with boys in sports (Ehrhardt & Money, 1967). Although the girls showed signs of "tomboyism," there were no indications of lesbianism and a normal, but delayed, heterosexual development was the rule (Money & Ehrhardt, 1972).

The two other clinical conditions which provide some insight into the role of prenatal hormones in human development are the androgen-insensitivity syndrome and Turner's syndrome. The androgen-insensitivity syndrome, which only affects males, is characterized by a discrepancy between genetic and genital sex. Although the males have the normal XY chromosomes and testes, they are born with female external genitalia of normal appearance (Masica, Money, Ehrhardt, & Lewis, 1969). The testes of such males produce androgens and estrogens but the target tissues are insensitive to the androgens. Individuals with Turner's syndrome develop with a chromosome complement of 44 (XO) or sometimes the second sex chromosome is present but fragmented. As a result of this genetic anomaly the gonads of such individuals remain undeveloped and the afflicted individuals are denied exposure to gonadal hormones either pre- or postnatally. Patients displaying Turner's syndrome differentiate morphologically as phenotypic females.

The behavioral consequences of these syndromes are poorly known because even fewer subjects have been studied than in the work with patients displaying the adrenogenital syndrome and progestin-induced pseudohermaphroditism. Money and Ehrhardt (1972) review the data available, mostly from their own studies at the Johns Hopkins Hospital. The 10 androgen-insensitive individuals studied show strong feminine orientation. For example, 8 of the 10 preferred marriage and home to a career and had played with dolls and with other girl's toys. Eight of the 10 had exclusively heterosexual relations with males and six of these reported normal levels of libido. Nine of the 10 rated themselves content with the female role. Thus, although genetically these individuals were male, their insensitivity to androgens resulted in their appearance as females and their behavioral development as feminine.

The results with Turner's syndrome patients are much the same. Their interest in physical activities, choice of play objects, clothing, and physical appearance are differentiated in a feminine rather than masculine direction (Ehrhardt, Greenburg, & Money, 1970). These results conform to the animal data demonstrating that in the absence of gonadal hormones behavioral development proceeds in a feminine direction. Quadagno *et al.* (1977) have suggested, as an alternative hypothesis to the findings of Money and his associates, that much of the modification in gender orientation is due to a self-fulfilling prophecy rather than prenatal endocrine influences. They suggest that the girls with adrenogenital syndrome and with progestin-induced pseudohermaphroditism were responding to parental attitudes during early development and that the parental influences shaped the behavior of their afflicted offspring toward a masculine orientation. With samples as small as those available and with the limitations of clinical data these interpretations are possible. However, the bulk of the animal literature supports the conclusion that perinatal endocrine influences play a strong role in shaping later behaviors and it seems unlikely that humans are immune to such influences.

C. Human Intelligence and Fetal Hormone Levels

In addition to modifications of psychosexual orientation, the fetally androgenized girls studied displayed an apparent elevation in IQ in comparison to expected values (Money, 1971; Money & Lewis, 1966). Sixty percent of a sample of 70 adrenogenital syndrome girls had IQ scores of 110 or above. Similarly, in a study of 10 girls with progestin-induced pseudohermaphroditism, Ehrhardt and Money (1967) found a mean IQ of 125 (SD ± 11.8). The conclusion that fetal androgenization resulted in elevated IQ received support from Dalton's (1968) findings on the educational achievement of 29 children born to mothers treated with progesterone because of toxemia of pregnancy. Teachers rated the progesterone-exposed children significantly higher than control children in all academic subjects. These latter findings are particularly impressive because comparisons were made with carefully selected control populations in this study.

Ehrhardt and Baker (1974) have recently had the opportunity to replicate the earlier work on fetally androgenized individuals. They have examined the consequences of the adrenogenital syndrome on 17 female and 10 male patients. All of the patients were receiving cortisone therapy and all of the girls had undergone surgery for genital correction. The siblings and the parents of the children with the adrenogenital syndrome were used as controls. Girls with the adrenogenital syndrome showed more boyish traits than the control girls. Still, the afflicted girls were not considered sexually abnormal by their parents or peers and were clearly identified in a female role.

The same sets of patients and controls were used by Baker and Ehrhardt (1974) to reexamine the possibility that elevated levels of prenatal androgens could improve intelligence. In this study, family socioeconomic status and genetic background were controlled by utilizing siblings and parents as control populations. Control for genetic background was not part of the design of the previous studies and may be an important consideration because both parents and some siblings carry the adrenogenital syndrome trait since the condition is transmitted by an autosomal recessive gene. The mean IQ of the patients with adrenogenital syndrome was significantly elevated from the norm but was not significantly different from their siblings or parents. Similarly, the mean IQs of male and female patients did not differ significantly. The values were 111 $\pm$21 for males and 113 $\pm$14 for females. Money and Lewis (1966) also had found no difference in IQ between the girls they studied with adrenogenital syndrome and their siblings.

The findings of elevated IQs among patients with the adrenogenital syndrome confirms the previous studies (Money & Lewis, 1966) but, as Quadagno *et al.* (1977) have suggested, the elevated IQs among the parents and siblings of these patients suggest that genetic factors or environmental conditions related to being reared in families with high intelligence could have influenced the high IQs observed. It thus seems, as Baker and Ehrhardt (1974) state, that "the enhancement of intellectual development cannot be attributed specifically to the prenatal and/or postnatal hormonal aspects of the adrenogenital syndrome, since patients did not differ in IQ from unaffected siblings and parents" (p. 72). A preliminary report by Reinisch (1976) presents results similar to those of Baker and Ehrhardt.

In summary, the results obtained from studies on humans with a variety of clinical syndromes conform remarkably well to the results of animal experimentation. Females exposed to androgenic substances prenatally appear to be masculinized in certain behavioral traits, and males denied exposure to prenatal androgens are feminized. The strongest evidence for the important role played by prenatal hormones in humans is seen in genetic males with androgen insensitivity. These individuals are clearly feminine in appearance and orientation yet carry the XY chromosome complement. The effects of early hormones during normal development on later human behavior are clearly subtle and subject to environmental modification. Nevertheless, the weight of animal experimentation and findings from clinical studies of humans indicate that prenatal endocrine concentrations may be partly responsible for differences between the sexes and also for variability among individuals within a sex.

IV. Sexual Differentiation in Birds

Birds differ from mammals with respect to the regulation of sexual development. This difference may have its origin in the reversal of sex chromosome distribution. The male bird, like the female mammal, is the homogametic sex. That is, it has two copies of the same sex chromosome (usually designated as ZZ in birds). Heterogamety is seen in the female bird (ZW) and the male mammal. If all aspects of morphological differentiation are considered, it is reasonably accurate to state that sexual differentiation in birds is the reverse of that in mammals with gonadal secretions being required for female rather than male development. It should be noted, however, that morphological sexual differentiation in birds includes some complexities not seen in mammals (Price et al., 1975).

The earliest research having relevance to the sexual differentiation of behavior in birds was that of Domm and Davis (1941, 1948). These investigators demonstrated that treatment of genetic male chickens with estrogen prenatally eliminates the display of masculine sexual behavior in adulthood. Perhaps because Domm and Davis did not view their research in the framework of sexual differentiation, many years passed before their study was followed up. J. A. Wilson and Glick (1970) replicated their finding, and, in addition, demonstrated that the demasculinization of genetic males by steroid treatment in ovo results from a reduction in responsiveness to subsequent androgen treatment. To recall our discussion of mammals for a moment, this phenomenon is analogous to the defeminization of genetic female rodents by neonatal androgen treatment in that sex steroid treatment in early life eliminates a behavior from the repertoire of the animal.

Adkins (1975) extended this research to another species and introduced a useful experimental tool. She injected Japanese quail eggs with either TP or EB about halfway through the incubation period. As adults, quail identified by plumage characteristics as males were placed on a short photoperiod which caused the testes to regress. This treatment resulted in functional castration without the necessity of physical caponization. When these functional castrates were injected with TP and placed with receptive females, the males that had been treated with sex steroids in ovo displayed much less masculine copulatory behavior than did control males that received an injection of the oil vehicle in ovo.

Previously (Section II,C,3) we saw that TP and EB exert similar effects upon behavioral differentiation in mammals. Now we find that these hormones appear to be interchangeable in demasculinizing male birds. Such interchangeability not only raises questions concerning the nature of hormone action in the sexual differentiation of normal animals, but also presents problems of protecting the developing animal from unwanted sex hormones. Because of the importance of these issues, a recent study has reevaluated the hormonal specificity of demasculinization in birds (Whitsett, Irvin, Edens, & Thaxton, 1977). Genetic male Japanese quail were injected *in ovo* with a variety of sex steroids at a dosage determined to be the minimal quantity of estradiol-17β that would eliminate the capability to display masculine sexual behavior. After caponization and TP treatment in adulthood, these animals were tested for their sexual response to receptive females. Masculine copulatory behavior was found to be reduced significantly in males treated with any of several estrogens prenatally, but not in those that had received testosterone (Fig. 4). It was concluded that the effectiveness of androgen in demasculinizing males in previous studies was probably due to the high levels of the propionate ester of testosterone that were administered *in ovo*. Thus it appears likely that the normal agent of behavioral demasculinization in the female quail is an estrogen, and that the testosterone secreted by the testis of the em-

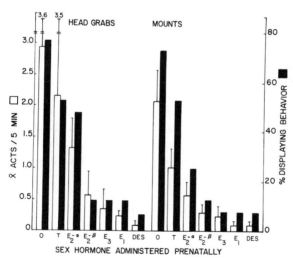

FIG. 4. Influence of prenatal treatment with various sex hormones on masculine sexual behavior of genetic male quail following caponization and 2 weeks of testosterone propionate treatment in adulthood. O = oil, T = testosterone, E_2-β = estradiol-17β, E_2-α = estradiol-17α, E_3 = estriol, E_1 = estrone, DES = diethylstilbestrol. From Whitsett *et al.* (1977).

bryonic male (Guichard, Cedard, Haffen, & Scheib, 1973) does not pose any developmental difficulties for the normal male.

In summary, the few studies of birds suggest the existence of a mechanism for behavioral differentiation that may be similar to that found in mammals (even though the sex requiring hormonal stimulation for differntiation is different in the two classes). A weakness of the bird research to date is that these studies indicate only that a behavior can be *suppressed* by the presence of sex steroid during prenatal development, not that a behavior can be augmented. One reason why feminization of behavior by prenatal estrogen has not been demonstrated is that, in quails and chickens, both sexes are capable of displaying feminine behavior given the proper hormonal environment in adulthood. In other words, the males of these two species exhibit latent bisexuality. Whether male bisexuality is representative of the galliformes or even the entire class of birds is unknown. A possible basis for this bisexuality has been proposed by Whitsett *et al.* (1977).

Birds are promising subjects for studies of sexual differentiation. Much is known about their embryology. Eggs are easily treated with hormones, and although prenatal gonadectomies present problems, anti-estrogens could be administered. Precocial birds may be reared in the absence of parental influences. The sexual behavior of certain species such as the Japanese quail is highly stereotyped, frequent in occurrence, and easily quantified. The existence of gross sex differences in brain structure in canaries and zebra finches suggests that birds may be excellent subjects for the study of the organizational effects of sex hormones (Nottebohm & Arnold, 1976). The apparent similarity of behavioral sexual differentiation in birds to that in mammals may reflect similar physiological mechanisms. Of possible relevance to this question is the recent demonstration by Martinez-Vargas, Gibson, Sar, and Stumpf (1975) that limited-capacity nuclear binding of $[^3H]$estradiol-17β by cells in the hypothalamus and preoptic of the chick embryo begins around Day 10 of incubation, which is during the stage of behavioral sexual differentiation in this species (J. A. Wilson & Glick, 1970).

V. Conclusions

Important sex differences in copulatory postures and other behaviors in mammals have their origin in the hormonal milieu of fetal and neonatal life. In the absence of gonadal hormones, mammals of either genetic sex differentiate as females. Testicular hormone results in a suppression of the ability to exhibit feminine behaviors in adulthood and in an enhancement of the potential for masculine behaviors. Humans appear to conform to the basic mammalian pattern, although the social environment exerts a greater influence on gender identity in humans than is true in other mammals. Sexual differentiation of behavior in birds is similar to that in mammals, in principle, although it is the female, rather than the male that requires gonadal hormone stimulation for normal differentiation. Major problems needing resolution are the locus and mode of action of the hormones responsible for neurobehavioral sexual differentiation and the evolutionary and physiological bases of bisexuality. A species sexuality continuum has been proposed in an attempt to initiate an analysis of bisexuality.

References

Adkins, E. K. Hormonal basis of sexual differentiation in the Japanese quail. *Journal of Comparative and Physiological Psychology*, 1975, **89**, 61–71.

Adler, N., & Bermant, G. Sexual behavior of male rats: Effects of reduced sensory feedback. *Journal of Comparative and Physiological Psychology*, 1966, **61**, 240–243.

Anderson, P. K., & Hill, J. L. Mus musculus: Experimental induction of territory formation. *Science*, 1965, **148**, 1753–1755.

Baker, S. W., & Ehrhardt, A. A. Prenatal androgen, intelligence, and cognitive sex differences. In R. C. Friedman, R. M. Richart, & R. L. van de Wiele (Eds.), *Sex differences in behavior*. New York: Wiley, 1974, Pp. 53–76.

Barnea, A., Weinstein, A., & Lindner, H. R. Uptake of androgens by the brain of the neonatal female rat. *Brain Research*, 1972, **46**, 391–402.

Beach, F. A. Hormonal factors controlling the differentiation, development, and display of copulatory behavior in the ramstergig and related species. In E. Tobach, L. R. Aronson, & E. Shaw (Eds.), *The biopsychology of development*. New York: Academic Press, 1971, Pp. 249–296.

Beach, F. A. Hormonal modification of sexually dimorphic behavior. *Psychoneuroendocrinology*, 1975, **1**, 3–23.

Beach, F. A., & Holz, A. M. Mating behavior in male rats castrated at various ages and injected with androgen. *Journal of Experimental Zoology*, 1946, **101**, 91–142.

Beach, F. A., Noble, R. G., & Orndoff, R. K. Effects of perinatal androgen treatment on responses of male rats to gonadal hormones in adulthood. *Journal of Comparative and Physiological Psychology*, 1969, **68**, 490–497.

Beeman, E. A. The effect of male hormone on aggressive behavior in mice. *Physiological Zoology*, 1947, **20**, 373–405.

Bronson, F. H., & Desjardins, C. Aggression in adult mice: Modification by neonatal injections of gonadal hormones. *Science*, 1968, **161**, 705–706.

Bronson, F. H., & Desjardins, C. Aggressive behavior and seminal vesicle function in mice: Differential sensitivity to androgen given neonatally. *Endocrinology*, 1969, **85**, 971–974.

Bronson, F. H., & Desjardins, C. Neonatal androgen administration and adult aggressiveness in female mice. *General and Comparative Endocrinology*, 1970, **15**, 320–325.

Clemens, L. G., & Coniglio, L. Influence of prenatal litter composition on mounting behavior of female rats. *American Zoologist*, 1971, **11**, 617. (Abstract)

Crowcroft, P., & Rowe, F. P. Social organization and territorial behaviour in the wild house-mouse (*Mus musculus* L.). *Proceedings of the Zoological Society of London*, 1963, **140**, 517–531.

Dalton, K. Ante-natal progesterone and intelligence. *British Journal of Psychiatry*, 1968, **114**, 1377–1382.

Dantchakoff, V. Rôle des hormones dans la manifestation des instincts sexuel. *Comptes Rendus Hebdomadaires des Séances de l'Académie des Sciences*, 1938, **206**, 945–947.

Debold, J. F., & Whalen, R. E. Differential sensitivity of mounting and lordosis control systems to early androgen treatment in male and female hamsters. *Hormones and Behavior*, 1975, **6**, 197–209.

Dörner, G., & Staudt, J. Structural changes in the preoptic anterior hypothalamic area of the male rat, following neonatal castration and androgen substitution. *Neuroendocrinology*, 1968, **3**, 136–140.

Dörner, G., & Staudt, J. Structural changes in the hypothalamic ventromedial nucleus of the male rat following neonatal castration and androgen treatment. *Neuroendocrinology*, 1969, **4**, 278–281.

Domm, L. V., & Davis, D. E. Sexual behavior of intersexual domestic fowl. *Proceedings of the Society for Experimental Biology and Medicine*, 1941, **48**, 665–667.

Domm, L. V., & Davis, D. E. The sexual behavior of intersexual domestic fowl. *Physiological Zoology*, 1948, **21**, 14–31.

Eaton, G. G. Effect of a single prepubertal injection of testosterone propionate on adult bisexual behavior of male hamsters castrated at birth. *Endocrinology*, 1970, **87**, 934–940.

Eaton, G. G., Goy, R. W., & Phoenix, C. H. Effects of testosterone treatment in adulthood on sexual behaviour of female pseudohermaphrodite rhesus monkeys. *Nature (London)*, 1973, **242**, 119–120.

Edwards, D. A. Mice: Fighting by neonatally androgenized females. *Science*, 1968, **161**, 1027–1028.

Edwards, D. A. Post-neonatal androgenization and adult aggressive behavior in female mice. *Physiology and Behavior*, 1970, **5**, 465–467.

Ehrhardt, A. A., & Baker, S. W. Fetal androgens, human central nervous system differentiation and behavior sex differences. In R. C. Friedman, R. M. Richart, & R. L. van de Wiele (Eds.), *Sex differences in behavior*. New York: Wiley, 1974. Pp. 33–52.

Ehrhardt, A. A., Greenberg, N., & Money, J. Female gender identity and absence of fetal hormones: Turner's syndrome. *Johns Hopkins Medical Journal*, 1970, **126**, 237–248.

Ehrhardt, A. A., & Money, J. Progestin-induced hermaphroditism: IQ and psychosexual identity in a study of ten girls. *Journal of Sex Research*, 1967, **3**, 83–100.

Erwin, J., & Anderson, B. Agonistic behavior of pregnant female monkeys (*Macaca nemestrina*): Possible influences of fetal gonadal hormones. *Psychological Reports*, 1975, **36**, 699–702.

Gandelman, R. Mice: Postpartum aggression elicited by the presence of an intruder. *Hormones and Behavior*, 1972, **3**, 23–28.

Gerall, A. A., McMurray, M. M., & Farrell, A. Suppression of the development of female hamster behaviour by implants of testosterone and non-aromatizable androgens administered neonatally. *Journal of Endocrinology*, 1975, **67**, 439–445.

Goldfoot, D. A., Feder, H. H., & Goy, R. W. Development of bisexuality in the male rat treated neonatally with androstenedione. *Journal of Comparative and Physiological Psychology*, 1969, **67**, 41–45.

Goldfoot, D. A., & van der Werff ten Bosch, J. J. Mounting behavior of female guinea pigs after prenatal and adult administration of the propionates of testosterone, dihydrotestosterone, and androstanediol. *Hormones and Behavior*, 1975, **6**, 139–148.

Gorski, R. A., & Shryne, J. Intracerebral antibiotics and androgenization of the neonatal female rat. *Neuroendocrinology*, 1972, **10**, 109–120.

Goy, R. W. Role of androgens in the establishment and regulation of behavioral sex differences in mammals. *Journal of Animal Science*, 1966, **25**, 21–35.

Goy, R. W. Experimental control of psychosexuality. *Philosophical Transactions of the Royal Society of London, Series B*, 1970, **259**, 149–162.

Goy, R. W. *Comparative aspects of bisexuality in mammals.* Paper presented at the Workshop on Research in Human Sexuality, Stony Brook, New York, June 1974.

Goy, R. W., Bridson, W. E., & Young, W. C. Period of maximal susceptibility of the prenatal female guinea pig to masculinizing actions of testosterone propionate. *Journal of Comparative and Physiological Psychology*, 1964, **57**, 166–174.

Goy, R. W., & Goldfoot, D. A. Hormonal influences on sexually dimorphic behavior. In R. O. Greep (Ed.), *Handbook of Physiology* (Sect. 7, Vol. 2, p. 1). Baltimore: Williams & Wilkins, 1973. Pp. 169–186.

Goy, R. W., & Resko, J. A. Gonadal hormones and behavior of normal and pseudohermaphroditic nonhuman female primates. *Recent Progress in Hormone Research*, 1972, **28**, 707–713.

Grady, K. L., Phoenix, C. H., & Young, W. C. Role of the developing rat testis in differentiation of neural tissues mediating mating behavior. *Journal of Comparative and Physiological Psychology*, 1965, **59**, 176–182.

Gray, L. E., Jr. *Aggression in female house mice.* Unpublished doctoral dissertation, North Carolina State University, 1976.

Guichard, A., Cedard, L., Haffen, K., & Scheib, D. Métabolisme de la prégnènolone et de la progesterone radio-actives par les gonades embryonnaires de caille (*Coturnix coturnix japonica*) en culture organotypique. *General and Comparative Endocrinology*, 1973, **21**, 478–484.

Harris, G. W., & Jacobson, D. Functional grafts of the anterior pituitary gland. *Proceedings of the Royal Society, Series B*, 1952, **139**, 263–276.

Hart, B. L. Manipulation of neonatal androgen: Effects on sexual responses and penile development in male rats. *Physiology and Behavior*, 1972, **8**, 841–845.

Heffner, L. J., & van Tienhoven, A. Effects of progesterone on uptake and retention of H-testosterone in the neonatal female rat. *Neuroendocrinology*, 1973, **12**, 129–141.

Jost, A. Problems of fetal endocrinology: The gonadal and hypophyseal hormones. *Recent Progress in Hormone Research*, 1953, **8**, 379–418.

Kinsey, A. C., Pomeroy, W. B., Martin, C. E., & Gebhard, P. H. *Sexual behavior in the human female.* Philadelphia: Saunders, 1953.

Kobayashi, F., & Gorski, R. A. Effects of antibiotics on androgenization of the neonatal female rat. *Endocrinology*, 1970, **86**, 285–289.

Larsson, K. Effects of neonatal castration upon the development of the mating behavior of the male rat. *Zeitschrift für Tierpsychologie*, 1966, **23**, 867–873.

Luttge, W. G., & Whalen, R. E. Dihydrotestosterone, androstenedione, testosterone: Comparative effectiveness in masculinizing and defeminizing reproductive systems in male and female rats. *Hormones and Behavior*, 1970, **1**, 265–281.

Martinez-Vargas, M. C., Gibson, D. B., Sar, M., & Stumpf, W. E. Estrogen target sites in the brain of the chick embryo. *Science*, 1975, **190**, 1307–1308.

Masica, D. N., Money, J. Ehrhardt, A. A., & Lewis, V. G. I.Q. fetal sex hormones and cognitive patterns: Studies in the testicular feminizing syndrome of androgen insensitivity. *Johns Hopkins Medical Journal*, 1969, **124**, 34–43.

Mittwoch, U. *Genetics of sex differentiation.* New York: Academic Press, 1973.

Money, J. Pre-natal hormones and intelligence: A possible relationship. *Impact of Science on Society*, 1971, **21**, 285–290.

Money, J., & Ehrhardt, A. A. Fetal hormones and the brain: Effect of sexual dimorphism on behavior—a review. *Archives of Sexual Behavior*, 1971, **1**, 241–262.

Money, J., & Ehrhardt, A. A. *Man and woman, boy and girl.* Baltimore: Johns Hopkins University Press, 1972.

Money, J., & Lewis, V. I.Q. genetics and accelerated growth: Adrenogenital syndrome. *Bulletin of Johns Hopkins Hospital*, 1966, **118**, 365–373.

Mullins, R. F., Jr., & Levine, S. Hormonal determinants during infancy of adult sexual behavior in the female rat. *Physiology and Behavior*, 1968, **3**, 333–338.

Nadler, R. D. Masculinization of female rats by intracranial implantation of androgen in infancy. *Journal of Comparative and Physiological Psychology*, 1968, **66**, 157–167.

Nadler, R. D. Intrahypothalamic exploration of androgen-sensitive brain loci in neonatal female rats. *Transactions of the New York Academy of Sciences*, 1972, **34**, 572–581.

Nottebohm, F., & Arnold, A. P. Sexual dimorphism in vocal control areas of the song-bird brain. *Science*, 1976, **194**, 211–213.

Owen, K., Peters, P. J., & Bronson, F. H. Differential responsiveness to replacement therapy of pre- and postpubertally castrated mice with respect to intermale aggression. *Hormones and Behavior*, 1973, **4**, 301–306.

Paup, D. C., Coniglio, L. P., & Clemens, L. G. Masculinization of the female golden hamster by neonatal treatment with androgen or estrogen. *Hormones and Behavior*, 1972, **3**, 123–131.

Peters, P. J., Bronson, F. H., & Whitsett, J. M. Neonatal castration and intermale aggression in mice. *Physiology and Behavior*, 1972, **8**, 265–268.

Pfaff, D. Nature of sex hormone effects on rat sex behavior: Specificity of effects and individual patterns of response. *Journal of Comparative and Physiological Psychology*, 1970, **73**, 349–358.

Pfeiffer, C. A. Sexual differences of the hypophyses and their determination by the gonads. *American Journal of Anatomy*, 1936, **58**, 195–225.

Phoenix, C. H. Prenatal testosterone in the nonhuman primate and its consequences for behavior. In R. C. Friedman, R. M. Richart, & R. L. van de Wiele (Eds.), *Sex differences in behavior*. New York: Wiley, 1974, Pp. 19–31.

Phoenix, C. H., Goy, R. W., Gerall, A. A., & Young, W. C. Organizing action of prenatally administered testosterone propionate on the tissues mediating mating behavior in the female guinea pig. *Endocrinology*, 1959, **65**, 369–382.

Phoenix, C. H., Goy, R. W., & Young, W. C. Sexual behavior: General aspects. In L. Martini & W. F. Ganong (Eds.), *Neuroendocrinology* (Vol. 2). New York: Academic Press, 1967. Pp. 163–196.

Price, D., Zaaijer, J. J. P., Ortiz, E., & Brinkmann, A. O. Current views on embryonic sex differentiation in reptiles, birds, and mammals. *American Zoologist*, 1975, **15**(Suppl. 1), 173–195.

Quadagno, D. M., Briscoe, R., & Quadagno, J. S. The effect of perinatal gonadal hormones on selected nonsexual behavior patterns: A critical assessment of the nonhuman and human literature. *Psychological Bul.*, 1977, **84**, 62–80.

Raisman, G., & Field, P. M. Sexual dimorphism in the preoptic area of the rat. *Science*, 1971, **173**, 731–733.

Raisman, G., & Field, P. M. Sexual dimorphism in the neuropil of the preoptic area of the rat and its dependence on neonatal androgen. *Brain Research*, 1973, **54**, 1–29.

Reddy, V. V. R., Naftolin, F., & Ryan, K. J. Conversion of androstenedione to estrone by neural tissues from fetal and neonatal rats. *Endocrinology*, 1974, **94**, 117–121.

Reinisch, J. M. Effects of prenatal hormone exposure on physical and psychological development in humans and animals: With a note on the state of the field. In E. J. Sachar (Ed.), *Hormones, behavior and psychopathology*. New York: Raven, 1976. Pp. 69–94.

Resko, J. A. Androgen secretion by the fetal and neonatal rhesus monkey. *Endocrinology,* 1970, **87**, 680–687.

Resko, J. A. The relationship between fetal hormones and the differentiation of the central nervous system in primates. In W. Montagna & W. A. Sadler (Eds.), *Reproductive behavior.* New York: Plenum Press, 1974. Pp. 211–222.

Resko, J. A. Fetal hormones and their effect on the differentiation of the central nervous system in primates. *Federation Proceedings,* 1975, **34**, 1650–1655.

Resko, J. A., Feder, H. H., & Goy, R. W. Androgen concentrations in plasma and testis of developing rats. *Journal of Endocrinology,* 1968, **40**, 485–491.

Resko, J. A., Malley, A., Begley, D., & Hess, D. L. Radioimmunoassay of testosterone during fetal development of the rhesus monkey. *Endocrinology,* 1973, **93**, 156–161.

Reyes, F. I., Boroditsky, R. S., Winter, J. S. D., & Faiman, C. Studies on human sexual development. II. Fetal and maternal serum gonadotropin and sex steroid concentrations. *Journal of Clinical Endocrinology and Metabolism,* 1974, **38**, 612–617.

Reyes, F. I., Winter, J. S. D., & Faiman, C. Studies on human sexual development. I. Fetal gonadal and adrenal sex steroids. *Journal of Clinical Endocrinology and Metabolism,* 1973, **37**, 74–78.

Rosenblum, L. A. *The development of social behavior in the rhesus monkey.* Unpublished doctoral dissertation, University of Wisconsin, 1961.

Salaman, D. F., & Birkett, S. Androgen-induced sexual differentiation of the brain is blocked by inhibitors of DNA & RNA synthesis. *Nature (London),* 1974, **247**, 109–112.

Sheridan, P. J., Sar, M., & Stumpf, W. E. Interaction of exogenous steroids in the developing rat brain. *Endocrinology,* 1974, **95**, 1749–1753.

Stern, J. J. Neonatal castration, androstenedione, and the mating behavior of the male rat. *Journal of Comparative and Physiological Psychology,* 1969, **69**, 608–612.

Sutherland, S. D., & Gorski, R. A. An evaluation of the inhibition of androgenization of the neonatal female rat brain by barbiturate. *Neuroendocrinology,* 1972, **10**, 94–108.

Swanson, H. H. Effects of castration at birth in hamsters of both sexes on luteinization of ovarian implants, oestrous cycles and sexual behaviour. *Journal of Reproduction and Fertility,* 1970, **21**, 183–186.

Swanson, H. H., & Crossley, D. A. Sexual behaviour in the golden hamster and its modification by neonatal administration of testosterone propionate. In M. Hamburgh & E. J. W. Barrington (Eds.), *Hormones in development.* New York: Appleton, 1971. Pp. 677–687.

Tiefer, L. Gonadal hormones and mating behavior in the adult golden hamster. *Hormones and Behavior,* 1970, **1**, 189–202.

Tollman, J., & King, J. A. The effects of testosterone propionate on aggression in male and female C57BL/10 mice. *British Journal of Animal Behaviour,* 1956, **4**, 147–149.

Turner, J. W., Jr. Influence of neonatal androgen on the display of territorial marking behavior in the gerbil. *Physiology and Behavior,* 1975, **15**, 265–270.

Wagner, J. W., Erwin, W., & Critchlow, V. Androgen sterilization produced by intracerebral implants of testosterone in neonatal female rats. *Endocrinology,* 1966, **79**, 1135–1142.

Ward, I. L., & Renz, F. J. Consequences of perinatal hormone manipulation on the adult sexual behavior of female rats. *Journal of Comparative and Physiological Psychology,* 1972, **78**, 349–355.

Warren, D. W., Haltmeyer, G. C., & Eik-Nes, K. B. Testosterone in the fetal rat testis. *Biology of Reproduction,* 1973, **8**, 560–565.

Wells, L. J., & van Wagenen, G. Androgen induced female pseudohermaphroditism in the monkey (*Macaca mulatta*): Anatomy of the reproductive organs. *Contributions to Embryology of the Carnegie Institute,* 1954, **35**, 93–106.

White, N., Mayo, S., & Edwards, D. A. Fighting in female mice as a function of the size of the opponent. *Psychonomic Science,* 1969, **16**, 14–15.

Whitsett, J. M., Bronson, F. H., Peters, P. J., & Hamilton, T. H. Neonatal organization of aggression in mice: Correlation of critical period with uptake of hormone. *Hormones and Behavior*, 1972, **3**, 11–21.

Whitsett, J. M., Irvin, E. W., Edens, F. W., & Thaxton, J. P. Demasculinization of male Japanese quail by prenatal estrogen treatment. *Hormones and Behavior*, 1977, **8**, 254–263.

Whitsett, J. M., & Vandenbergh, J. G. Influence of testosterone propionate administered neonatally on puberty and bisexual behavior in female hamsters. *Journal of Comparative and Physiological Psychology*, 1975, **88**, 248–255.

Wilkins, L., Jones, H. W., Holman, G. H., & Stempfel, R. S., Jr. Masculinization of the female fetus associated with administration of oral and intramuscular progestins during gestation: Non-adrenal female pseudohermaphrodism. *Journal of Clinical Endocrinology and Metabolism*, 1958, **18**, 559–585.

Wilson, J. A., & Glick, B. Ontogeny of mating behavior in the chicken. *American Journal of Physiology*, 1970, **218**, 951–955.

Wilson, J. D., & Gloyna, R. E. The intranuclear metabolism of testosterone in the accessory organs of reproduction. *Recent Progress in Hormone Research*, 1970, **26**, 309–336.

Wilson, J. G., Hamilton, J. B., & Young, W. C. Influence of age and presence of the ovaries on reproductive function of rats injected with androgens. *Endocrinology*, 1941, **29**, 784–789.

Young, W. C., Goy, R. W., & Phoenix, C. H. Hormones and sexual behavior. *Science*, 1964, **143**, 212–218.

HORMONAL MEDIATION OF THE EFFECTS OF PRENATAL STRESS ON OFFSPRING BEHAVIOR

JUSTIN M. JOFFE[1]

Department of Psychology
University of Vermont
Burlington, Vermont

[1]Author's research reported in Sections IV and V was supported by a grant from the United States Public Health Service, National Institute of Child Health and Human Development (HD-05571). I am most grateful to Dr. Karmela Milković and Dr. Bruce S. Kapp for their helpful comments and constructive criticism.

Facts have a less intrinsic value than they used to have. . . . More must now be extracted from
them in their mutual relations. They must be manipulated into the web of some inconclusive
hypothesis, or otherwise they may as well die an unrecorded death, because their independence
only helps to block the already but too narrow path which leads towards omniscience.

Anonymous, 1875, p. 423

I. Introduction

There is a large body of evidence showing that the development and later
behavior of an immature organism can be affected by agents such as radiation, disease, drugs and hormones, and nutrition. In the last 20 years interest
has been extended to examinations of the effects of events operating during
the earliest stages of development—that is, during life prior to birth.

When mammals are the subject of investigation, the design and conduct
of experiments on the effects of prenatal events present particular problems
since two organisms, related in a unique and complex manner, are involved.
Many of the difficulties center on the relative inaccessibility of the developing organism and the consequent need to consider and evaluate the mediating influence of the mother, who provides the immediate environment of
her developing embryo and fetus. In the investigation of any prenatal
variable the response of the mother to the experimental manipulation is of
interest in designing the experiment or in interpreting the results. Concern
with the maternal response may be less in the case of agents such as radiation, where it is possible for the agent to affect the fetus without maternal
involvement (although maternal involvement may occur: see Joffe, 1969,
pp. 35–43), than in the case of others, such as hormonal manipulations,
where the fetus may be affected, for example, by the agent itself, by a meta-
bolite of maternal origin, or by a change in maternal hormone levels produced by the agent administered.

In addition there are certain kinds of variables that do not involve direct
manipulations of the internal state of the mother but that are assumed to
produce some or all of their effect on the offspring as a result of the response
of the mother to the treatment. Most of these procedures, which are described in the next section, have been referred to by the researchers employ-
ing them or by reviewers (Archer & Blackman, 1971; Joffe, 1969) as prenatal
stressors. The brief introductory overview of procedures that have been
used (Section I,A) and of the effects of prenatal stress on offspring behavior

(Section I,B) is limited to experiments on rats and mice since research related to mediating mechanisms, which is considered later in this chapter, has been confined to these two species. It will be seen that the available evidence on hormonal mediation of prenatal stress effects is sometimes contradictory and that there are many questions on which little or no information is available. The purpose of nevertheless advancing tentative hypotheses and attempting to evaluate them is twofold. It provides a method of organizing the available evidence and provides vantage points from which to view the field. The vantage points provided by the hypotheses are undoubtedly temporary but may help to provide a somewhat better view of the terrain than is possible without them.

A. Prenatal Stress Procedures

The procedures are grouped into four categories for the sake of convenience. Since the essential components of each procedure have not been identified, other groupings would be equally defensible. After they have been briefly described, the question of whether it is appropriate collectively to label them prenatal stress procedures is considered. Reviews of most of the experiments cited can be found in Archer and Blackman (1971) and Joffe (1969).

1. "Psychological" Stressors

This category includes one type of procedure, which generally does not subject animals to painful or physically stressful events during pregnancy.
a. CS-Exposure Procedure. Females are exposed during pregnancy to a signal previously paired with electric shock. This procedure, introduced by Thompson (1957), generally involves training females prior to mating to avoid shock (unconditioned stimulus: US) on presentation of a signal (conditioned stimulus: CS) by crossing to the opposite side of a two-compartment shuttlebox. The females are then mated and are reintroduced to the shuttlebox during gestation. Usually no further shock is given during gestation. In many experiments the avoidance response is prevented on some or all of the pregnancy trials by introducing or locking a barrier between the two halves of the box. Variations of this general paradigm constitute the most commonly used technique of imposing prenatal stress (Ader & Belfer, 1962; Bell, Hendry, & Miller, 1967; Doyle & Yule, 1959a, 1959b, 1959c; Hockman, 1961; Joffe, 1965a; Morra, 1965a, 1965b; Porter & Wehmer, 1969; Smith, Heseltine, & Corson, 1971; Smith, Joffe, & Heseltine, 1975; Thompson & Quinby, 1964; Thompson, Watson, & Charlesworth, 1962; Wehmer, Porter, & Scales, 1970). However, no two experimenters have used precisely the same procedures. For example, some have reexposed animals to the CS in

their home cages rather than returning them to the apparatus (Smith *et al.*, 1971, 1975), some have administered occasional shocks during gestation while most have not, and there have been variations in most parameters of the basic experimental procedure, including the number of conditioning trials, number of conditioning sessions, shock intensity, nature and duration of the conditioned stimulus, nature of the unconditioned stimulus (shock alone or shock plus airblast), design of apparatus (shuttlebox or operant chamber), type of avoidance response required (shuttle response or lever press, or both), number of trials and number of sessions during gestation, and the period of gestation at which reexposure occurred.

2. PHYSICAL STRESSORS

This category includes procedures which appear to be physically stressful, or to markedly increase levels of physical stimulation relative to controls, without necessarily involving pain.

   a. Handling.   Rats were handled for brief periods (3 to 10 minutes) two or three times a day during pregnancy (Ader & Conklin, 1963; Ader & Plaut, 1968).

   b. Aversive Procedures.   Female mice were subjected to three procedures each day—forced swimming, being tilted from side to side in a "tilt box," and placement in a brightly lit open field (DeFries, 1964; DeFries & Weir, 1964; DeFries, Weir, & Hegmann, 1967; Weir & DeFries, 1964).

   c. Crowding.   Pregnant mice were crowded by placing groups of 15 mice in cages 6 × 12 × 5½ in., normally accommodating 5 mice (Keeley, 1962) or by placing females in an 8 × 11 ,× 5 in. cage with ten "aggressive" males during the second trimester of pregnancy (Lieberman, 1963).

3. PAIN STRESS

This category includes procedures with components that are either definitely or probably painful.

   a. Conditioning.   In one study pregnant rats were subjected to an escape-conditioning procedure in which signaled shock is terminated by pressing a lever (Hutchings & Gibbon, 1970). In another study, pregnant rats received 20 avoidance conditioning trials per day for 4 days in a shuttlebox (Bell *et al.*, 1967).

   b. Conflict.   Prior to mating and during gestation female rats lived in cages in which they were required to cross an electrified floor to obtain food or water, except for 1 hour in every 24 when shock was switched off (Joffe, 1965b).

   c. Shock.   Pregnant rats received unsignaled footshock (Joffe, 1977).

   d. Audiogenic Seizures.   Pregnant rats were subjected to audiogenic seizures twice a day (Thompson & Sontag, 1956).

e. Injections.   Saline or distilled water was administered by subcutaneous or intraperitoneal injection to pregnant rats (Havlena & Werboff, 1963a).

4. PREMATING PROCEDURES

Both the procedures in this category could be grouped in other categories but for the fact that subjects received no treatment after mating; consequently, the procedures need to be distinguished from those in the other categories.

a. Premating Avoidance Conditioning.   Female rats were given avoidance conditioning training daily for 14 days (Joffe, 1965a) or twice daily for 10 days (Wehmer *et al.*, 1970) prior to mating, with no further disturbance during pregnancy.

b. Immobilization.   For 4 hours each day for 7 days prior to mating, female rats were placed in wire-screen cocoons which severely restrict motion (Lane & Hyde, 1973).

Procedures involving variables such as loud noise, electric shock, or injection of fluids may affect the fetus directly. Effects on offspring have also been obtained with procedures that do not appear capable of having direct effects on the fetus (for example, handling during pregnancy: Ader & Conklin, 1963; Ader & Plaut, 1968; CS-exposure with a change in illumination as the CS: Joffe, 1965a). Unlikely as direct effects may appear to be in these cases, the possibility cannot be excluded until appropriate control procedures have been used. However, effects have been obtained in studies in which the prenatal treatment is administered only prior to mating (Joffe, 1965a; Lane & Hyde, 1973), and in these cases no direct effects on the fetus are possible since no treatment is applied to the mother following conception. These studies indicate that the prenatal effects must be mediated by the maternal response to the treatments in some cases, and suggest that the maternal response may play a role in other cases as well. A procedure which fails to exclude the possibility of direct effects on the fetus may nevertheless possess advantages. For example, it may allow the experimenter to control variables such as the timing and intensity of prenatal stress that may be difficult to manipulate when procedures that are less likely to produce direct effects— such as the CS-exposure procedure—are used (Joffe, 1969, pp. 144–145). These advantages may outweigh the drawback of failing to exclude the possibility of direct effects on the fetus.

The answer to the question of what the diverse procedures listed above have in common has influenced the development of hypotheses about mediating mechanisms. Providing them with a common label suggests that a single mechanism, or set of mechanisms, is thought to be involved. The label itself suggests what mechanisms are considered likely to mediate the effects.

Labeling a procedure a *stressor* implies that it produces certain physiological responses. As originally defined (Selye, 1950), a stressor was an agent or event that produced pituitary-adrenal, thymico-lymphatic, and gastrointestinal changes. Over the years evidence has accumulated which suggests that stressors produce responses in a wide variety of endocrine systems (e.g., Mason, 1968a, 1968b), while at the same time emphasis has been placed on the pituitary-adrenal component of Selye's triad. Pituitary-adrenal activation has come to be regarded as a necessary, if not sufficient, requirement for a procedure to be considered stressful.

Although abundant evidence exists on the pituitary-adrenal effects of many of the physical stress and pain stress procedures, very little evidence is available on the pituitary-adrenal effects of the most frequently used prenatal stress procedure, the CS-exposure paradigm. In an investigation of the effects of CS-exposure on pregnant rats, Joffe, Mulick, Ley and Rawson (1978) found that plasma corticosterone levels on day 3 and day 12 of gestation were higher following reexposure to the shuttlebox than in pregnant rats with the same premating avoidance experience that were blood sampled immediately on removal from their cages. That is, the reexposure procedure resulted in pituitary-adrenal activation. Another finding in the same experiment raised the question of what it is about the CS-exposure procedure that produces pituitary-adrenal activation: Exposure to the shuttlebox increased corticosterone levels in pregnant rats that had received no avoidance conditioning prior to mating to the same level as that seen in the CS-exposure group.[2] However, the elevated corticosterone levels in the CS-exposure group qualify the procedure as stressful whatever component of the total situation is responsible for the increase.

There is sufficient evidence available to conclude that most of the physical stress and pain stress procedures listed above meet the minimal definition of stress procedures. In some cases the evidence is direct. For example, handling has been shown to raise the level of plasma corticosterone in pregnant rats (Grota & Ader, 1970), crowding to produce adrenal hypertrophy in

---

[2]This finding in turn raises the possibility that the effects of the CS procedure on offspring have little to do with the avoidance conditioning but are due instead to handling and general disturbance required by the procedure of reexposing the animals to the CS/shuttlebox situation. Hutchings and Gibbon (1970) found that the effects on offspring of prenatal handling were the same as those of escape conditioning during pregnancy, but the effects of the CS-exposure procedure have been found to differ from those of prenatal handling (Hockman, 1961; Morra, 1965a). In addition, the effects of CS-exposure procedures on offspring vary as a function of the number of avoidance training and reexposure trials and the number of shocks (Thompson & Quinby, 1964) or the number of avoidance training trials alone (Morra, 1965b). In these latter experiments variables such as handling during gestation are similar across all groups, and consequently differences in the effects of various conditioning parameters are not attributable to the handling during gestation necessitated by the procedure.

some species of mice (reviewed by Christian, 1975), and shock (for example, Bassett, Carincross, & King, 1973) and escape conditioning (Bassett *et al.*, 1973) to raise levels of plasma corticosterone in rats. In cases in which no data are available on pituitary-adrenal response to the procedure, an inference can reasonably be made that it produces pituitary-adrenal activation, since the procedure contains one or more components (such as handling or shock) which themselves produce pituitary-adrenal activation. Evidence is available on pregnant animals only in the cases of handling and crowding, and the intensity and duration of pituitary-adrenal activation in response to other procedures may not be the same in pregnant animals as in nonpregnant females or in males. However, there is no reason to suppose that pituitary-adrenal activation would be absent in pregnant animals in response to procedures which produce marked activation in nonpregnant females or in males.

Even less evidence is available on the effects of premating procedures on pituitary-adrenal function during gestation. There is little question that avoidance conditioning and immobilization produce pituitary-adrenal activation during the period they are administered. For example, Zimmerman and Critchlow (1969) reported substantial increases in plasma corticosterone levels of rats following immobilization. In the studies of the effects of premating stress on behavior, however, no further treatment is administered during gestation and the question arises as to whether there are changes in pituitary-adrenal hormonal levels—for example, in response to routine environmental events—during gestation. In an attempt to assess this possibility with regard to premating avoidance conditioning, Joffe *et al.* (1978) took blood samples on day 3, 12, or 21 of gestation from females that had received premating avoidance conditioning only. Blood was taken immediately on removal of an animal from its cage and a second sample was taken 15 minutes later. Neither immediate nor 15 minutes levels of plasma corticosterone of animals that had had premating avoidance conditioning differed from levels in untreated controls on any of the 3 days. It is possible that assessments made at different times of day, on different days of gestation, at different times after exposure to the procedure, and so on might have provided evidence of effects. No evidence at all is available on the effects of premating immobilization on pituitary-adrenal function during gestation. In the light of the negative evidence on one premating procedure and the absence of evidence on the other, premating procedures are classified as prenatal stressors with less confidence than those in the other categories.

B. *Behavioral Effects of Prenatal Stress*

Although the various procedures probably produce common pituitary-adrenal changes, it is not surprising that the findings of different experiments show a great deal of inconsistency. Experiments typically differ in many respects, including the species and strains of subjects used, the postnatal experience of the offspring, their age at testing, the types of tests used, and the behavioral measurements taken. Because of this diversity no brief overall summary or general statements about findings can be made.

Fortunately, at least one common denominator exists in that the great majority of investigators have tested offspring in some type of open-field apparatus (Hall, 1934; Broadhurst, 1960) in which ambulatory activity and number of fecal boluses deposited generally constitute the main measures. Data are available on the effects of prenatal treatments of offspring open-field activity in eight of the 11 subcategories outlines in the previous section. Only in the cases of gestational conditioning (Bell *et al.*, 1967; Hutchings & Gibbon, 1970), premating immobilization (Lane & Hyde, 1973), and audiogenic seizure treatment (Thompson & Sontag, 1956) was open-field activity not measured. (In the last study, activity of offspring in an activity cage was unaffected by the prenatal treatment.) In two of the remaining categories the evidence is entirely negative: open-field activity of offspring of females subjected to handling (Ader & Conklin, 1963) or conflict (Joffe, 1965b) was not significantly affected. In the remaining six subcategories, open-field activity of offspring was measured in 22 of 26 experiments and significantly affected in each case. Many of the studies included several experimental groups and offspring activity was seldom affected in all groups, so a box score somewhat oversimplifies the picture. More detailed summaries can be found in Joffe (1969) and Archer & Blackman (1971, Table I). The point here is that open-field activity of offspring is more often affected by prenatal treatments (apparently without regard to the specific nature of the procedure) than any other behavioral measure thus far investigated, making it a useful "marker" in investigations of mediating mechanisms—this usefulness is independent of questions about the "meaning" of open-field activity as a measure of behavior.

In some cases the prenatal treatment has increased offspring activity and in other cases decreased it, and to avoid complicating matters, the preceding description of effects has been deliberately silent on the direction of the effects. The direction in a given case appears to be dependent largely on variables other than the type, timing, and intensity of the prenatal stress procedure. Some of these other variables are discussed below.

Other open-field measures (defecation, latency of initial activity, activity in the center of the field) have been reported less frequently and are affected with less regularity. It seems appropriate to assume that the effects on activity are not necessarily related to changes in "emotionality." This latter characteristic is defined in terms of open-field defecation scores (Broadhurst, 1960; Hall, 1934, 1938), and these are affected by prenatal stress procedures less frequently than are activity scores.

Various types of learning tasks (such as mazes and avoidance conditioning situations) and "timidity tests" (e.g., time taken by animals to emerge from their cage or to approach food) have been used occasionally, as well as other behavioral tests in one or two investigations (for details, see Archer & Blackman, 1971, or Joffe, 1969). Generally, effects on behavior in most of these tests have been inconsistent from one experiment to another, and too few tests have been used regularly enough to provide a firm impression of trends. Nevertheless, effects on such behavioral measures, as well as on other measures of offspring growth and development, are potentially capable of helping to illuminate the process mediating the effects of prenatal stress.

The occurrence and direction of effects on offspring, including their open-field activity, appear to be influenced by variables such as the age and sex of offspring, their postnatal experience, the characteristics of the test and the testing procedures, and, most clearly, by the strain of rats or mice used. For example, a number of studies (DeFries, 1964; DeFries, et al., 1967; Joffe, 1965a) indicate that, aside from the effects being similar in rats and mice, the direction of the effects is dependent on certain characteristics of the strain of subjects used. This dependence of the direction of the effects on the genotype of the experimental subjects emerged clearly in two investigations. DeFries (1964) mated two strains of mice (BALB/cCrgl and C57BL/Crgl) in all possible combinations (a 2 × 2 diallel cross: see Broadhurst, 1967). Half the pregnant females of each strain were stressed during pregnancy by subjecting them to daily sessions of forced swimming, tilting from one side of a box to the other while a loud tone was sounded at intervals, and exposing them to a brightly illuminated open field. Although offspring were reared by their natural mothers, leaving open the possibility that effects on offspring were postnatally mediated (Joffe, 1969, Chapter 2), the effects on the open-field activity of their offspring are interesting. These are shown in Fig. 1. Prenatal stresses clearly had a different effect on offspring of different genotypes. The activity of offspring of the strain characterized by higher activity (BALB) was decreased, and that of offspring of the low-active strain (C57) increased, by prenatal stress. The different effect of stress on offspring of different genotypes nurtured in the intrauterine environments of mothers of the same strain (CC and CB, or BC and BB: Fig. 1) indicates that the differential effect can be due to the genotype of the offspring, while the different effect of stress on offspring of the same genotype (CB and BC) nurtured in mothers of different strains indicates that the differential effect can also be due to the genotype of the mother.

Similar conclusions emerge from the findings of a study by Joffe (1965a; see also Joffe, 1969, Chapter 8). In this case two strains of rats, Maudsley reactives (MR) and nonreactives (MNR) (Broadhurst, 1960, 1962) were used in a diallel cross. The stress procedure that affected offspring activity was

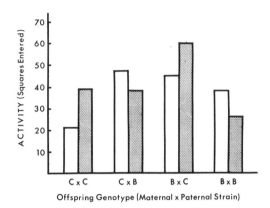

Fɪɢ. 1.   Open-field activity of offspring from two inbred strains of mice and their reciprocal crosses (B: BALB/cCrgl strain; C: C57BL/Crgl strain). Open bars indicate means of offspring of control females, shaded bars means of offspring of females stressed during gestation (DeFries, 1964).

avoidance conditioning given to females prior to mating. The females were not disturbed during pregnancy and offspring were cross-fostered at birth to untreated females so that any effects are attributable to influences operating prenatally. As in DeFries's (1964) experiment, the activity of offspring of the more active strain (MNR, in this case) was decreased, and the activity of offspring of the less active strain (MR) was increased by prenatal stress; in addition, the direction of the stress effect on the reciprocal crosses was dependent on maternal genotype.

There is, then, a considerable amount of evidence indicating that prenatal stress can affect the behavior of offspring, particularly their activity in an open field. The precise nature of the effect may be dependent on many other variables, one set of which, the genotypes of mother and fetus, have been shown to influence the effect in a systematic way.

II. Hormonal Mediation: Background

A question that, for obvious reasons, was posed at an early stage of investigation was one regarding the manner in which prenatal stress effects are mediated. Thompson (1957) suggested that the effects might be due to endocrine changes in the mother, resulting from the experimental procedures, being transmitted to the fetuses. Although it is not the only possibility, the nature of the maternal-placental-fetal relationship makes it probable that some blood-borne substance is involved. There is no neural connection between mother and fetus, and, although there is no continuity of circulation between them, a large variety of chemical substances in the mother's blood can be transmitted across the placenta and into the fetal circulatory system (Hagerman and Villee, 1960). Indeed, permeability of the placenta to many substances is essential for the nourishment, respiration, and excretion of the fetus (see Zamenhof and van Marthens, this volume).

If one postulates that prenatal effects are mediated by the transport of chemical substances from mother to fetus, then hormones appear to be the most likely chemical substances. Indeed, as mentioned earlier, involvement of hormonal changes is implicit in the use of the term "stress" (Selye, 1950). Furthermore, if hormonal changes are suspected it is reasonable to postulate that the effects are mediated by the maternal pituitary-adrenal system, since this system is activated by a variety of stressors (Sayers & Sayers, 1947).

The detailed proposal regarding the mediation of prenatal stress effects by pituitary-adrenocortical hormones is derived from two sources: (a) Evidence on the relationship of the maternal and fetal pituitary-adrenocortical systems (more correctly, hypothalamo-pituitary-adrenocortical systems, but brain mechanisms are not considered directly here) and (b) Hypotheses concerning the possible role of the pituitary-adrenocortical system in the mediation of the effects of neonatal environmental variables on later behavior.

A. Relationship of Maternal and Fetal Pituitary-Adrenocortical (PAC) Systems

Adrenalectomy of pregnant rats results in marked hypertrophy of fetal and neonatal adrenals (Angervall, 1962; Ingle & Fisher, 1938) and increased levels of plasma corticosterone in the offspring at birth (Thoman, Sproul, & Levine, 1970) (see Fig. 2A). Administration of cortisone (Courrier, Colonge, & Baclesse, 1951; Knobil & Briggs, 1955) or of dexamethasone or corticosterone (Paul & D'Angelo, 1972) to the pregnant rat produces fetal adrenal atrophy (see Fig. 2B). That these effects are not due directly to changes in maternal ACTH levels, which are increased in adrenalectomized animals and decreased in those given corticosteroids (including dexamethasone), is indicated by the effect of administering ACTH to pregnant females. Such treatment produces fetal adrenal atrophy (Jones, Lloyd, & Wyatt, 1953; Migeon, Prystowsky, Grumbach, & Byron, 1956), not the hypertrophy which would be expected if the ACTH acted directly on the fetal adrenals (see Fig. 2C).

These and related studies provide convincing evidence that corticosteroids cross the placenta, a conclusion confirmed by the detection of radioactivity in fetuses shortly after injecting the mothers with radioactively labeled corticosterone (Zarrow, Philpott, & Denenberg, 1970). ACTH, like

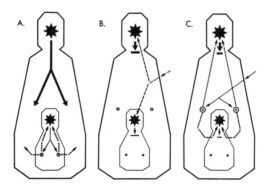

FIG. 2. Relationship of maternal and fetal pituitary-adrenocortical systems. Diagrammatic summary of endocrine effects and hormonal changes produced by (A) Maternal adrenalectomy (which produces fetal adrenal hypertrophy); (B) Administration of corticosteroids to the mother (maternal and fetal adrenal atrophy); and (C) Administration of ACTH to the mother (maternal adrenal hypertrophy, fetal adrenal atrophy). Large shapes represent the mother, small ones the fetus. Stars indicate the pituitary gland and circles the adrenals. Solid lines represent ACTH, with stimulating effects on adrenal cortical hormone release, broken lines corticosteroids, with inhibitory effects on pituitary ACTH release.

most proteins (Zamenhof & van Marthens, this volume), normally does not cross the placenta (Milković, Paunović, Ronkulin, Bobanović, & Milković, 1966). Thus, adrenalectomy of the mother lowers the level of adrenal steriods in fetal circulation. This disinhibits ACTH output by the fetal pituitary after the 18th day of gestation, when the fetal PAC system of the rat is functional (Milković, Milković, & Paunović, 1973). The increased levels of fetal ACTH produce fetal adrenal hypertrophy and an accompanying increase in fetal adrenal corticosterone production. The increased fetal corticosterone maintains corticosterone in the adrenalectomized mother at normal levels as steroids pass from the fetus to the mother (Dupouy, Coffigny, & Magre, 1975; Milković, Paunović, Kniewald, & Milković, 1973).

Conversely, administering ACTH to the mother results in increased levels of steroids (of maternal adrenal origin) in the fetus. These steroids suppress ACTH output by the fetal pituitary with consequent atrophy of the fetal adrenals. Administration of corticosteroids (corticosterone, cortisone, and dexamethasone have been investigated) to the mother produces effects on the fetus which are similar to those of ACTH administration although the effects on the mother are dissimilar. The exogenous corticosteroids suppress both maternal and fetal ACTH output, with resultant adrenal atrophy and reduced adrenocortical output. The levels of circulating corticosteroids remain high but endogenous production is suppressed.

The mechanisms and effects of the different treatments are summarized diagrammatically in Fig. 2.

B. Effects of Neonatal Manipulations on Behavior and the Pituitary-Adrenocortical System

Hypotheses concerning hormonal mediation of prenatal stress effects were developed from hypotheses concerning hormonal mediation of the effects of neonatal events on later behavior. Consequently, a brief outline of these earlier hypotheses is presented here.

Various postnatal manipulations of immature rodents, such as neonatal handling and shock, which have been shown to have widespread effects on their development and behavior (Denenberg, 1962; Levine, 1962a), also produce pituitary-adrenocortical changes. For example, under certain conditions neonatal manipulations may increase corticosterone levels in the newborn rat (Denenberg, Brumaghim, Haltmeyer, & Zarrow, 1967; Gray, 1971). Neonatal manipulations have also been found to affect the maturation of the diurnal rhythm of corticosterone secretion (Ader, 1969), the development of the PAC response to stress (Levine, 1968), and the functioning of the PAC system in adulthood (Ader & Grota, 1969; Haltmeyer, Denenberg, & Zarrow, 1967; Levine, 1962b; Levine, Haltmeyer, Karas, & Denenberg, 1967). In addition, there are data indicating that direct manipulations of the neonatal PAC system affect later behavior (e.g., Howard & Granoff, 1968; Howard, 1973; Nyakas, 1973; Schapiro, 1968). These various lines of evidence resulted in the development of an hypothesis regarding the manner in which early experience effects are mediated. This hypothesis is analogous to proposals concerning the "organizational" influence on the central nervous system of gonadal hormones during the perinatal period (see Whitsett & Vandenbergh, this volume).

The earliest statement of the hypothesis that the effects of neonatal manipulations are mediated by PAC hormones was made by Levine and Mullins (1966). They proposed that various forms of early stimulation (handling, shock, etc.) produce an increase in circulating corticosterone which modifies central neural function which in turn alters the manner in which the PAC system responds to environmental events in later life. It should be noted that the hypothesis invokes the PAC system as a mediator of the effects of neonatal stimulation in two distinct ways. First, it is the response of the PAC system that induces the changes in the functioning of the central nervous system. Second, it is the altered functioning of the PAC system which is responsible for the altered behavior seen in the adult animal after neonatal stimulation. Results not in accord with one part of the hypothesis do not necessarily detract from the validity of the other part. For example, evidence indicating that, say, thyroid activation was needed in order for neonatal manipulations to affect behavior would not exclude the possibility that thyroid changes in the neonate modified the functioning of central nervous system mechanisms controlling the PAC system. Conversely, evidence indicating that behavioral changes following neonatal manipulations occurred without accompanying modification of PAC function would not exclude the possibility that central nervous system mechanisms affecting the behavior were modified by a PAC response to neonatal stimulation.

Investigators (Joffe, 1969, p. 109; Joffe & Levine, 1969) reasoned that if, in fact, early postnatal experience can modify the functioning of brain areas responsible for adrenal functioning in adults, it is likely that prenatal treatments, particularly those producing changes in pituitary-adrenal hormonal levels, produce effects in the same way. Stress would alter the level of hormones circulating in the mother and hence perhaps in the fetus, and these hormones might alter fetal brain function directly—assuming the fetal brain is sensitive to such effects prenatally—or indirectly by altering the functioning of the fetal adrenals. If the altered adrenal functioning persisted into the postnatal period it could presumably lead to effects on brain functioning at this stage. Hypotheses that are derived from this line of reasoning are presented more formally in the next section.

III. Hormonal Mediation of Prenatal Stress Effects: Hypotheses

The general proposal that the effects of prenatal stress on offspring behavior are mediated by the pituitary-adrenal system can now be stated more explicitly in the form of a number of hypotheses.

1. Activation of the maternal pituitary-adrenal system in response to prenatal stress procedures increases levels of fetal glucocorticoids, particularly (in rats) corticosterone.

2. The pituitary-adrenal hormonal changes resulting from stress to the mother produce long-term changes in the functioning of areas of the fetal central nervous system. The observed effects on behavior are due to these changes in neural or neuroendocrine mechanisms subserving the behavior.

3. The fetal central neural mechanisms affected are those controlling the functioning of the pituitary-adrenal system, so that changes in pituitary-adrenal functioning should occur in offspring of animals stressed during gestation.

4. The effects on behavior are produced by changes in the functioning of the pituitary-adrenal system of the offspring. Therefore, behavioral effects should not occur in the absence of changes in pituitary-adrenal functioning, and the behavior in question should be affected by direct manipulations of pituitary-adrenal functioning.

The first two hypotheses, which state that behavioral effects of prenatal stress are due to CNS changes resulting from altered levels of pituitary-adrenal hormones during development, are more important than, and independent of, the third and fourth hypotheses. These latter subsidiary hypotheses postulate that the CNS changes involve neuroendocrine mechanisms associated with pituitary-adrenal function and that the altered pituitary-adrenal functioning in the offspring produces the behavioral effects. However, it is clear that prenatal pituitary-adrenal activation could produce effects on mechanisms controlling systems other than the pituitary-adrenal system and, conversely, that mechanisms controlling the pituitary-adrenal system of offspring could be altered by prenatal changes in other hormonal systems. Consequently evidence on the effects of prenatal pituitary-adrenal changes on fetal brain mechanisms and offspring behavior does not bear directly on the question of whether behavioral effects of prenatal treatments are the result of offspring having modified pituitary-adrenal function (and vice versa).

IV. Evidence

A. Effects of Prenatal Hormonal Manipulations on Offspring Behavior

Hypotheses 1 and 2 imply that alterations of maternal pituitary-adrenal function should themselves affect the behavior of offspring.

1. ADRENAL MEDULLARY HORMONES

Initially, experimenters concerned with the mediation of prenatal stress effects concentrated on determining if the adrenal medullary hormones, epinephrine and norepinephrine, produced effects on offspring similar to the effects of prenatal stress.

Thompson and Olian (1961) investigated the effects of prenatal epinephrine injections in three strains of mice and found that the effects on the open-field activity of the offspring were dependent on strain; scores of a low-active strain (A/Jax) were increased by epinephrine, those of a high-active strain (C57BL/6) decreased, and scores of a medium active strain (BALB/Ci) were not significantly affected. As Young (1967) has pointed out, the scores presented by Thompson and Olian suggest a prenatal treatment by test condition interaction, but the data were not given the statistical treatment appropriate to detect this effect.

The importance of parental characteristics in determining the direction of the effect on offspring activity was again shown in a later experiment by Thompson's group, this time using rats. Thompson et al. (1962) found that the direction of the effects of epinephrine injections in the second trimester was dependent upon parental activity levels. In this study the activity of offspring of high-active parents was *increased* by the parental epinephrine injections, that of offspring of low-active parents *decreased* by the epinephrine injections. (A variety of procedures in this study differed from those used by Thompson & Olian, 1961, making it impossible to pinpoint reasons for this discrepancy.) Open-field defecation was significantly increased by the prenatal epinephrine in both groups. Under stressful testing conditions (open-field testing following electric shock) activity of offspring in both activity level groups was decreased by prenatal epinephrine injections.

Thompson and Goldenberg (1962) examined the effects of two dosages of epinephrine administered in different trimesters of pregnancy on the viability, weight, and adrenal size of rat offspring, and later Thompson, Goldenberg, Watson, and Watson (1963) reported the effects on behavior. There were no effects on viability, but offspring in the high-dosage group were lighter than the others at 180 and 200 days of age and the adrenals of all groups injected in the first or second trimester—including the saline-injected group—were lighter than the adrenals of uninjected controls. Open-field activity of male offspring of mothers injected with epinephrine or saline in the second trimester was depressed; the effect on females was not significant. Scores in a runway and a water maze were unaffected, as were error scores in a Hebb–Williams maze, but time scores in the maze showed that offspring of females injected (with epinephrine or saline) in the second and third trimester were slower than controls.

No other studies on this topic have precisely replicated these experiments so it is not surprising that, while further experiments confirm the general proposition that epinephrine will affect the behavior of offspring, other studies do not report similar findings. Variations in the various parameters discussed earlier are sufficient to account for these differences.

Young (1963) used a number of control groups: Aside from a group of rats receiving epinephrine injections during gestation there was a saline-injected group, a group which received handling equivalent to that involved in the injection procedure, and an undisturbed group. Offspring were tested in an open field and a Hebb–Williams maze at either 30 or 60 days of age. There were no significant differences in activity at either age, but open-field defecation and urination (combined) were significantly greater in offspring of epinephrine-treated mothers than in offspring of the other three groups at 30, but not at 60, days of age. Epinephrine group offspring were slower in the Hebb–Williams maze at both ages.

In a subsequent experiment, Young (1964) used both epinephrine and norepinephrine treatments and, in addition, postnatal manipulation (rotation) of offspring (rats). In this experiment, effects on open-field defecation were not found, but epinephrine reduced activity (regardless of postnatal treatment) as in most of the studies by Thompson and his colleagues. Both epinephrine and norepinephrine produced inferior maze performance at both 30 and 60 days of age. Bell, Drucker, and Woodruff (1965) also found that epinephrine administration during gestation reduced open-field activity of rat offspring.

There is little point in comparing the findings of these experiments with those of the effects of prenatal stress since the results in both areas are sufficiently variable to produce similar or discrepant findings at will depending on the studies selected for comparison. The variation in so many parameters, including strain of subjects, does not enable one to find a suitable comparison of epinephrine and stress treatments, except in the case of a study by DeFries *et al.* (1967) in which females received either stress or epinephrine injections. These experimenters used a diallel cross of two mouse strains (BALB/cJ and C57BL/6J). Essentially, four replications of the cross were used: (i) a variety of stress procedures (enforced swimming, "tilt box," open field) were administered daily from 10 days after mating; (ii) undisturbed controls; (iii) epinephrine on Days 10 and 11 of gestation; (iv) vehicle injections.

Offspring were tested in an open field at 37–43 days of age. The effects of stress procedures (compared to untreated controls) were similar to those found previously by DeFries (1964), with offspring of high-active fathers showing reduced activity and those of low-active fathers showing increased activity. In addition, there was a similar interaction of epinephrine treatment with paternal strain, but in this case the direction of the effects was reversed, with activity of offspring of high-active fathers *increased* and that of offspring of low-active fathers *decreased.* That is, in both strains of mice stress altered offspring activity in a direction different to that of epinephrine. The difference in the direction of effects of stress as compared to epinephrine led DeFries *et al.* (1967) to conclude that the effects of epinephrine injections do not mimic those of stress. However, the difference in the periods at which the two treatments were administered rather than the nature of the stressors might account for the different effects on offspring behavior.

Generally, it seems that these kinds of experiments are unlikely to shed much light on the processes underlying the effects of prenatal stress. Epinephrine injections produce release of ACTH and an increase in the circulating level of corticosteroids so that effects on the fetus could be the result of transfer of either medullary or cortical hormones; thus, in a sense, injections of medullary hormones can be considered simply as a different stress procedure. Nevertheless, these investigations were valuable in that they were the first to indicate that hormones involved in the response to stress are capable of affecting offspring behavior.

2. PITUITARY-ADRENOCORTICAL (PAC) HORMONES

Experiments on effects other than behavioral ones provide evidence that the effects of prenatally administered PAC hormones and stress are comparable in at least one area. Prenatal cortisone (Fraser & Fainstat, 1951; Kalter & Warkany, 1959) or corticosterone (Blaustein, Feller, & Rosenzweig, 1971) can cause a high incidence of cleft palate in mice. The incidence varies with the strain of mouse (Kalter, 1954, 1961, 1965; Warkany & Kalter, 1962). Similarly, stressing pregnant mice (using a restraint or immobilization procedure) around day 14 of gestation produces cleft palate in the fetuses (Rosenzweig & Blaustein, 1970), and the incidence is similar in corticosterone-injected and stressed groups (Barlow, McElhatton, Morrison, & Sullivan, 1974; Barlow, McElhatton, & Sullivan, 1975).

Prenatal hormonal manipulations known to have marked effects on fetal and neonatal adrenal size and function (Section II, A) have been found to affect offspring behavior, but the picture is far from consistent. Behavioral effects once again appear to be dependent on variables such as strain, age, sex, postnatal experience of offspring, and the test procedures used. While age, sex, and experience have been investigated in some experiments, no systematic investigation of strain has been carried out. Unfortunately, assessment of the role of strain by comparing the results of different experiments is precluded by variations across experiments in other parameters, such as test procedures and the dose or timing of prenatal hormonal manipulations. In other words, when different strains have been used so have different test procedures or hormonal manipulations. Consequently, it is not possible to pinpoint reasons for contradictory findings. In the following brief review, variables that may account for differences in results are identified only to suggest where clarification is needed.

a. Maternal Adrenalectomy. The effects of prenatal maternal adrenalectomy on offspring behavior have been particularly variable. Effects on offspring open-field behavior have been reported: A significant increase in the activity of offspring of adrenalectomized female rats was detected, but only in offspring which had received prior testing in an avoidance conditioning task (Joffe, Milković, & Levine, 1972). However, in studies using different strains of rats, open-field activity of offspring of adrenalectomized females was not significantly affected even when the open-field testing followed avoidance conditioning (Smith, Joffe, and Heseltine, 1975; J. M. Joffe, J. A. Mulick, & J. A. Peterson, unpublished). In a fourth experiment, in which no systematic manipulation was made of the experience of rat offspring prior to open-field testing, no effects of prenatal maternal adrenalectomy on open-field behavior were obtained (Havlena & Werboff, 1963b). Aside from strain of subjects, these experiments differed in the time (in relation to mating) that adrenalectomy was performed, postnatal treatment of offspring, and age of offspring at testing.

The absence of effects on open-field behavior in all but one experiment is not attributable to an inability of adrenalectomy to affect offspring behavior since other effects on behavior have been found more frequently. Shuttlebox avoidance conditioning scores of offspring have been affected by prenatal maternal adrenalectomy; offspring of adrenalectomized female rats made more avoidances in two studies (Joffe et al., 1972a; Joffe et al., unpublished), although in the former the effect was significant only in female offspring. The absence of an effect in the third study in which offspring avoidance conditioning was investigated (Smith et al., 1975) may be attributable to a modification of the conditioning paradigm. Smith et al. (1975), unlike other investigators, used a conditioning procedure in which, during the intertrial interval, the floor remained electrified on the side of the box to which the rate would be required to cross on the following CS presentation. This eliminates intertrial responding and may, as a result, affect conditioning scores. Joffe et al. (unpublished) found that in a conditioning paradigm in which a rat was free to make intertrial responses, the improved avoidance conditioning of offspring of adrenalectomized mothers was accompanied by a significant increase in intertrial responding. Taken together, then, the findings of the studies suggest that improved conditioning may be due principally to increased activity in the shuttlebox. This possibility is given some support by the finding that, in a passive-avoidance test, offspring of adrenalectomized females reentered the box in which they had received shock sooner than offspring of controls (Joffe et al., unpublished).

Some evidence is available on the effects of prenatal maternal adrenalectomy on other behaviors of rat offspring. Havlena and Werboff (1963b) found no effect on performance in a timidity test, and Joffe et al. (unpublished) found no effects on scores in a reaction-to-handling test (in which the experimenter rates an animal's startle response, vocalization, and resistance to being picked up).

   b. *Exogenous Administration of Hormones.* Less evidence is available on the effects of other prenatal manipulations of the maternal PAC system on offspring behavior. Increases in ACTH levels of pregnant rats, whether produced by subcutaneous implantation of an ACTH-secreting tumor (Joffe et al., 1972a) or by ACTH injections (Joffe, 1977) did not affect avoidance conditioning scores of offspring but significantly affected their open-field activity. In earlier studies the effect was related to test order: Offspring of tumor-implanted females tested after avoidance conditioning were significantly more active than littermates tested without prior conditioning experience (Joffe et al., 1972a). Offspring of ACTH-injected females (Joffe, 1977) were significantly less active than offspring of saline-injected controls regardless of prior test experience.

   In a study by Smith et al. (1975), treatment of pregnant rats with dexamethasone (a potent synthetic glucocorticoid which, like natural glucocorticoids, inhibits ACTH release: Purves & Sirett, 1965) failed to affect off-spring open-field activity significantly when low doses (8 to 14 μg/rat/day) were administered prior to and during gestation, but a higher dose (20 μg/rat/day) administered during gestation resulted in a significant increase in the activity of female offspring (Joffe, 1977).

However, Grota (1970) found that offspring of rats administered dexamethasone in their drinking water during gestation did not differ from control offspring in a reaction-to-handling test, although the highest dose of dexamethasone used was probably higher than the doses used in the studies cited above. Only the amount of dexamethasone dissolved in 8 oz. of drinking water is reported, not the amount ingested. The highest dose ingested was probably over 30 μg/rat/day. Grota administered the drug from day 2 only until day 17 of gestation, which raises the possibility that effects depend on modified corticosteroid levels during the last few days of gestation, when the fetal PAC system is functional. (The fetal pituitary begins to secrete ACTH between day 17 and day 18 of gestation: S. Milković et al., 1973.) Grota did find that the highest dose of dexamethasone increased the resting level of plasma corticosterone in male offspring in adulthood.

Maternal Hypophysectomy. Obias (1957) found no effects of maternal hypophysectomy on day 13 of gestation on the physical development of offspring or their performance in a water maze. The incidence of perinatal deaths was high in both mothers and offspring.

Conclusion. As in the case of adrenal medullary hormones, a comparison of the effects of prenatal PAC hormonal manipulations on offspring behavior with the effects of prenatal stress is precluded by the inconsistency of the effects of both categories of treatments. In any case, it is unlikely that experimental manipulations of hormonal levels would mimic, in pattern and quality, the complex of changes that actually result from prenatal stress techniques. Thus identical effects would not necessarily be expected. At least the studies described, by indicating that prenatal PAC hormonal manipulations can in certain cases affect offspring behavior—in particular, open-field activity—leave open the possibility that prenatal stress effects are mediated by the PAC system.

B. Effects of Prenatal Stress on the Pituitary-Adrenocortical System of the Offspring

Experiments on this topic are relevant to Hypotheses 1 (altered hormonal levels in the mother are reflected in changes in fetal levels), 3 (Changes in PAC function occur in offspring of prenatally stressed females), and 4 (behavioral effects are the result of effects on the PAC system of the offspring).

There is abundant evidence that direct manipulation of the maternal PAC system affects fetal and neonatal hormonal levels and adrenal size (see Section II, A). Furthermore, stressors such as maternal starvation (Picon, 1957), exposure of the mother to low temperatures or chronic pain (Milković, Winget, Romić, & Levine, 1974), or injection of the mother with formalin (Schnürer, 1963) produce fetal adrenal atrophy similar to that produced by injecting the mother with ACTH or corticosteroids. However, there is very little evidence as to the effects of any of the prenatal stress procedures described in Section I, A on hormonal levels in the fetus.

In an attempt to assess the effects of the CS-exposure procedure on fetal adrenal function, J. M. Joffe, J. A. Mulick, K. F. Ley, and R. A. Rawson (unpublished) examined fetal adrenal weights and corticosterone levels. They found no effects of the procedure on either measure in rat fetuses delivered by caesarean section during the last 24 hours of gestation. However, the stress of the caesarean delivery may have masked any effects of the prenatal stress procedure on plasma corticosterone levels. Furthermore, as indexed by neonatal rats' adrenal size and plasma corticosterone levels, daily sessions of electric shock during gestation also did not affect fetal levels of PAC hormones (J. M. Joffe, J. A. Mulick, & J. A. Peterson, unpublished; Joffe, 1977). The paucity of direct measures of plasma corticosterone levels in fetuses of stressed and unstressed mothers leaves unanswered the question of the immediate effects of stress on fetal hormonal levels (Hypothesis 1).

In two experiments (J. M. Joffe, J. A. Mulick, & J. A. Peterson, unpublished; Joffe, 1977) gestational stress (specifically, electric shock) also failed to affect resting levels of plasma corticosterone, or levels 15 minutes after the stress of the first blood sample in older rat offspring (measures obtained from adult animals in the first case and from 33–38 day old animals in the second). This finding provides no support for the hypothesis that fetal neural mechanisms controlling PAC function are affected by prenatal stress (Hypothesis 3). However, handling pregnant rats has been found to affect PAC function in adult offspring (Ader & Plaut, 1968). Plasma corticosterone levels following electric shock were similar in offspring of handled and control females, but levels following the apparently milder stimulation of being picked up were lower in female offspring of handled mothers (although there were no differences between experimental and control males). This finding provides some support for the implication of hypothesis 3 (that changes in PAC function occur in offspring of prenatally stressed animals), but only with regard to the particular prenatal stress procedure used. Although evidence on the PAC effects of other procedures is negative, insufficient evidence is available to reach a conclusion concerning the hypothesis that fetal central neural mechanisms controlling the PAC system are modified by prenatal stress.

Since behavioral effects of prenatal stress have been demonstrated in experiments in which no detectable effects on PAC function were found (e.g., Joffe, 1977), Hypothesis 4—which states that PAC changes produce the behavioral effects—also lacks support.

C. Behavioral Effects of Modification of Pituitary-Adrenocortical Function in Adult Animals

If, as Hypothesis 4 states, the effects of prenatal stress on offspring behavior are the consequence of modified PAC function in the offspring, then modifying PAC function in other ways should affect behavior in the same situations. The situation of most relevance in this regard is the open-field test, since open-field activity is most often reported to be affected by prenatal stress (see Section I, B).

Much of the evidence on the relationship between open-field behavior and PAC functioning is inconsistent when studies in which correlational techniques or indirect manipulations of PAC function have been used are examined (e.g., see Ader, 1975). However, investigations using direct experimental manipulation of PAC status have produced less ambiguous findings. Moyer (1958) found that adrenalectomy significantly increased open-field defecation in female rats. This finding was confirmed by Joffe, Mulick, and Rawson (1972) who showed, in addition, that the effect occurs in both males and females and that it is not due to a general increase in defecation since home cage defecation was reduced in adrenalectomized animals. Furthermore, dexamethasone administration also increases open-field defecation in females (Mulick, Joffe, & Peterson, 1975; Joffe, Mulick, Peterson, & Paunović, 1976) but not in males (Mulick et al., 1975).

In those studies in which open-field activity was measured, however, the effects of endocrine manipulations were slight (Joffe et al., 1972b) or nonsignificant (Joffe et al., 1976; Mulick et al., 1975). Thus, although PAC manipulations reliably affect open-field defecation, they have little effect on activity, the measure most frequently affected by prenatal stress. The evidence contradicts the implication of Hypothesis 4, that behaviors affected by prenatal stress should be affected by direct manipulations of the PAC system. Consequently, the hypothesis itself—that behavioral effects of prenatal stress are the result of PAC changes in the offspring—is not supported.

D. Modification of Prenatal Stress Effects by Manipulation of the Maternal Pituitary-Adrenocortical System

Although the effects of prenatal manipulations of PAC hormonal levels are far from consistent, they do establish that modification of the PAC system is often sufficient to affect offspring behavior (Section IV, A). Investigations of the hypothesis that such PAC hormonal changes are necessary if prenatal manipulations are to affect offspring behavior (Hypotheses 1 and 2) have been based on the following proposition: If activation of the maternal PAC system mediates the effects of prenatal stress, procedures which attenuate or abolish the PAC response to stress should attenuate the effects of prenatal stress on offspring. Evidence from two experiments using this approach is available.

In the first investigation (Smith *et al.*, 1975) female rats were subjected to prenatal stress under conditions in which the adrenocortical response to stress was absent (adrenalectomy) or attenuated by the administration of dexamethasone in the drinking water prior to mating and throughout gestation. A third group received chlorpromazine in the drinking water. Chlorpromazine can raise ACTH levels and inhibit stress-induced ACTH release, but the effects are dependent on dose (DeWied, 1967) and since postpartum maternal adrenal weights were unaffected by chlorpromazine in the Smith *et al.* (1975) study it is unclear whether chlorpromazine modified PAC function. A fourth group of females was hormonally unmanipulated. Half the females in each of the four groups were subjected to avoidance conditioning prior to mating and exposure to the CS in the home cage throughout pregnancy. Four times a day buzzers identical to those in the shuttleboxes were sounded for 10 seconds every minute for 30 minutes. All offspring were fostered at birth to lactating females that had received neither stress nor drug treatment. The effects of adrenalectomy and dexamethasone treatments themselves were described earlier (Section IV, A). The concern here is with modifications of the effects of stress attributable to manipulations of the maternal PAC system.

The prenatal stress procedure resulted in significant reductions in the birth and weaning weights of offspring of hormonally untreated ("control") females. As can be seen in Fig. 3 these effects were prevented by treatments attenuating the maternal PAC response to stress. One behavioral measure in the Smith *et al.* (1975) study showed attenuation of the stress effect. The number of avoidances performed by 50- to 55-day-old female (but not male) offspring of otherwise untreated mothers was significantly reduced by prenatal stress, while the avoidance conditioning scores of offspring of chlorpromazine-treated or adrenalectomized mothers were unaffected by stress. However, the avoidance scores of female offspring of dexamethasone-treated females were significantly increased by prenatal stress, indicating that the attenuation of the PAC response to stress produced by dexamethasone failed to prevent prenatal stress from affecting offspring behavior.

Other measures of offspring development and behavior in the Smith *et al.* (1975) study provide a complex picture. In a food deprivation test at 42 days of age the mortality of male (but not female) offspring of control females

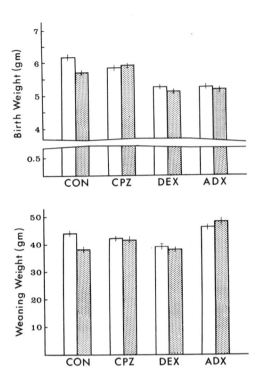

FIG. 3.   Mean (± standard error) body weights at birth (above) and weaning (below) of offspring of unstressed females (open bars) and females stressed during gestation (shaded bars). Mothers otherwise were untreated (CON), given chlorpromazine (CPZ) or dexamethasone (DEX) in their drinking water, or were adrenalectomized (ADX). From Smith *et al.* (1975). Copyright 1975 by Pergamon Press and reproduced by permission.

and of females with modified PAC function was reduced by prenatal stress, and the weight loss of different subgroups of offspring in the same test at 69 days of age was reduced by prenatal stress regardless of maternal PAC status. Similarly, the ability of offspring to compete for food in a social dominance test was reduced by prenatal stress in all groups. In sum, on a number of measures prenatal stress affected the offspring of females with modified PAC function in the same way that it affected offspring of otherwise untreated females, contradicting the notion that PAC hormonal changes are necessary for prenatal stress to affect offspring.

The effects on the open-field activity of offspring in the Smith *et al.* (1975) study are perhaps of most interest. Activity scores of animals tested at 30 days of age were unaffected by prenatal stress or PAC manipulations. However, activity scores of other subgroups of offspring tested between 50 and 60 days of age showed a variety of effects which are summarized in Fig. 4.

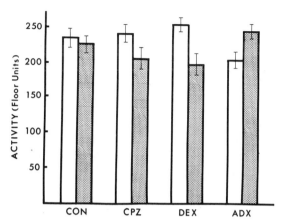

FIG. 4. Mean ($\pm$ standard error) open-field activity scores of offspring of unstressed females (open bars) and females stressed during gestation (shaded bars). Mothers were otherwise untreated (CON), given chlorpromazine (CPZ) or dexamethasone (DEX) in their drinking water, or adrenalectomized (ADX). From Smith *et al.* (1975).

Prenatal stress did not significantly affect the activity of offspring of control females or chlorpromzaine-treated females. However, the effects of stress can be said to have been potentiated by maternal adrenalectomy or dexamethasone treatment. Prenatal stress produced a significant decrease in the activity of offspring of dexamethasone-treated females and a significant increase in the activity of offspring of adrenalectomized females. That is, prenatal stress failed to affect offspring of hormonally unmanipulated females but affected offspring of females with an attenuated PAC response. If PAC activation were the mechanism responsible for the effects of prenatal stress on offspring behavior, prenatal stress should not have produced significant effects on offspring behavior in groups in which PAC responsiveness to stress was attenuated by hormonal treatments.

The question of whether attenuation of the maternal PAC response to stress attenuates the effects of prenatal stress on offspring behavior was investigated in one other experiment. Joffe (1977) used a different prenatal stress procedure (electric shock during gestation), a higher dose of dexamethasone (20 μg/rat/day) with more precise control of dosage achieved by injecting the drug rather than putting it in the drinking water, and an additional method of attenuating the maternal PAC response to stress. ACTH injection, which increases adrenocortical output to near maximal levels, was used to attenuate any further maternal PAC response to shock during gestation in one group of rats. Daily injections of the appropriate drug (dexamethasone or ACTH) or of saline vehicle were started on day 2 of gestation and the daily stress sessions (15 unsignaled 3 second foot-shocks during a 15 minute period) on Day 7. All offspring were fostered at birth to untreated mothers.

Both dexamethasone and ACTH attenuated the effects of stress on birth weight. The birth weight of offspring of saline-injected females was significantly *increased* by prenatal stress, while in the dexamethasone and ACTH groups the birth weight of offspring of stressed mothers did not differ significantly from that of offspring of unstressed mothers. The data from the Smith *et al.* (1975) and Joffe (1977) experiments clearly implicate the maternal PAC system in the mediation of the effects of stress on birth weight: Attenuating the maternal PAC response to stress during gestation prevents stress from affecting the birth weight of offspring.

Other measures of the effects of stress on offspring (Joffe, 1977) show a similar variety of patterns to that seen in the previous experiment (Smith *et al.*, 1975). Mortality rates from birth to weaning were high in all groups and there were significantly more deaths in ACTH–Stress than in ACTH–No Stress offspring. This potentiation of a stress effect in one of the two groups in which the maternal PAC response to stress was attenuated is not in accord with the supposition that PAC activation mediates the effects of prenatal stress. Active and passive avoidance conditioning of offspring were affected by neither stress nor PAC manipulations. As in the Smith *et al.* (1975) experiment, open-field behavior of offspring tested prior to puberty was unaffected by prenatal stress or hormones, but activity scores of separate groups of offspring tested later (86–96 days of age in this case) were affected.

The detection of effects in older animals that are not seen in younger ones (in this experiment and the one previously discussed) is of some interest. While the emergence of effects in older animals could implicate any number of age-correlated changes, the one that suggests itself in this context is the change in hormonal functioning following puberty. In both studies effects were not detected in offspring tested prior to puberty but there were marked effects of the same treatments in animals tested after puberty, suggesting the need for systematic investigation of the interaction of the PAC and pituitary-gonadal systems in mediating effects of prenatal stress.

The effects of prenatal treatments on the open-field activity of older offspring are shown in Fig. 5. Slight support for the hypothesis of PAC mediation is found in the attenuation of the prenatal stress effect on open-field activity in the dexamethasone group. Whereas prenatal stress produced a significant reduction in activity of offspring of saline-treated females, the effect of prenatal stress on activity of offspring of dexamethasone-treated females was not significant. However, the data as a whole provide evidence contradicting the hypothesis. Unlike the finding with dexamethasone, injecting females with ACTH during gestation failed to prevent stress from affecting the activity of their offspring; in addition, the effect of stress on offspring

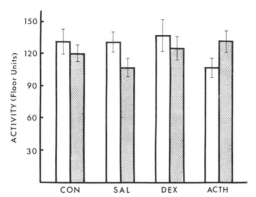

FIG. 5. Mean (± standard error) open-field activity scores of offspring of unstressed females (open bars) and females stressed during gestation (shaded bars). Mothers were otherwise untreated (CON), or injected with saline (SAL), dexamethasone (DEX), or ACTH during gestation. From Joffe, 1977.

of ACTH-treated females was in the opposite direction to the effect of stress on saline-injected controls. If the effects of stress were a result of maternal PAC activation, the attenuation of the PAC response to stress by ACTH-injection should have attenuated the behavioral effect of prenatal stress.

In summary, the effects of prenatal stress on birth weights (and, in one study, on weaning weights) are attenuated by inactivation of the maternal PAC system. In no case in which prenatal stress affected offspring behavior in controls were the effects consistently attenuated by manipulations of the maternal PAC system. In certain cases prenatal stress had similar effects on offspring of mothers with attenuated PAC functioning to those it had on offspring of mothers in which PAC function was not manipulated (mortality in a food deprivation test, weight loss in food deprivation and social dominance tests: Smith *et al.*, 1975); in other cases prenatal stress affected offspring of hormonally treated females when offspring of hormonally unmanipulated females were unaffected (open-field activity: Smith *et al.*, 1975; preweaning mortality: Joffe, 1977); in yet other cases prenatal stress significantly affected offspring of hormonally treated females but the direction of the effect was opposite to the direction of the effect on controls (avoidance conditioning of female offspring: Smith *et al.*, 1975; open-field activity: Joffe, 1977). It can only be said that attenuation of the maternal PAC response to stress potentiates, reverses, or fails to modify, the effects of prenatal stress on offspring behavior. It does not block them.

V. Implications and Conclusions

The evidence available makes it appear unlikely that the effects of pre-natal stress on offspring behavior are due to altered levels of PAC hormones during development or that the effects are attributable to changes in brain mechanisms involved in PAC functioning in the offspring. Some types of prenatal stress procedures alter fetal glucocorticoid levels (Hypothesis 1: Section IV, B), but even if these changes were found consistently with all procedures they could not account for the behavioral effects on offspring since behavioral effects are found in circumstances in which PAC involve-ment is attenuated or prevented (Section IV D). This contradicts a major implication of hypotheses 1 and 2. It also remains possible that some types of prenatal stress alter brain mechanisms controlling PAC function (hypo-thesis 3: Sections IV, B and D), but even if this evidence were consistent such changes could not account for the behavioral effects of stress (Hypothesis 4) since direct manipulations of PAC function do not produce effects on behavior similar to those of prenatal stress (Section IV, C) and behavioral effects of prenatal stress are found in the absence of PAC effects (Section IV, B).

It remains necessary to offer some alternative possibilities. To do so, it is helpful to consider in more detail the effects of prenatal treatments on the open-field activity of offspring.

A. Effects of Prenatal Hormonal Manipulations on Open-Field Activity of Offspring

The effects on the open-field activity of offspring of the PAC manipula-tions used in the two experiments described in Section IV, D (Smith *et al.*, 1975; Joffe, 1977) are summarized in Table I. In this table, "Treatment effect" indicates the effect that the hormone or surgical treatment itself had on the open-field activity of offspring. For example, " +(9)" for the first dexamethasone (DEX) group listed indicates that the offspring of unstressed mothers administered dexamethasone during gestation were 9% more active than the offspring of hormonally unmanipulated (control) unstressed females. It will be recalled that in other experiments (Joffe *et al.*, 1972a; Joffe *et al.*, unpublished; Havlena & Werboff, 1963b: see Section IV, A) prenatal maternal adrenalectomy has been found to leave offspring activity un-affected or to produce effects dependent on the previous test experience of the offspring. The latter qualification applies also to the effects of increased ACTH levels produced by a different technique, subcutaneous implantation of an ACTH-secreting tumor (Joffe *et al.*, 1972a: see Section IV,A). Never-theless, it is helpful to attempt to determine if offspring activity is related to any of the prenatal PAC hormonal levels in mother or fetus. A summary of

TABLE I

SUMMARY OF THE EFFECTS OF HORMONES OR ADRENALECTOMY (ADX) AND OF STRESS
ON OPEN-FIELD ACTIVITY OF OFFSPRING[a]

Data	Treatment	Treatment effect	Stress effect
Smith *et al.* (1975)	CON	—	−(4)
	DEX	+(9)	−(22)[b]
	ADX	−(13)	+(20)[b]
Joffe (1977): Male offspring	SAL	—	−(10)[b]
	DEX	−(10)	−(5)
	ACTH	−(29)[b]	+(47)[b]
Female offspring	SAL	—	−(25)[b]
	DEX	+(15)[b]	−(11)[b]
	ACTH	−(16)[b]	+(18)[b]

[a]"Treatment effect" indicates whether the treatment itself increased (+) or decreased (−) activity of offspring of unstressed females in comparison with offspring of unstressed hormonally unmanipulated controls (CON) (Smith *et al.*, 1975) or in comparison with offspring of unstressed saline-treated controls (SAL) (Joffe, 1977). "Stress effect" indicates whether stress increased or decreased activity of offspring compared to offspring of unstressed females that received the same treatment. Numbers in parenthesis indicate the percentage increase or decrease. Data from Joffe (1977) for male and female offspring are presented separately because dexamethasone (DEX) significantly affected the score of females but not of males.

[b]Statistically significant ($p < .05$).

the effects of dexamethasone, ACTH, and adrenalectomy on maternal, fetal, and neonatal PAC function is shown in Table II. This table is based on data from experiments described in Section II, A.

As shown in Table II, ACTH, by stimulating the maternal adrenal, raises levels of circulating corticosterone. Dexamethasone, although it attenuates ACTH release and thus inhibits adrenal corticosterone production, is itself a corticosteroid. Consequently, both ACTH and dexamethasone raise the net levels of circulating corticosteroids in both mother and fetus (Table II). However, the effects of ACTH and dexamethasone on offspring activity are generally dissimilar (Table I: "Treatment effect"), which suggests that their effects are not mediated by changes in net levels of corticosteroids.

However, if a distinction is made between levels of natural and synthetic corticosteroids—that is, between corticosterone and dexamethasone—a different picture emerges. The need for such a distinction is suggested by the finding that dexamethasone and corticosterone show different patterns of binding in rat brain (DeKloet, Wallach, & McEwen, 1975), which raises the possibility that any behavioral effects the two substances have will be different despite the comparability of their effects on PAC function. If one looks, then, not at net levels of corticosteroids but rather at levels of corticosterone (Table II), open-field activity can be related to levels of fetal or

TABLE II

EFFECTS OF VARIOUS MATERNAL HORMONAL MANIPULATIONS ON ADRENAL SIZE AND HORMONAL LEVELS IN MOTHER AND FETUS LATE IN GESTATION AND IN THE NEONATE[a]

Maternal treatment	Effects on mother					Effects on fetus						Effects on neonate		
	Adrenal weight	ACTH	Corticosteroids			Adrenal weight	ACTH	Corticosteroids				Adrenal weight	ACTH	Corticosteroids
			Ex[b]	En[c]	Net			Ex[b]	Mat[d]	En[c]	Net			
DEX	−	−	+	−	+	−	−	+	+	−	+	−	−	−
ACTH	+	+	0	+	+	−	−	0	+	−	+	−/0[e]	?	−/0[e]
ADX	−	+	0	−	0	+	+	+	−	+	0	+	?	+

[a] Increased size or elevated hormonal levels indicated by "+," decreased size or levels by "−," and no difference from untreated controls by "0." DEX: dexamethasone; ADX: adrenalectomy.
[b] Exogenous.
[c] Endogenous.
[d] Of maternal origin.
[e] Unaffected in some experiments.

maternal steroids. The effect of dexamethasone on offspring activity might be attributable to the decreased levels of corticosterone in mothers and fetuses (both maternal and fetal production of corticosterone are suppressed by dexamethasone: Paul and D'Angelo, 1972). The failure of adrenalectomy to produce significant effects on activity may be due to the absence of a significant change in maternal and fetal corticosterone levels (K. Milković et al., 1973, 1974; Dupouy et al., 1975: see Section II, A and Table II). The decreased activity of offspring of ACTH-treated females may be due to the increased prenatal levels of corticosterone of maternal origin (Milković et al., 1974). In other words, there is some indication that the open-field activity of offspring is inversely related to prenatal levels of fetal and maternal corticosterone.

In addition, an inverse relationship is seen between maternal ACTH levels and offspring activity. Activity is increased in offspring of mothers with low ACTH levels during gestation (dexamethasone groups), slightly decreased in offspring of mothers with increased ACTH levels (adrenalectomy), and significantly decreased in cases where maternal ACTH levels are substantially increased (ACTH-treatment). Insufficient data are currently available to decide which of the two hormonal levels—corticosterone or ACTH—is the better predictor of offspring activity.

B. Modification of Prenatal Stress Effects on Open-Field Activity by Maternal Hormonal Manipulations

The effects of treatments used to modify the maternal PAC response to stress on the occurrence and direction of the effect of prenatal stress on offspring activity are summarized in Table I. In this table, "Stress effect" indicates the direction and magnitude of the difference in the open-field activity scores of offspring of stressed females in a particular treatment group in comparison with offspring of unstressed females that received the same hormonal or surgical treatment.

The direction of the effect of stress appears with some consistency to be opposite to the effect of the hormonal treatment (or surgery) itself. With one exception (Joffe, 1977: dexamethasone-group males), where the effects are small, stress reversed the effect of the drug or other treatment. This reversal by prenatal stress of the effect of the treatment itself is reminiscent of the different direction of activity changes in response to stress in rodents of different genotypes (see Section I, B). It appears that when either a genetic or a pharmacological variable acts to produce a deviation in activity level from some intermediate level, stress tends to counteract this deviation. In addition, it appears that to some extent the greater the deviation that the treatment produces the larger the effect of stress, as if stress "overcorrects" by an amount roughly proportional to the size of the treatment effect. What this implies about the involvement of hormones and neuroendocrine mechanisms in the mediation of prenatal stress effects is obscure, but efforts to determine if the principle holds for other agents that have prenatal effects on offspring activity may aid in the search for mediating processes.

It appears that the activity levels of offspring of unstressed females are inversely related to maternal ACTH levels and to maternal and fetal corticosterone levels produced by the treatments and that the effect of stress is in the opposite direction to the effect of the treatment itself. Consequently, the direction of the effect of stress can be related to maternal ACTH levels or maternal and fetal corticosterone levels. Stress reduced offspring activity in all cases indicated in Table I except those in which maternal ACTH levels were raised (adrenalectomy and ACTH treatments). The relationship of the stress effects to fetal (or maternal) corticosterone levels is less clearcut. Stress produced decreased activity in the dexamethasone groups, in which prenatal corticosterone levels were low, and resulted in increased activity in the ACTH group, in which prenatal corticosterone levels were increased. However, it also produced an increase in the activity of offspring of adrenalectomized females, in which prenatal corticosterone levels were similar to those of controls. This would lead one to predict that the effects of prenatal stress on activity would be the same in offspring of adrenalectomized and hormonally unmanipulated females; this prediction is contradicted by the available data (Table I).

C. Hypotheses

Hypotheses can be formulated which encompass the effects of both drugs and stress either in terms of maternal ACTH levels or fetal corticosterone levels. However, corticosterone levels were less clearly related to activity or to the effects of stress than ACTH levels, and an hypothesis framed in terms of corticosterone levels results in a prediction of the effects of stress on the activity of offspring of adrenalectomized females contrary to the existing data. Basing an hypothesis on both ACTH and corticosterone levels does not result in different predictions of drug and stress effects in the cases of dexamethasone and ACTH administration or adrenalectomy (although it does predict an effect of corticosterone administration different from the one predicted by the hypothesis based on ACTH alone). In addition, it is less parsimonious than basing one on ACTH levels alone.

The proposal centering on maternal ACTH levels is that offspring activity is related in a curvilinear, U-shaped manner to the level of a maternal factor (or group of factors), modifiable independently by changes in ACTH levels and by stress. This hypothesis can encompass both the inverse relationship between maternal ACTH levels and offspring activity and the tendency of stress to raise the activity of offspring of females with high ACTH levels while lowering the activity of offspring of females with low ACTH levels. If one assumes that both ACTH and stress increase the level of this factor (one can assume that they both decrease the level without altering the principle of the explanation), treatments which reduce ACTH levels (such as dexamethasone) would reduce the amount of this factor, moving groups to the left on the descending arm of the U, with a consequent increase in the activity of offspring. The decrease in activity due to stress in control, saline-injected, and dexamethasone groups would be attributable to movement of scores to the right on the descending arm of the U as levels of the maternal factor were increased by stress. Adrenalectomy and ACTH treatments alone would similarly reduce activity as raised levels of ACTH increased the level of the maternal factor—ACTH would move the group to near the nadir of the curve—and stress applied to adrenalectomized or ACTH-treated females would further increase the level of the maternal factor, moving groups further to the right and onto the ascending arm of the U, thus resulting in increased offspring activity.

Assuming the factor to be chemical but not necessarily hormonal, it is possible at present to specify only a few of the characteristics it would have to possess:

1. It is neither an adrenal hormone nor ACTH itself;
2. Its level is altered by both stress and ACTH;
3. The direction of the change produced by stress and ACTH is the same;
4. It can readily cross the placenta.

Obviously far more specification of the nature of this factor is needed before it can be regarded as more than hypothetical, but in the meantime the proposal is of some help in summarizing the effects of hormones and stress on offspring behavior and, even without identification of the factor, the postulated relationship has heuristic value.

The lack of evidence that would enable the factor to be identified is, in part, a consequence of the limitation, in past research, of the search for mediating mechanisms to the PAC system. Thus, although the hypothesis is tentative and the major conclusion of this review—that the effects of prenatal stress on offspring behavior are probably not mediated by the maternal or fetal PAC systems—negative, they may contribute to the discovery of mediating mechanisms by widening the focus of the search.

References

Ader, R. Early experiences accelerate maturation of the 24-hour adrenocortical rhythm. *Science*, 1969, **163**, 1225–1226.

Ader, R. Early experience and hormones: emotional behavior and adrenocortical function.

140

JUSTIN M. JOFFE

In B. E. Eleftheriou and R. Sprott (Eds.), *Hormonal correlates of behavior.* New York: Plenum, 1975. Pp. 7–33.

Ader, R., & Belfer, M. L. Prenatal maternal anxiety and offspring emotionality in the rat. *Psychological Reports,* 1962, **10**, 711–718.

Ader, R., & Conklin, P. M. Handling of pregnant rats: effects on emotionality of their offspring. *Science,* 1963, **142**, 411–412.

Ader, R., & Grota, L. J. The effects of early experience on adrenocortical reactivity. *Physiology and Behavior,* 1969, **4**, 303–305.

Ader, R., & Plaut, S. M. Effects of prenatal maternal handling and differential housing on offspring emotionality, plasma corticosterone levels, and susceptibility to gastric erosions. *Psychosomatic Medicine,* 1968, **30**, 277–286.

Angervall, L. Adrenalectomy in pregnant rats. Effects on offspring. *Acta Endrocrinologica,* 1962, **41**, 546–560.

Anonymous. White's "Selborne." *Nature,* 1875, **11**, 423–424.

Archer, J. E., & Blackman, D. E. Prenatal psychological stress and offspring behavior in rats and mice. *Developmental Psychobiology,* 1971, **4**, 193–248.

Barlow, S. M., McElhatton, P., Morrison, P., & Sullivan, F. M. Effects of stress during pregnancy on plasma corticosterone levels and foetal development in the mouse. *Journal of Physiology,* 1974, **239**, 55P–65P.

Barlow, S. M., McElhatton, P. R., & Sullivan, F. M. The relation between maternal restraint and food deprivation, plasma corticosterone, and induction of cleft palate in the offspring of mice. *Teratology,* 1975, **12**, 97–103.

Bassett, J. R., Cairncross, K. D., & King, M. G. Parameters of novelty, shock predictability, and response contingency in corticosterone release in the rat. *Physiology and Behavior,* 1973, **10**, 901–907.

Bell, R. W., Drucker, R. R., & Woodruff, A. B. The effects of prenatal injections of adrenalin chloride and d-amphetamine sulfate on subsequent emotionality and ulcer-proneness of offspring. *Psychonomic Science,* 1965, **2**, 269–270.

Bell, R. W., Hendry, G. H., & Miller, C. E. Prenatal maternal conditioned fear and subsequent ulcer-proneness in the rat. *Psychonomic Science,* 1967, **9**, 269–270.

Blaustein, F. M., Feller, R., & Rosenzweig, S. Effect of ACTH and adrenal hormones on cleft palate frequency in CD-1 mice. *Journal of Dental Research,* 1971, **50**, 609–612.

Broadhurst, P. L. Experiments in psychogenetics: applications of biometrical genetics to behaviour. In H. J. Eysenck (Ed.), *Experiments in personality.* Vol. 1. *Psychogenetics and Psychopharmacology.* London: Routledge & Kegan Paul, 1960. Pp. 1–102.

Broadhurst, P. L. A note on further progress in a psychogenetic selection experiment. *Psychological Reports,* 1962, **10**, 65–66.

Broadhurst, P. L. An introduction to the diallel cross. In J. Hirsch (Ed.), *Behavior-genetic analysis.* New York: McGraw-Hill, 1967. Pp. 287–304.

Christian, J. J. Hormonal control of population growth. In B. E. Eleftheriou & R. L. Sprott (Eds.), *Hormonal correlates of behavior.* New York: Plenum, 1975. Pp. 205–274.

Courrier, R., Colonge, A., & Baclesse, M. Action de la cortisone administrée à la mere sur la surrenale du foetus de rat. *Comptes Rendus Hebdomadaire des Séances de l'Académie des Sciences,* 1951, **233**, 333–336.

DeFries, J. C. Prenatal maternal stress in mice. Differential effects on behavior. *Journal of Heredity,* 1964, **55**, 289–295.

DeFries, J. C., & Weir, M. W. Open field behavior of C57BL/6J mice as a function of age, experience, and prenatal maternal stress. *Psychonomic Science,* 1964, **1**, 389–390.

DeFries, J. C. Weir, M. W., & Hegmann, J. P. Differential effects of prenatal maternal stress on offspring behavior in mice as a function of genotype and stress. *Journal of Comparative and Physiological Psychology,* 1967, **63**, 332–334.

DeKloet, R., Wallach, G., & McEwen, B. S. Differences in corticosterone and dexamethasone binding to rat brain and pituitary. *Endocrinology*, 1975, **96**, 598–609.

Denenberg, V. H. The effects of early experience. In E. S. E. Hafez (Ed.), *The behavior of domestic animals*. London: Balliere, Tindall, & Cox, 1962. Pp. 109–138.

Denenberg, V. H., Brumaghim, J. T., Haltmeyer, G. C., & Zarrow, M. X. Increased adrenocortical activity in the neonatal rat following handling. *Endocrinology*, 1967, **81**, 1047–1052.

DeWied, D. Chlorpromazine and endocrine function. *Pharmacological Review*, 1967, **19**, 251–288.

Doyle, G. A., & Yule, E. P. Grooming activities and freezing behavior in relation to emotionality in albino rats. *Animal Behavior*, 1959, **7**, 18–22. (a)

Doyle, G. A., & Yule, E. P. Early experience and emotionality. I. The effects of prenatal maternal anxiety on the emotionality of albino rats. *South African Journal of Social Science*, 1959, **10**, 57–65. (b)

Doyle, G. A., & Yule, E. P. Early experience and emotionality. II. The effects of handling and gentling on the offspring of emotional albino rats. *South African Journal of Social Science*, 1959, **10**, 67–77. (c)

Dupouy, J. P., Coffigny, H., & Magre, S. Maternal and foetal corticosterone levels during late pregnancy in rats. *Journal of Endocrinology*, 1975, **65**, 347–352.

Fraser, F. C., & Fainstat, T. D. Production of congenital defects in the offspring of pregnant mice treated with cortisone. *Pediatrics*, 1951, **8**, 527–533.

Gray, P. Pituitary-adrenocortical response to stress in the neonatal rat. *Endocrinology*, 1971, **89**, 1126–1128.

Grota, L. J. Effects of dexamethasone on the development of emotionality and adrenocortical reactivity. *Proceedings, 78th Annual Convention, American Psychological Association*, 1970, 203–204.

Grota, L. J., & Ader, R. Adrenocortical function in pregnant rats: handling and the 24-hour rhythm. *Physiology and Behavior*, 1970, **5**, 739–741.

Hagerman, D. C., & Villee, C. A. Transport functions of the placenta. *Physiological Review*, 1960, **40**, 313–330.

Hall, C. S. Emotional behavior in the rat. I. Defecation and urination as measures of individual differences in emotionality. *Journal of Comparative Psychology*, 1934, **18**, 385–403.

Hall, C. S. The inheritance of emotionality. *Sigma Xi Quarterly*, 1938, **26**, 17–37.

Haltmeyer, G. C., Denenberg, V. H., & Zarrow, M. X. Modification of the plasma corticosterone response as a function of infantile stimulation and electric shock parameters. *Physiology and Behavior*, 1967, **2**, 61–63.

Havlena, J., & Werboff, J. Postnatal effects of control fluids administered to gravid rats. *Psychological Reports*, 1963, **12**, 127—131. (a)

Havlena, J., & Werboff, J. Adrenalectomy of the pregnant rat and behavior of the offspring. *Psychological Reports*, 1963, **12**, 348–350. (b)

Hockman, C. H. Prenatal maternal stress in the rat: its effects on emotional behavior in the offspring. *Journal of Comparative and Physiological Psychology*, 1961, **54**, 679–684.

Howard, E. Increased reactivity and impaired adaptability in operant behavior of adult mice given corticosterone in infancy. *Journal of Comparative and Physiological Psychology*, 1973, **85**, 211–220.

Howard, E., & Granoff, D. M. Increased voluntary running and decreased motor coordination in mice after neonatal corticosterone implantation. *Experimental Neurology*, 1968, **22**, 661–673.

Hutchings, D. E., & Gibbon, J. Preliminary study of behavioral and teratogenic effects of two "stress" procedures administered during different periods of gestation in the rat. *Psychological Reports*, 1970, **26**, 239–246.

Ingle, D. C., & Fisher, G. T. Effect of adrenalectomy during gestation on the size of the adrenal glands of newborn rats. *Proceedings of the Society for Experimental Biology and Medicine*, 1938, **39**, 149–150.

Joffe, J. M. Genotype and prenatal and premating stress interact to affect adult behavior in rats. *Science*, 1965, **150**, 1844–1845. (a)

Joffe, J. M. Emotionality and intelligence of offspring in relation to prenatal maternal conflict in albino rats. *Journal of General Psychology*, 1965, **73**, 1–11. (b)

Joffe, J. M. *Prenatal Determinants of Behavior*. Oxford: Pergamon, 1969.

Joffe, J. M. Modification of prenatal stress effects by dexamethasone and adrenocorticotrophin. *Physiology and Behavior*, 1977, **19**, 601–606.

Joffe, J. M., & Levine, S. Effects of prenatal stress on offspring behavior in relation to maternal and offspring adrenal function. XIX International Congress of Psychology, London, 1969.

Joffe, J. M., Milković, K., & Levine, S. Effects of change in maternal pituitary-adrenal function on behavior of rat offspring. *Physiology and Behavior*, 1972, **8**, 425–430. (a)

Joffe, J. M., Mulick, J. A., Ley, K. F., Jr., & Rawson, R. A. Effects of prenatal stress on maternal corticosterone levels and behavior during gestation. *Bulletin of the Psychonomic Society*, 1978, in press.

Joffe, J. M., Mulick, J. A., Peterson, J. A., & Paunović, J. Sex-difference in the effect of dexamethasone on open-field behavior in rats: gonadal hormones. *Physiology and Behavior*, 1976, **16**, 543–546.

Joffe, J. M., Mulick, J. A., & Rawson, R. A. Effects of adrenalectomy on open-field behavior in rats. *Hormones and Behavior*, 1972, **3**, 87–96. (b)

Jones, J. M., Lloyd, C. W., & Wyatt, T. C. A study of the interrelationships of maternal and fetal adrenal glands of rats. *Endocrinology*, 1953, **53**, 182–191.

Kalter, H. The inheritance of susceptibility to the teratogenic action of cortisone in mice. *Genetics*, 1954, **39**, 185–196.

Kalter, H. On the possible origin of a strain difference between C3H and CBA mice. *Genetics*, 1961, **46**, 874 (Abstr.).

Kalter, H. Experimental investigation of teratogenic action. *Annals of the New York Academy of Sciences*, 1965, **123**, 287–294.

Kalter, H., & Warkany, J. Experimental production of congenital malformations in mammals by metabolic procedures. *Physiological Review*, 1959, **39**, 69—115.

Keeley, K. Prenatal influence on behavior of offspring of crowded mice. *Science*, 1962, **135**, 44–45.

Knobil, E., & Briggs, F. N. Fetal-maternal endocrine interrelations: the hypophyseal-adrenal system. *Endocrinology*, 1955, **57**, 147–152.

Lane, E. A., & Hyde, T. S. The effects of maternal stress on fertility and sex ratio—a pilot study with rats. *Journal of Abnormal Psychology*, 1973, **82**, 78–80.

Levine, S. The psychophysiological effects of infantile stimulation. In E. L. Bliss (Ed.), *Roots of behavior*. New York: Hoeber, 1962. Pp. 246–253. (a)

Levine, S. Plasma free corticosteroid response to electric shock in rats stimulated in infancy. *Science*, 1962, **135**, 795–796. (b)

Levine, S. Influence of infantile stimulation on the response to stress during preweaning development. *Developmental Psychobiology*, 1968, **1**, 67–70.

Levine, S., Haltmeyer, G. C., Karas, G. G., & Denenberg, V. H. Physiological and behavioral effects of infantile stimulation. *Physiology and Behavior*, 1967, **2**, 55–59.

Levine, S., & Mullins, R. F., Jr. Hormonal influence on brain organization in infant rats. *Science*, 1966, **152**, 1585–1592.

Lieberman, M. W. Early developmental stress and later behavior. *Science*, 1963, **141**, 824–825.

Mason, J. W. Organization of the multiple endocrine responses to avoidance in the monkey. *Psychosomatic Medicine*, 1968, **30**, 774–790. (a)

Mason, J. W. "Overall" hormonal balance as a key to endocrine organization. *Psychosomatic Medicine*, 1968, **30**, 791–808. (b)

Migeon, C. J., Prystowsky, H., Grumbach, M. M., & Byron, M. C. Placental passage of 17 hydroxycorticosteroids: comparison of levels in maternal and fetal plasma and effect of ACTH and hydrocortisone administration. *Journal of Clinical Investigation*, 1956, **35**, 488–493.

Milković, K., Paunović, J., Kniewald, Z., & Milković, S. Maintenance of the plasma corticosterone concentration of adrenalectomized rats by the fetal adrenal glands. *Endocrinology*, 1973, **93**, 115–118.

Milković, K., Winget, C., Romić, R., and Levine, S. Effect of adrenocortical activity of pregnant rat on the foetal pituitary-adrenocortical system. *Periodicum Biologorum*, 1974, **76**, 77–83.

Milković, S., Milković, K., & Paunović, J. The initiation of fetal adrenocorticotrophic activity in the rat. *Endocrinology*, 1973, **92**, 380–384.

Milković, S., Paunović, J., Ronkulin, J., Bobanović, T., & Milković, K. Some studies of the placental permeability to ACTH. *Bulletin Scientifique. Conseil des Académies de la RSF Yugoslavie, Section A—Zagreb*, 1966, **11**, 108–109.

Morra, M. Prenatal sound stimulation on postnatal rat offspring open-field behaviors. *Psychological Record*, 1965, **15**, 571–575. (a)

Morra, M. Level of maternal stress during two pregnancy periods on rat offspring behavior. *Psychonomic Science*, 1965, **3**, 7–8. (b)

Moyer, K. E. Effect of adrenalectomy on emotional elimination. *Journal of Genetic Psychology*. 1958, **92**, 11–16.

Mulick, J. A., Joffe, J. M., & Peterson, J. M. Sex differences in the effects of dexamethasone phosphate on behavior in rats. *Physiology and Behavior*, 1975, **14**, 37–42.

Nyakas, C. Influence of corticosterone and ACTH on the postnatal development of learning and memory functions. *Hormones and Brain Function*, (Budapest, 1971), 1973, 83–89.

Obias, M. D. Maternal behavior of hypophysectomized gravid albino rats and the development and performance of their progeny. *Journal of Comparative and Physiological Psychology*, 1957, **50**, 120–124.

Paul, D. H., & D'Angelo, S. A. Dexamethasone and corticosterone administration to pregnant rats: effects on pituitary-adrenocortical function in the newborn. *Proceedings of the Society for Experimental Biology and Medicine*, 1972, **142**, 1360–1364.

Picon, L. O. Influence de l'hypophysectomie et de la surrenalectomie de la ratte gestante sur le poids des foetus. *Comptes Rendus des Séances de la Société de Biologie et de ses Filiales*, 1957, **151**, 1314–1317.

Porter, R. H., & Wehmer, F. Maternal and infantile influences upon exploratory behavior and emotional reactivity in the albino rat. *Developmental Psychobiology*, 1969, **2**, 19–25.

Purves, H. D., & Sirett, N. E. Assay of corticotrophin in dexamethasone-treated rats. *Endocrinology*, 1965, **77**, 336–374.

Rosenzweig, S., & Blaustein, F. M. Cleft palate in A/J mice resulting from restraint and deprivation of food and water. *Teratology*, 1970, **3**, 47–52.

Sayers, G., & Sayers, M. A. Regulation of pituitary adrenocorticotrophic activity during the response of the rat to acute stress. *Endocrinology*, 1947, **40**, 265–273.

Schapiro, S. Some physiological, biochemical, and behavioral consequences of neonatal hormone administration: cortisol and thyroxine. *General and Comparative Endocrinology*, 1968, **10**, 214–288.

Schnürer, L. Maternal and foetal responses to chronic stress in pregnancy. A study in albino rats. *Acta Endocrinologica*, 1963, **43**, Suppl. 80.

Selye, H. *The physiology and pathology of exposure to stress*. Montreal: Acta, 1950.

Smith, D. J., Heseltine, G. F. D., & Corson, J. A. Pre-pregnancy and prenatal stress in five consecutive pregnancies: effects on female rats and their offspring. *Life Sciences*, 1971, **10**, 1233–1242.

Smith, D. J., Joffe, J. M., & Heseltine, G. F. D. Modification of prenatal stress effects in rats by adrenalectomy, dexamethasone and chlorpromazine. *Physiology and Behavior*, 1975, **15**, 461–470.

Thoman, E., Sproul, M., & Levine, S. Influence of adrenalectomy in pregnant rats on reproductive processes: effects on the foetus and offspring. *Journal of Endocrinology*, 1970, **46**, 297–303.

Thompson, W. D., & Sontag, L. W. Behavioral effects in the offspring of rats subjected to audiogenic seizure during the gestational period. *Journal of Comparative and Physiological Psychology*, 1956, **49**, 454–456.

Thompson, W. R. Influence of prenatal maternal anxiety on emotionality in young rats. *Science*, 1957, **125**, 698–699.

Thompson, W. R., & Goldenberg, L. Some physiological effects of maternal adrenalin injection during pregnancy in rat offspring. *Psychological Reports*, 1962, **10**, 759–774.

Thompson, W. R., Goldenberg, L., Watson, J., & Watson, M. Behavioral effects of maternal adrenalin injection during pregnancy in rat offspring. *Psychological Reports*, 1963, **12**, 279–284.

Thompson, W. R., & Olian, S. Some effects on offspring behavior of maternal adrenalin injection during pregnancy in three inbred mouse strains *Psychological Reports*, 1961, **8**, 87–90.

Thompson, W. R., & Quinby, S. Prenatal maternal anxiety and offspring behavior: parental activity and level of anxiety. *Journal of Genetic Psychology*, 1964, **105**, 359–371.

Thompson, W. R., Watson, J., & Charlesworth, W. R. The effects of prenatal maternal stress on offspring behavior in rats. *Psychological Monographs*, 1962, **76**, No. 38 (Whole No. 557).

Warkany, J., & Kalter, H. Maternal impressions and congenital malformations. *Plastic and Reconstructive Surgery*, 1962, **30**, 628–637.

Wehmer, F., Porter, R., & Scales, B. Prenatal and pregnancy stress in rats affects behavior of grandpups. *Nature*, 1970, **227**, 622.

Weir, M. W., & DeFries, J. C. Prenatal maternal influence on behavior in mice. Evidence of a genetic basis. *Journal of Comparative and Physiological Psychology*, 1964, **58**, 412–417.

Young, R. D. Effect of prenatal maternal injection of epinephrine on postnatal offspring behavior. *Journal of Comparative and Physiological Psychology*, 1963, **56**, 929–932.

Young, R. D. Effect of prenatal drugs and neonatal stimulation on later behavior. *Journal of Comparative and Physiological Psychology*, 1964, **58**, 309–311.

Young, R. D. Developmental psychopharmacology: a beginning. *Psychological Bulletin*, 1967, **67**, 73–86.

Zarrow, M. X., Philpott, J. E., & Denenberg, V. H. Passage of ^{14}C-4- corticosterone from the rat mother to the foetus and neonate. *Nature*, 1970, **226**, 1058–1059.

Zimmerman, E., & Critchlow, V. Negative feedback and pituitary-adrenal function in female rats. *American Journal of Physiology*, 1969, **216**, 148–155.

Section 2

NUTRITION

INTRODUCTION

Although it has long been appreciated that adequate nourishment of the pregnant mother must be crucial to the welfare of the developing embryo and fetus, it has been only in the last decade or so that highly analytic experiments have been conducted which specify the long-term anatomical, physiological, behavioral, and possible psychological concommitants of prenatal undernutrition. The reason for the emphasis on prenatal nutrition is that that is the period not only of general bodily formation, but most especially the formation of the brain. Although the multiplication of cells continues in some areas of the brain for a short while after birth in certain species, the mammalian brain (including the human brain) generally gets most of its nerve cells or neurons during the prenatal period. Each neuron has an axon and many dendrites, these providing the links (synapses) between neurons inside as well as outside of the central nervous system (i.e., central–central connections as well as central–peripheral connections to sense organs and to muscles). While, as will be seen in Section 3, the number and branching of the dendrites remain susceptible to all sorts of influences into adulthood, no new neurons are generated in the brain after the early formative period. In addition to neural cells, the brain is composed of glial cells which surround the neurons and are thought to serve a "support" function, in the sense of providing metabolic exchange, among other things. The glial cells usually form after the cerebral neurons have proliferated, so the glial cells may still be actively mutliplying in fairly large numbers for a while after birth in species such as our own. The third gross component of the brain (roughly 20% or so) is made up of extracellular tissues.

In the first chapter in this section, Stephen Zamenhof and Edith van Marthens describe in elegant and clear detail the highly complicated nutritional interrelationships between the pregnant mother and her fetus, emphasizing the influences of nutrition on various aspects of prenatal brain development. Besides describing how inadequate prenatal nutrition causes suboptimal brain growth in the fetal period, these authors also show that these deficits can be trans-generational and thus diminish the brain growth of the granddaughters and grandsons even when the daughters of the original malnourished mother have been placed on entirely adequate diets after birth. Dr. Zamenhof and Dr. van Marthens also present some evidence of impaired learning ability in the second-generation offspring, which themselves had never been overtly deprived of adequate nutrition. On the positive side, Dr. Zamenhof and Dr. van Marthens also describe some admittedly rare instances of "superoptimal" brain growth brought about presumably by complex improvements in the intrauterine environment during gestation.

It will come perhaps as a surprise that the extensive behavioral testing of offspring of undernourished mothers does not provide clear and consistent evidence of long-term learning deficits. In the second chapter in this section, Peter Leathwood reviews the extensive animal literature on this topic and shows that developmental lags or delays are the most prominent outcome of fetal undernourishment, and these are usually overcome in time. The human data on the question of fetal dietary insufficiency also do not show irreversible deficits in school, professional, and other achievements. It is perhaps important here to share Dr. Zamenhof's and Dr. van Marthens' caution with respect to both the animal and the human findings of "no effect." The behavioral tests for the animals are usually rather simple maze and conditioning tasks, which may not tax the higher "cognitive" abilities of the subjects. It certainly is possible that learning deficits could be revealed, for example, on the most difficult problems of the Hebb-Williams maze that were otherwise not discernible in simpler tasks. The reviews at hand certainly indicate the need for much more intensive and extensive "testing of the limits" than has heretofore been the case in the behavioral analysis of the effects of prenatal undernutrition.

NUTRITIONAL INFLUENCES ON PRENATAL BRAIN DEVELOPMENT

S. ZAMENHOF AND E. VAN MARTHENS

Mental Retardation Research Center
and Brain Research Institute
U.C.L.A. School of Medicine
Los Angeles, California

I. Introduction

A. General Scope

This chapter will deal with those factors affecting early brain development that can be classified as nutritional. It is customary in chapters of this kind to discuss only the known pertinent aspects; this tends to give the general impression that much is known about the subject. We feel that in a field so new and complex such an impression would be misleading; in this chapter,

149

therefore, we will depart from this custom and will endeavor to discuss also other *unknown* aspects that may be of importance. The emphasis will be on *prenatal* influences on brain development.

B. Definitions

1. The term *nutrients* usually refers to carbohydrates, proteins, and vitamins. However, any complete discussion should also include minerals, because their deficiency has been shown to result in fetal malnutrition. Oxygen and water also fully participate in synthetic reactions but these substances are not considered as nutrients because they are usually abundant. This is unfortunate because their abundance in the maternal organism does not preclude their deficiency in the fetus, especially in cases of oxygen deficiency caused by placental insufficiency (see Section IV,B).

2. *Brain development* includes (a) synthesis or "growth" of brain cell components (proteins, nucleic acids, etc.), (b) actual cell proliferation or multiplication, (c) cell death, (d) cell migration, and (e) cell differentiation, which also includes increase (growth) in cell size. All these processes are in essence chemical reactions that are closely interdependent and are under the control of regulatory mechanisms, as yet not well understood. As chemical reactions, they include rate-limiting steps that form a multitude of closely overlapping checks: if one factor becomes abundant, the next one becomes the rate-limiting step, and so on.

3. *Fetal malnutrition* and *maternal malnutrition*. Rate-limiting steps may appear also in auxiliary systems that (a) deliver the nutrients to the site of synthesis of brain cell components, and (b) remove from the site the unwanted products of reaction (metabolic waste). Thus, for instance, the visible outcome of such rate-limiting steps, *fetal malnutrition*, may have several components, of which the two best known are (1) *maternal malnutrition* that results in deficiency of nutrients for the fetus, and/or (2) *placental* (uteroplacental) *insufficiency* that results in deficient delivery of available nutrients through the placenta to the fetus. The two components sometimes have the same cause, and sometimes are independent. These aspects will be discussed further on. Other components of fetal malnutrition may be decreased uterine blood flow, decreased umbilical blood flow, etc.

C. Prenatal Flow of Nutrients to the Site of Developing Brain

Figure 1 is a schematic representation of the flow of nutrients to the site of synthesis of neuronal (neuroblast) and glial (glioblast) components of the embryo or fetus.[1] The individual nutrients will be discussed later. Even

---

[1]Neuroblast and glioblast are the immature stages of a neuron and glial cell, respectively.

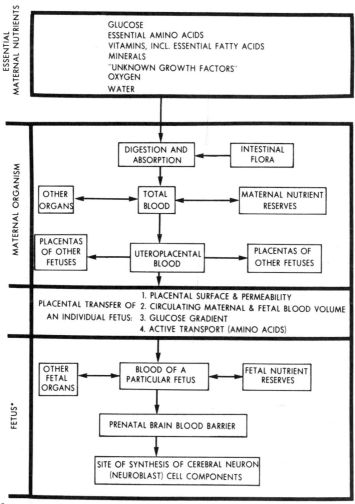

FIG. 1. Schematic representation of the flow of essential nutrients to the site of synthesis of neuronal (neuroblast) cell components. From Zamenhof and van Marthens (1974), reprinted by permission of Dr. W. Junk b.v. Publishers, The Hague, The Netherlands.

this simplified schematic flow is still very complex and illustrates the multitude of potential regulatory sites on which such neuronal and glial proliferation depends.

Maternal dietary nutrients, digested, absorbed, and ultimately available in the blood, can be supplemented by substances (such as nonessential amino acids) manufactured in maternal organs, primarily the liver, and by vitamins manufactured by the intestinal flora. Amounts of nutrients may be further decreased on increased by the participation of maternal nutrient reserves. In particular, one of the hormones mobilizing these reserves is pituitary growth hormone; the blood level of this hormone is known to increase during fasting and during pregnancy.

It is now well recognized that the fetus is not a parasite which extracts from the maternal organism all it needs. When pregnant animals are faced with nutritional insufficiencies, it's the fetal development and/or survival that is affected, because the diet is inadequate to support two lives rather than one. This is particularly well demonstrated in the rat: maternal dietary protein deprivation around the time of implantation results in resorption of fetuses. This failure was traced to faulty implantation and placentation (see review in Zamenhof, van Marthens, & Grauel, 1971b).

It is obvious that proper placental transfer of nutrients to the fetus is a key requirement for normal fetal development. In the case just described, absence of proper placentation, resulting from the regulatory action of lack of protein, precluded subsequent transfer of nutrients even if they later became available. As will be discussed further on, maternal malnutrition itself is one of the conditions causing placental underdevelopment. Thus, lack of nutrients may have a twofold effect: deficiency of transfer to the fetus on top of deficiency of substances to be transferred. This deficiency of transfer due to placental underdevelopment might also affect the passage of "nutrients" present in abundance, such as oxygen and water, as well as the removal of waste material from the fetus.

A well-developed placenta (including its maternal blood supply) is only one of the requirements for proper placental transfer of nutrients. As will be discussed further on, glucose is the main energy source for the fetus. The factor determining the passage of glucose through the placenta appears to be the concentration gradient (although the carrier is probably also involved). Glucose concentrations in maternal and fetal blood are, in turn, hormonally regulated. Thus it is possible, for example, to increase glucose transport to the fetus by introducing more insulin into the fetus, so lowering fetal blood glucose level and thus increasing the gradient (Picon, 1967). On the other hand, the passage of amino acids through the placenta involves active transport: the concentration of amino acids is higher in fetal than in maternal blood (see review in Blaxter, 1964, pp. 191, 192).

In cases of multiple births, an important factor in fetal nutrition is the competition between fetuses for all nutrients and for space. In many animals, including humans, neonatal body weight is correlated with the number of fetuses in the litter (McKeown & Record, 1952; Venge, 1950). In humans, in one study (Babson, Kangas, Young, & Bramhall, 1964) 20 sets of twins of the same sex and with weight differences of 300 g or more at birth (gestation period of at least 36 weeks) were examined for intellectual achievement at the mean age of 8.5 years: the results showed that the twin underweight at birth exhibited a significantly lower level of intellectual achievement in the areas examined. Other studies also point in this direction (Drillen, 1970; Hohenauer, 1971; Kaelber & Pugh, 1969; Scarr, 1969; Willerman & Churchill, 1967). In cases of maternal dietary restriction, one twin may develop normally, thus taking advantage of the other whose brain becomes underdeveloped (Usher, 1970).

In summary, many factors other than maternal dietary restriction may also contribute to the nutrient deficiency at the site of synthesis of neuronal and glial components of the embryo or fetus.

II. Nutrients in Prenatal Brain Development

The assessments of fetal nutrient requirements is a difficult and largely unsolved problem; the following examples will illustrate the situation.

1. In almost all experiments the nutrients are delivered not to the fetus *per se*, but to the mother. As discussed in the Introduction (Fig. 1), the maternal nutrients (after intestinal absorption) are enriched or impoverished by the participation of maternal nutrient reserves, and the amounts that reach the placenta are essentially unknown and variable. Thus, for instance, fetuses survive even if (for a part of pregnancy) maternal diet is completely protein-free (Zamenhof et al., 1971b). An obviously wrong conclusion would be that the fetus can temporarily synthesize its proteins without any supply of essential amino acids; the more logical conclusion would be that these amino acids are supplied by the mother from her nutrient reserves. Thus, the *actual* fetal nutrient supply at a given moment is *quantitatively* unknown.

2. The actual fetal requirements are also not completely known *qualitatively*. In the past it was assumed that the kind of nutrients a fetus needs must be the same as that of the mother. Recently, however, it was found that for human newborns (but not for the mother) cysteine is an essential amino acid (Sturman, Gaull, & Raiha, 1970). It could be the embryos and fetuses only gradually acquire the ability to synthesize amino acids that used to be considered "nonessential"; if so, then the essential or nonessential nature of specific amino acids may largely depend on age, especially at the embryonic stage.

The limited recent information on prenatal nutrients in brain development is summarized in the following paragraphs. For some general information on nutrients in embryonic and fetal growth the reader is referred to a review by Giroud (1970).

A. Carbohydrates and Energy Sources

Glucose is the main energy source for the fetus. Other sugars (especially fructose) may also be utilized but they cross the placenta at a much slower rate, and glucose alone would be sufficient (see review in Alexander, Britton, Cohen, & Nixon, 1969). Lipids are oxidized only to a small extent by fetal organs (see review in Hahn, 1972). In the absence of glucose, gluconeogenesis may occur and glucogenic amino acids may be converted into glucose in the maternal liver; however, mammalian *fetal* liver is still unable to synthesize glucose (Yarnell, Nelson & Wagle, 1966). In maternal organisms essential amino acids are, to a considerable degree, spared from oxidation especially on protein-calorie-deficient diets (McFarlane & von Holt, 1969); in particular, lysine is efficiently conserved (Yamashita & Ashida, 1969). It must again be pointed out that most of this information pertains essentially to the maternal organism, and that much less is known about the ontogeny of anabolic and catabolic enzymatic systems in the embryo and the fetus.

The excess of glucose in the fetus is converted into glycogen and stored in the placenta and in the fetal liver. Liver glycogen is of importance especially in hypoxia during and after labor: if the amount of glycogen stored is insufficient brain damage may occur (see reviews in Dawes, 1968; Minkowski, Roux, & Tordet-Caridroit, 1974; J. C. Sinclair, Saigal, & Yeung, 1974).

B. Amino Acids

Except for some immunoglobulins, the proteins as such do not cross the placenta in any significant amounts (Dancis & Schneider, 1975). [It should be noted that, once in the fetal blood, proteins would reach the fetal cerebrospinal fluid due to the immaturity of the blood–brain barrier (Adinolfi, Beck, Haddad, & Seller, 1976)]. The nutrient value of food proteins resides essentially in single amino acids that have been absorbed in maternal intestines. However, dipeptides can be also absorbed in intestines; their role in fetal nutrition is essentially unknown.

The uncertainty as to the full list of amino acids essential for the embryo and fetus has already been discussed. However, it appears certain that at least all those amino acids that are known to be essential for the mother, are also essential for the fetus. Thus, omission of any single one of them from the maternal diet should hinder protein synthesis by the fetus. This, indeed, has been demonstrated: the omission of a single essential amino acid, tryptophan, lysine, or methionine from the maternal diet has an inhibitory effect on fetal brain development similar to that produced by the omission of proteins as a whole (Zamenhof, Hall, Grauel, van Marthens, & Donahue, 1974b).

Many foods of plant origin are deficient in one or more of the essential amino acids (especially lysine and tryptophan). The stimulatory effect of food fortification (addition of lysine or lysine plus threonine) on prenatal and postnatal brain development (brain weight, protein, and cell number) has been demonstrated recently in rats (Chase & Jansen, 1976).

The proper formulation of a diet, synthetic with respect to amino acids, is a complex and not completely solved problem (review in Zamenhof *et al.*, 1974b). Proper formulation is important because the levels of dietary amino acids influence the size of the free amino acid pool, which, in turn, could be one of the principal regulators of protein synthesis in the cell and thus could regulate development (Miller, 1970). A formulation proper for one strain may not be so for another strain. Possibly, differential intestinal absorption is involved; much more work on this subject is still needed.

C. Vitamins and Essential Fatty Acids

Vitamin and essential fatty acid requirements for proper fetal growth are to be expected, but often difficult to demonstrate; they are needed in such small amounts that the maternal organism is usually able to provide enough of them. To demonstrate any effects the maternal organism usually has also to be deprived before the onset of pregnancy. It should be also pointed out that the reported studies usually do not rule out the possibility that the effect of vitamin deficiency is indirect, e.g., through reduced food intake.

The majority of the studies on vitamin deficiency in fetal development refer to *teratogenic* effects (see reviews in Giroud, 1970; E. M. Johnson, 1965; Kalter, 1968; see also the chapter by Hutchings in this volume). The deficiency may act in the "critical" (very early) period of organogenesis,[2] and results in a small percentage of gross deformities that attracted attention of earlier investigators. The vitamins, whose severe deficiencies were so studied, were A, B_1, B_2, B_6, B_{12}, C, D, E, K, choline, folic acid, nicotinic acid, and pantothenic acid (see review in Dodge, Prensky, & Feigin, 1975, pp. 422–499). With reference to brain development, the most often observed abnormalities were hydrocephaly and exencephaly (in deficiency or excess of vitamin A; deficiencies of vitamins B_1, B_2, B_{12}, E, folic acid, nicotinic acid, and pantothenic acid). The resulting organisms were often nonviable.

In contrast to the studies just cited, this review is mostly concerned with *quantitative* brain growth deficiencies that occur after the period of organogenesis and result in an impairment of cell number (proliferation), differentiation, and function, of essentially all fetuses rather than in gross nonviable

[2] Organogenesis is defined here as the formation of an organ.

abnormalities of only a few. In the field of vitamins such studies have thus far been infrequent. With reference to vitamin A it was reported that an *excess* of this vitamin, given to pregnant mice during the later stages of gestation, influences the development of the cerebral cortex not only by interfering with the production of cells in the neuroepithelial zone but also by affecting the differentiation of existing neuroblasts; as a result, some of the newborns appeared to have abnormal patterns of behavior (Langman & Welch, 1967). In general, there appears to exist in humans a placental transfer mechanism favoring the fetus for some vitamins. For example, fetal cord levels are higher than maternal levels for thiamine, biotin, vitamin C, riboflavin, niacinamide, and pantothenate; this, however, is not true for folate, vitamin B_6, and B_{12} (Kaminetzky, Baker, Frank, & Langer, 1974). Thus, deficiencies in the latter three vitamins in the maternal diet should particularly affect the fetus and indeed have been demonstrated.

Folate is essential for deoxyribonucleic acid (DNA) synthesis (methylation of uracil deoxyribotide to form thymidylate) and therefore for cell proliferation. Folate deficiency in the mother has been implicated in low birth weight or malformation of the fetus, including anencephaly (Hibbard, Hibbard, & Jeffcoate, 1965; Kitay, 1969).

Deficiency in vitamin E during pregnancy was reported to result in fewer mitoses in the neural tube, and later in a smaller brain that showed a marked increase in the number of glial cells, but a decrease in number of neurons (Verma & Wei King, 1967).

Vitamin B_6 deficiency in pregnant rats resulted in small fetuses with neurologic defects (Davis, Nelson, & Shepard, 1970). Fetal brain weights and brain DNA and RNA (ribonucleic acid) contents were also somewhat lower than in controls (Driskell & Kirksey, 1971; Moon & Kirksey, 1972). Postnatal B_6 deficiency resulted in lower contents of brain lipids (Kurtz, Levy, & Kanfer, 1972; Williamson & Coniglio, 1971), and lower pituitary levels of growth hormone (Huber & Gershoff, 1965).

Low levels of vitamin B_{12} or choline before and during pregnancy (rat) result in offspring with stunted growth, congenital hydrocephalus, and alterations in nucleic acids and protein in the brain (Newberne, Ahlstrom, & Rogers, 1970; Woodard & Newberne, 1966). On the other hand, high levels of B_{12} administered during pregnancy result in larger offspring with heavier neonatal brain weight and brain lipid content (Newberne, 1963; Newberne & Young, 1973). Growth hormone has been implicated in the mobilization of B_{12} from tissue depots (Rosenthal, Tanaka, & Glass, 1969).

It has been pointed out that a diet which is considered fully adequate for postnatal development when consumed by the mother does not necessarily provide an adequate nutritional environment for the developing fetus. A B_{12} level which is adequate for the adult, may be only marginally adequate for fetal development, and inadequate during any stressful situation (Newberne & Young, 1973).

The effect of *low essential fatty acids* (linoleic acid family) during gestation and lactation on brain weight and brain lipids had been studied by Svennerholm, Alling, Bruce, Karlsson, and Sapia (1972). No change in these parameters could be demonstrated; on the other hand, A. J. Sinclair and Crawford (1971) and Steinberg, Clarke, and Ramwell (1968) found a decrease in brain weight and a change in brain lipid composition. Again, to demonstrate any effect, the deficient diet had to be fed long before mating.

D. Minerals, Trace Elements, and Unknown Growth Factors

Although logically, minerals should be essential requirements in fetal nutrition, because every new cell must contain them, studies of these requirements are lagging behind studies of protein and calorie (energy) needs; this is because ordinary maternal diet often contains enough minerals to cover these requirements. During pregnancy, maternal demands for calcium, phosphorus (especially for nucleic acid synthesis), sodium, potassium, magnesium, iodine, and iron increase considerably due to the growth of the fetus and the increased volume of blood. Yet, no systematic studies of the effects of deficiencies of these elements on fetal brain development have been reported.

In 1968–1969 it was reported that zinc deficiency during pregnancy affects the behavior of the mother (failure to groom the infants and to build nest, see Apgar, 1968) and of her offspring (as tested in the Lashley III maze and in pole-jump conditioned-avoidance test, see Caldwell & Oberleas, 1969). Further research has demonstrated that zinc is an indispensable trace element associated with many enzymes and needed for cell replication in general and DNA synthesis in particular (see review in Chesters, 1974; Loeb, 1974); zinc deficiency in pregnancy may have teratogenic effects (see review in Hambridge, 1974). It has also been demonstrated recently that a zinc deficiency in prenatal life (Eckhert & Hurley, 1976; McKenzie, Fosmire, & Sandstead, 1975) results in deficient brain DNA synthesis during neuronal proliferation.

There are no comparable studies on the effect of deficiency of other trace elements on fetal brain development. It takes special purified diets and special precautions in living quarters to demonstrate trace-element requirements in animal diets. When, however, this is accomplished, it can be shown that boron, chromium, copper, cobalt, fluorine, manganese, molybdenum, nickel, silicon, tin, vanadium, among other trace elements, are required in the adult rat diet and during pregnancy (Giroud, 1970; Schwarz, 1974; see also review in Dodge *et al.*, 1975, pp. 392–405). In addition, there may be a need for unknown (organic?) substance(s) (Schwarz, 1970). It is of interest that even a carefully designed synthetic diet is inferior to natural stock diet in supporting fetal growth in general, and the growth of fetal brain in particular (Zamenhof *et al.*, 1974b).

III. Regulatory Factors and Timing in Prenatal Brain Development

The progress of prenatal brain development can be followed by measuring gross parameters, such as brain volume, weight, cell number, and protein content: other important parameters such as extent of dendritic tree, myelination, or number of synapses, etc., are either nonexistent at the early period of development, or are in the (transient) state of first appearance, and therefore thus far have not been used for quantitative evaluation of prenatal brain.

Brain weight, brain volume, head circumference, and cortical dimensions, the parameters most often reported in the literature, represent a composite of many factors, of which quantitatively the most important is water content (85% in the brain of neonatal rat). These parameters may undergo spurious changes and therefore are now considered less informative than those listed below. It must, however, be pointed out, that in a *large* sample of a *normal* population all the above parameters, as well as those to be mentioned later, are well correlated (Clark & Zamenhof, 1973; Zamenhof, Grauel, & van Marthens, 1971a; Zamenhof, Guthrie, & Clarkson, 1974a; Zamenhof & Holzman, 1973). Such correlations are more significant for neonatal brains than for postnatal or adult ones (Clark & Zamenhof, 1973; Zamenhof, Guthrie, & Clarkson, 1974a).

Among the parameters more useful than the brain weight, one may mention the total brain protein content: it tells not only about past synthetic activities but also about potential for future development, in the sense that postnatal neuron differentiation is likely to depend on neuronal protein content at birth. Another useful parameter is the protein content per cell, related also to cell size. A convenient index of the amount of protein per cell is the ratio: total protein/total DNA (see discussion further on).

Brain cell number, when properly understood in the ontogeny of neuron and glia cells, is a characteristic index of prenatal brain development. Actual total cell count on histological slides is a procedure that is both very laborious and subject to considerable error, especially since the count on each section has to be multiplied by the volume of the section, and integrated through all sections, to obtain total count per brain. The *cell density* can be measured on histological slides but the interpretation of this parameter is often misleading; lower density may mean poor cell multiplication, but it may also mean a later stage in development (migration of cells away from each other). In general, total brain cell number appears to be a more meaningful parameter than cell density.

One should also add that obtaining cell counts from histological slides is subject to considerable error, unless a rather large number of samples are taken from various brain regions: the number of cells and the cell densities change dramatically from one brain region to another. This criticism applies also to methods of estimation of total cell number as described later: whenever possible one should attempt to analyze various brain regions separately.

A method recently suggested is to replace the time-consuming and inaccurate histological slide procedure by counting cells in suspension, in a hemocytometer (Varon & Rainborn, 1969). A convenient quantitative method for bringing cells into suspension involves fixation, followed by mild ultrasonication (H. A. Johnson & Erner, 1972; Zamenhof, 1976a, 1976b).

The most often used method for cell enumeration is by determination of the deoxyribonucleic acid (DNA) content of the cells. Normal neuron and glia cells at birth are essentially diploid and the amount of DNA per diploid cell of a given species is constant (Vendrely, 1952). Although there have been reports of polyploid neurons, they involve cerebellar Purkinje cells (Lapham, 1968; Lentz & Lapham, 1969), Betz cells of the motor cortex (Herman & Lapham, 1969), or large pyramidal cells in the hippocampus of the mature brain (Herman & Lapham, 1969), but not cells in the neonatal cerebral cortex. Thus, determination of neonatal brain DNA is a convenient and objective quantitative method for determination of total neonatal brain cell numbers. Such determinations will be relied upon throughout this review (Zamenhof, Bursztyn, Rich, & Zamenhof, 1964; Zamenhof, van Marthens, Grauel, & Stillinger, 1972c).

From the DNA values per brain, the actual total number of brain cells can can be calculated by dividing by a (constant) DNA content per cell (6×10^{-6} μg for the rat) (Leslie, 1955; Zamenhof et al., 1964).

The total amount of brain DNA in the developing chick and rat reaches a transient plateau at hatching or at birth (Fig. 2). The constancy of the amounts of DNA in neonatal brains suggests one or more stringent regulatory mechanisms that are not easily disturbed. The outcome must be the precise and controlled slowing down of cortical neuron DNA synthesis toward the end of pregnancy. What are the controlling factors? Can we experimentally interfere with them? To illustrate the importance of this problem one may point out that if the neurons of a nonhuman primate brain (such as a gorilla brain) were allowed to undergo one more round of cell divisions, such a brain would reach the number of neurons in the human brain (around 13 billion in the whole brain).

Figure 3 represents a list of some of the obvious environmental factors

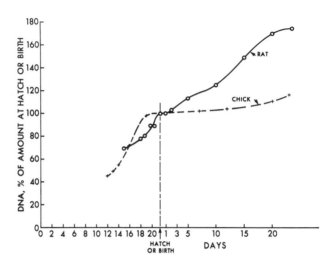

FIG. 2.   DNA synthesis in developing chick (+) and rat (O) brain (cerebral hemispheres). Abscissa-embryonal (fetal) age before hatching or birth and age after hatching or birth. Ordinate-DNA, in percentage of the amount at birth. From Zamenhof, van Marthens, and Bursztyn (1971), reprinted by permission of Appleton-Century-Crofts, Educational Division, Meredith Corp.

that could influence DNA synthesis and neonatal brain cell number. We have arbitrarily divided these factors into two groups: (1) regulatory processes and (2) embryonal and fetal nutrition *per se*, but it is to be understood that there is a great deal of overlapping in this scheme. Also, it is obvious that the list is far from complete. A more complete study should include migration and differentiation of neuroblasts, but about these processes we know very little. Essentially therefore, we will be discussing DNA synthesis and undifferentiated cell division only in ependymal and subependymal layers (germinal matrix) next to the ventricle where there is a good nutrient supply and where mitoses mostly (or exclusively) occur. Any failure leading to the infarction of this germinal matrix may result in mental retardation (Towbin, 1969).

First, one may think that the cell divisions eventually slow down and stop because of "contact inhibition". However, in these matrix layers the cells are already tightly packed even very early in development; thus, "contact inhibition" is probably not responsible for the slowing of cell division. A likely factor is the regulation of *nutrient availability*. This regulation may be hormonal, and both maternal and (later) fetal hormones may be involved. (The importance of hormones for the early development of brain and behavior has been well presented in the previous chapter by Whitsett and Vandenbergh.)

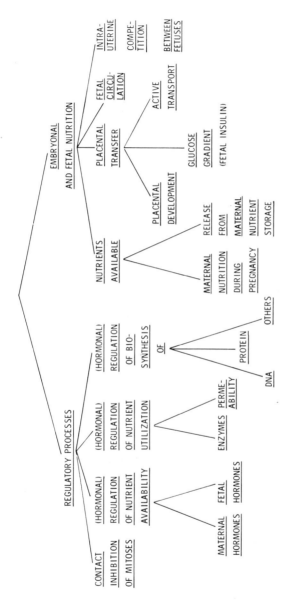

FIG. 3. Some possible natural environmental factors determining the number of brain cells in newborn mammals. From Zamenhof and van Marthens (1971), reprinted by permission of the University of California Press.

In addition to the availability of nutrients, there must be a control of *nutrient utilization*. For this utilization very special enzymes (for example, those of the Krebs cycle) and special permeabilities are needed, and all these may be dependent on gene derepression and again on hormonal regulation. Successful nutrient utilization does not exclude the need for very special enzymes (such as DNA polymerase) to synthesize a new quota of cell constituents (DNA, protein, etc.) prior to cell division. These enzymes also must be dependent on gene derepression and might be dependent on hormonal regulation.

Embryonal and fetal nutrition *per se* was discussed in the Introduction in connection with Fig. 1.

Although it is possible to compile lists of factors that *might* regulate cell divisions in the prenatal brain, the *actual* intricate process that takes place is still essentially unknown (Goss, 1972). An attempt to demonstrate some enzymatic systems involved in the regulation of DNA replication in the brain has been made by Margolis (1969). He first determined the DNA content of cerebral hemispheres, optic lobes, and cerebellum in chicken brains from the 11th day of embryonic life to 6 weeks after hatching. Each region showed a characteristic pattern of variation during development. The cerebellum showed the most rapid and the optic lobes the least rapid rate of DNA increase during the period studied. The concentration of DNA within these regions decreased continuously with age except for that of the cerebellum which passed through a maximum just before hatching.

The nature of the DNA-polymerase activity in soluble extracts from these brain regions seemed to be similar to the properties reported for this enzyme activity in other vertebrate tissues. At nearly every age the level of enzyme activity was highest in extracts from the embryonic cerebellum. The particulate fraction from brain homogenates decreased the DNA-polymerase activity observed in soluble brain extracts. The data obtained indicate that this inhibition was the result of dephosphorylation of the deoxynucleoside triphosphate substrates by an ATPase in the brain particulate fraction whose activity increases during ontogeny. This activity, then, may contribute to the determination of final DNA level of the particular part of the brain, and therefore also the final brain cell number.

Such a complex regulatory system consists of a multitude of overlapping checks so that if one factor is enhanced, the next one becomes a rate-limiting step. Because of this complexity, rapid progress in understanding these processes is unlikely in the near future. At present, most of the research is limited to the description of end result: the precise timing of cellular events in the prenatal brain.

A discussion of organogenesis in the central nervous system of the very young embryo is outside of the scope of this chapter. For a detailed study of this and subsequent periods of neurogenesis, the reader is referred to an excellent review by Berry (1974); for a review of early postnatal brain differentiation, see Dodge *et al.* (1975, pp. 6–18).

In the rat, the cerebral vesicle is formed on about the 10th or 11th day of pregnancy; during the subsequent proliferative stage the cells in ependymal and subependymal layer adjacent to the ventricle, fed by nutrients arriving through the ventricle, undergo vigorous mitoses. Around Day 14 they begin migration to the pial surface, to form primitive cortex. The neuroblasts that were formed earliest form the deepest layers of the cortex; the cells formed later pass through the deep layer to form more superficial layers. The latest neuroblasts to form in the fetal rat (Day 21) are found in superficial layer I; with few exceptions noted later in this chapter, the mitotic period is essentially concluded at birth (Berry, 1974; Berry & Rogers, 1965; Berry, Rogers, & Eayrs, 1964; Herschkowitz & Rossi, 1972). Essentially the same pattern, with proper correction for different length of pregnancy, has been found in mice (Angevine & Sidman, 1961) and in the rhesus monkey (Rakic, 1974); in the latter, the neuroblast proliferation ceases 2 months before birth.

Cell proliferation has been also studied by following the DNA increase (as discussed previously). In rats (Fig. 2), DNA increase before birth is preponderantly due to increase in number of neuroblasts; glioblasts start to proliferate at Day 18 of pregnancy (Berry & Rogers, 1965) and continue after birth until weaning; the postnatal increase in DNA is also due to non-neural elements (blood vessels, blood cells). In humans, a detailed study of the curve of DNA increase revealed that neuron proliferation in our species ceases about the 18th week of pregnancy (Dobbing & Sands, 1970, 1973), while increase in DNA continues prenatally, and in the postnatal period until the 6th (Winick, 1968) or even the 18th month (Dobbing & Sands, 1973). The proliferation of cerebellar neuroblasts and glioblasts in rats and humans takes place postnatally, except for Purkinje and Golgi II cells which originate during the early prenatal period. Another exception, in the cerebrum, consists of the short-axoned neurons whose proliferation may occur after birth (Altman & Das, 1966).

In contrast to neuron proliferation and migration, in most mammals the bulk of neuronal differentiation occurs postnatally. Nevertheless, it is likely that the extent of ultimate differentiation depends on the integrity, nutritional status, and size of cells at the end of the fetal period of development (i.e., at birth).

It is a general biological principle that the number of cells in any organ is most altered if the interfering agent acts during the period of most rapid cell proliferation in this organ. Thus, the number of cerebral neurons should be most "vulnerable" prenatally, at least in rats and humans among other mammalian species. Slight changes in the cell cycle may affect the rate of mitosis and may have a great effect on the final cell number (Herschkowitz & Rossi, 1972). Infarction of the actively proliferating ependymal or subependymal layer very early in pregnancy in humans results in a smaller, defective brain, and is responsible for a large proportion of cases of mental retardation (Towbin, 1969, 1970). Towbin feels that all of us have had only *suboptimal* pre- and perinatal chances for brain development: "Gestation and birth form an inexorable leveling mechanism; with the brain blighted at birth, the potential of mentation may be reduced from that of a genius to that of a plain child, or less. The damage may be slight, imperceptible clinically, or, it may spell the difference between brothers, one a dexterous athlete, the other an awkward child. Substantially, it is said, all of us have a touch of cerebral palsy and mental retardation, some more, some less—the endowment pathologically of gestation and birth" (Towbin, 1969, p. 160). Thus, the actual brain development in most cases may be below the genetic potential of the species in general or of an individual in particular.

The infarction discussed in the preceeding paragraph may be caused by many factors but one of them appears to be prenatal malnutrition. This subject will be discussed in the next section.

IV. Prenatal Malnutrition and Brain Development

At present, there is no indication that the fetal brain requires different nutrients than the rest of the fetus. What makes brain development somewhat special is the strict timetable of events (see preceding section): pregnancy operates on a tight schedule and a delayed or slowed down synthetic process in the brain may result it an irreversible anatomical brain deficiency. Whether such deficiency is always coupled with functional (mental; behavioral) deficiency is still unclear. This subject is well discussed by Leathwood in the next chapter in this volume. Early malnutrition alone might result in a brain with a marginally sufficient functional state; if, however, any other stressful conditions (poverty, deprived social brackground, etc.) are also present, a clear inadequacy may appear. Needless to say, these other stressful conditions indeed *are* almost always present in the situations in which human malnutrition occurs. One may also add that the brain functions tested in animals, and even in human infants and young adults, are often rather simple; it is conceivable that the very highest functions of human brain, so precious to modern society, would prove to be impaired by any anatomical deficiency that still leaves the brain good enough for simple functions. As an example, one may mention the recent work on the behavioral effects of mild prenatal hypoxia in the rat (McCullough & Blackman, 1976): the effects were not demonstrable in a simple Hebb-Williams maze, but easily demonstrable in a difficult Hebb-Williams maze.

The anatomical deficiency may be in neuron number, glia number, amount of neuronal protein stored for postnatal neuronal differentiation, concentration of neurotransmitters, etc. In severe cases of prenatal malnutrition these deficiencies are easy to demonstrate. In mild cases the deficiency may often be subtle and difficult to notice: for instance, it may affect not the total number of brain cells but just the neuron/glia ratio, or not the total number of neurons but just their distribution in individual layers (distortion of brain cytoarchitectonics), or not the final concentration of neurotransmitters in the mature brain but their temporary deficiency in a critical period of synaptogenesis. Because of difficulties in demonstrating such mild cases, some workers tend to disregard them, claiming that the "plasticity" of the brain takes care of "compensation" for the deficiencies. While such compensation may be sufficient in lower animals, one must be aware of the possibility that in humans such small deficiencies may well lead to a brain whose highest functions could be at suboptimal level.

General nutrient requirements in prenatal brain development have already been discussed in Section II. In this section we shall discuss only severe cases of fetal malnutrition because they result in well-demonstrated brain deficiencies. Since fetal malnutrition has at least two distinct components, maternal malnutrition and placental insufficiency, these are discussed separately.

A. Maternal Malnutrition

As indicated schematically in Fig. 1 and as discussed in the previous sections, the nutrients consumed by the pregnant female do not bear a one-to-one relationship to the nutrients ultimately reaching the site of proliferation of fetal neuroblasts: many regulatory factors intervene, and they may augment or decrease the quantities of nutrients that actually reach their destination. Nevertheless, *maternal* nutrients do have a profound influence on fetal brain development. The effect of *infant* nutrition on *infant* brain development was studied rather early; the study of maternal nutrients (prenatal nutrition) is a more recent development. Early studies included the behavioral aspects of early malnutrition (Caldwell & Churchill, 1967; Cowley & Griesel, 1959, 1963, 1966), but the brain itself was not investigated. The effects of malnutrition on *postnatal* brain development have been studied previously by Dickerson, Dobbing and McCance (1967), Dobbing and Widdowson (1965), Winick and Noble (1966), and Zeman (1967). All these and most subsequent studies were done on animals, not only because of the ban on human experimentation but also because human data, even if available, do not differentiate precisely enough between various periods and various kinds of malnutrition.

In 1968, we demonstrated (Zamenhof, van Marthens, & Margolis, 1968) that when female rats were maintained on an 8 or 27% casein diet for 1 month before mating and throughout gestation, the brains of newborn rats from females on the 8% casein diet contained significantly less DNA and protein compared to the progeny of the females on the 27% casein diet. The data on DNA indicate that there are fewer cells; the protein content per cell was also lower. If, at birth, the brain cells are predominantly neurons, and their number becomes final at that time (see Section III), then such dietary restriction may result in some permanent brain neuron deficiency. The quantitative alteration in number as well as the qualitative change (protein per cell) may constitute a basis for the impaired behavior of the offspring from protein-deprived mothers.

Around that time Winick (1969) and Zeman and Stanbrough (1969) independently worked on similar problems in rats so that our results were soon confirmed.

In the guinea pig, an animal more mature in brain development at birth, intrauterine malnutrition also resulted in significant reduction in neonatal body weight and brain weight, brain cell number, protein, cholesterol, and cerebroside and sulfatide content (Chase, Dabiere, Welch, & O'Brien, 1971).

Also of interest were our findings that malnutrition during pregnancy only was much less harmful than malnutrition started 1 month before mating and continued through pregnancy. Thus, there was evidence that maternal nutrient reserves at the beginning of pregnancy are an important factor in determining the outcome of malnourished pregnancy.

In a further study, Winick (1970b) assessed cell divisions in various discrete rat brain regions by the use of autoradiography, after injecting the mother with tritiated thymidine. In this way, he demonstrated differential regional sensitivity by the 16th day of gestation in the brains of fetuses of protein-restricted mothers. The cerebral white and gray matter were mildly affected. The area adjacent to the third ventricle and the subiculum were moderately affected, whereas the cerebellum and the area directly adjacent to the lateral ventricle were markedly affected. These data demonstrated again that the magnitude of the effect produced on cell division is directly related to the actual rate of cell division at the time the insult is applied.

Theoretical considerations of the mechanisms by which protein (amino acid) deficiency may affect DNA and RNA synthesis, have been discussed by Brasel (1974); Winick's and Brasel's group found changes in the activities of polymerases and nucleases during malnutrition. The change in several enzymatic activities in the leukocytes of malnourished pregnant women has also been demonstrated (Metcoff, 1974; Metcoff, Mameesh, Jacobson, Costiloe, Crosby, Sandstead, & McClain, 1976).

To investigate further the problem of *timing* of prenatal malnutrition, we decided to divide the pregnancy itself into shorter periods of malnutrition; in order to get demonstrable effects, the dietary restriction of the mother had to be more extreme: i.e., the diet had to be free of protein.

Pregnant rats were fed such a protein-free diet during five periods of pregnancy: Days 0 to 10, 10 to 15, 13 to 18, 15 to 20, or 10 to 20, and an adequate protein diet during the remaining time until parturition (Zamenhof, van Marthens, & Grauel, 1971b). In 62% of the dams fed a protein-free diet from 0 to Day 10, there was a failure to litter. There was no significant change in the food intake in any of the groups; yet there were significant decreases in body weights, cerebral weights, cerebral DNA, and cerebral protein of their offspring, even though, until Day 15, the total protein increment of the embryo and its supporting tissue constitutes only an insignificant fraction (1.3%) of the average maternal protein intake.

Thus, the observed effects are unlikely to be due to an actual deficiency of amino acids *per se* as required for embryonal protein synthesis. Work in other laboratories (review in Zamenhof *et al.*, 1971b) demonstrated that the disturbance can be traced to deficient placental development caused by a deficiency in estrogen and progesterone, caused, in turn, by a deficiency in maternal pituitary gonadotropic hormones. The latter might presumably be triggered by a change in amino acid balance (or serum proteins) acting in the pituitary and/or the hypothalamus that produces pituitary hormone-releasing factors. After Day 11, when the placenta starts to assume the hormonal functions of the maternal pituitary, the deficiency in placental development may further contribute to the overall effect. Winick (1970a) also reported the adverse effects of maternal protein restriction on placental development as early as Day 13 in rats.

Our data on cesarean sections on Day 16 and 20 of pregnancy, following deprivation from Days 10 to 15 also indicate deficient placental development. This deficiency persists to term (cesarean section on Day 20).

After Day 15, the total protein increments of the rat fetus and its supporting tissue cease to be insignificant. Brain underdevelopment due to protein deprivation after this time may be due to a direct deficiency of amino acids required for protein synthesis. The adverse effect on the development of the placenta may also continue. The most pronounced effects were obtained by protein deprivation from Day 10 to Day 20. This, indeed, seems to indicate the cumulative effect of both direct deficiency of amino acids and underdevelopment of the placenta.

In a recent study (Zamenhof, van Marthens, & Shimomaye, 1976b), total maternal protein deprivation was applied on Days 0–6, 0–7, or 0–10 of pregnancy, with normal diet afterwards. Deprivation on Days 0–6 had no effects on the formation of decidua, but deprivation on Days 0–7 reduced this formation to 55%. The number of corpora lutea of pregnancy and the size of the implantation sites (decidua) were the same in all three cases. However, on Day 16, the 0- to 10-day-deprived fetus, compared to the 0- to 6-day-deprived fetus, had significantly lower body weight, cerebral weight, cerebral DNA, and cerebral protein even though at Day 10 the actual protein needs of the embryo are still negligable. Placental weight and placental protein were also significantly lower. If appears that 7–10 days is the most susceptible period for early fetal resorption or underdevelopment caused by regulatory systems triggered by maternal protein deprivation.

Thus, at least in the rat, pregnancy operates on a very tight schedule and the mechanisms involved are, as can be seen, quite complex. It is of interest that one of these mechanisms (resorption of fetuses) must have been developed during evolution to protect the mother, in this case against organisms with different genomes (fetuses). Evidently, in time of emergency (protein deprivation) it is better to preserve a normal mother than to produce subnormal offspring. Obviously, the selection during the evolution here favored mechanisms fittest for the species as a whole, rather than selection of the fittest individual genomes (best fetuses).

The finding (Dobbing & Sands, 1970, 1973) that in the human neuronal proliferation terminates early has been recently interpreted (Dobbing, 1974; Dobbing & Sands, 1973) to mean that in the human the proliferation of brain neurons cannot be affected by prenatal malnutrition because that early in pregnancy the nutrient requirements of the fetus are still negligible (the notion of the "highly protected second trimester"). We disagree with this interpretation. We do not feel that even very early pregnancy is highly protected. As discussed earlier, there is evidence that rat embryos are usually destroyed (resorbed) a few days after implantation if the maternal diet lacks protein. This occurs even though at that stage the rat embryo requires (comparatively) even less protein than a human fetus in the second trimester. Embryos that do survive exhibit deficient placenta and brain development. Clearly, what decides about the destruction of the embryo is some regulatory mechanism and not the amount of food required by the embryo at that time.

Transgenerational effects: In the course of the preceding experiments we obtained evidence that the normally nourished female offspring (F_1) of mothers (F_0) malnourished during pregnancy produce offspring (F_2) that have significantly lower brain parameters (Zamenhof, van Marthens, & Grauel, 1971d, 1972a). This transfer of deficiencies to the next (F_2) generation is only through F_1 females, but not through F_1 males; clearly, it is not a Mendelian inheritance. The learning ability of the F_2 offspring (above) was tested in a water maze, and found to be significantly impaired; this study was then repeated in a specially designed computerized maze (Bressler, Ellison, & Zamenhof, 1975), with similar results.

Several possible explanations of these results have to be considered. Poor lactation of F_0 nursing mothers was not the cause since the effects on the brain in F_2 in another group was essentially the same although the nursing mothers were never protein-restricted.

Other possible explanations of this effect on brain development in F_2 animals are the following: due to protein restriction of F_0 mothers before delivery, the F_1 offspring are born handicapped, not only with regard to the brain (Zamenhof et al.; 1968) but also in other respects. Hall and Zeman (1968) have reported that the offspring of rats similarly protein-restricted during pregnancy suffer from retardation of kidney development and altered kidney function. Lee and Chow (1968) have reported that the restricted progeny showed reduced feed efficiency and low nitrogen balance; they excreted more amino acids than the controls. Thus, each progeny (F_1) may indeed suffer from cryptic malnutrition, even when postnatally given full access to normal food. As a result, the progeny (F_2) of F_1 had a cerebral cell deficiency in accordance with previous findings (Zamenhof et al., 1968).

Another possibility is that the F_1 organs affected were endocrine glands. Stephan, Chow, Frohman, and Chow (1971) have recently shown that similar F_1 animals had smaller pituitaries containing lower concentrations of growth harmone. Deficiencies of this and possibly other maternal (F_1) hormones may well affect fetal brain development of the F_2 offspring.

Other cases of maternal inheritance are, of course, well known. But the implications of the preceding case are of particular interest. They reveal the existence of a long-range regulatory mechanism which, generation after generation, cumulatively adjusts the size of individuals and their organs (within genetic limits) to the nutritional opportunities confronting a given strain. Thus, what we consider a deficiency may actually mean an adjustment that has a selective value for survival of the species. A recent study of birth weights (Ounsted, 1969) indicates that such phenomena may also be operating in humans: the degree of constraint imposed on the fetus is correlated with the degree of constraint experienced by the mother when she herself was a fetus.

Essential amino acids: In all the preceding experiments maternal dietary restriction was in protein as such. However, what reaches the fetus is not the intact protein but the amino acids. Thus, as a next step, we investigated the effect of exclusion of single amino acids, especially essential amino acids, from maternal diet.

A protein-free diet containing a complete chemically defined mixture of L-amino acids (AA) or this mixture deprived of one of the essential amino acids, tryptophan, lysine, or methionine, respectively, was fed to pregnant rats (Zamenhof et al., 1974b). The feeding period was 0–21 or 10–21 days of pregnancy. At birth the following neonatal parameters were measured: body weight, cerebral weight, cerebral DNA (cell number), and cerebral protein, as well as placental weight, placental DNA, and placental protein. As compared with normal (pelleted) stock diet, the AA diet resulted in small but significant decreases in body weight and cerebral parameters, but not in the placental parameters. Thus, it still remains uncertain whether our present knowledge of nutritional factors for optimal fetal development is sufficient to devise a fautless synthetic diet for pregnancy: the need for "unknown growth factors"[3] cannot yet be excluded.

Omission of tryptophan, lysine, or methionine, respectively, from the AA diet resulted in offspring significantly inferior to the full AA diet offspring in all parameters; the deficiencies were essentially similar to those produced in our previous study by total protein deprivation (Zamenhof et al., 1971b). Thus, omission of a single essential amino acid during pregnancy may be as harmful as total absence of dietary protein. Such a finding may be of particular importance in view of the well-known single or double essential amino acid deficiencies in many foods of plant origin.

In all the preceding experiments the maternal dietary restriction was in protein only, while caloric intake was kept normal. However, since glucose is the main energy source for the fetus, it was of interest to see whether restriction of caloric intake alone (with normal protein intake) would also affect prenatal brain development. We found (Zamenhof, van Marthens, & Grauel, 1971c, 1971e) that such a restriction of caloric intake to one-third of normal, even during the second half of pregnancy only, resulted in highly significant decreases in neonatal body weight, placental weight, neonatal cerebral weight, cerebral DNA (cell number), and cerebral protein. In this connection, it is of interest that Habicht, Yarbrough, Lechtig, and Klein (1973) obtained evidence of the importance of caloric supplementation in prevention of incidence of "small for date" human infants.

An attempt was also made to visualize the effects of prenatal caloric malnutrition on neonatal and older brains. Cerebral cell number, although intimately involved in brain performance (Holloway, 1968; Welker, Johnson, & Pubols, 1964), is not directly related to other putative factors of brain function such as the extent of the neuronal dendritic tree (Clendinnen & Eayrs, 1961; Welker et al., 1964). Cortical thickness and cortical cross-sectional area, on the other hand, should reflect both the cell number and the development of cellular arborization. We were, therefore, concerned with the problem whether cortical thickness and area are also reduced by prenatal caloric restriction (Clark, Zamenhof, van Marthens, Grauel, & Kruger, 1973).

[3]The term "unknown growth factors" is meant here to cover either unknown substances necessary for growth, or unknown circumstances (digestion, absorption, etc.) affecting nutrient utilization.

At birth, at 10 days of age, and at adulthood the brains were dissected out; on some, cerebral DNA (cell number) and cerebral protein were determined as described earlier. Other brains were fixed for histological study. Serial 50-μm frozen coronal sections were cut, mounted, and stained for quantitative study. Stained sections at the rostral and caudal poles of the corpus callosum were selected and their projections traced for subsequent measurements (Fig. 4).

It was found that not only cerebral parameters of the offspring (weight, DNA, protein) but also cortical dimensions (thickness at several positions, width, area) are significantly reduced when pregnant rats are maintained on caloric-deficient diets. The reduction in cortical thickness is approximately double that expected from the reduction in cerebral weight, which suggests that the cortex itself is more affected by such malnutrition than the cerebrum as a whole. It was also found that all these decreases were more pronounced at birth than at 10 days or than in later development. Thus, for visualization of prenatal deficiencies one should study the brain at birth or shortly thereafter. If it is more difficult to demonstrate the deficiencies later on, this may not mean rehabilitation has occurred after birth because by then the neurons have practically ceased to proliferate; it may just mean

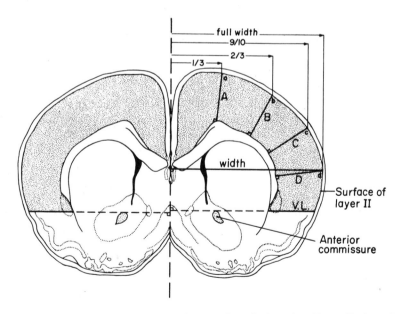

FIG. 4. Illustration of measurements on the rostral cerebral section. From Clark *et al.* (1973), reprinted by permission of Elsevier Scientific Publishing Co., Amsterdam, The Netherlands.

that after birth some of the damages become more elusive due to differentiation and considerable brain expansion.

Siassi and Siassi (1973) studied the effect of prenatal or early (0–10
days) postnatal protein-calorie deficiency in maternal diet on development
of the somatosensory cortex of the offspring. Cerebral weight, volume,
and dimensions were significantly lower at postnatal Days 10 and 21 even
when postnatal nutrition was normal. The number of glia cells was reduced
to a greater extent than was the number of neurons. Prenatal malnutrition
resulted in a greater permanent deficiency than did postnatal malnutrition.

B. Placental Insufficiency

All the preceding work was concerned with one component of fetal
malnutrition, namely maternal malnutrition during pregnancy. Wigglesworth (1964) laid the foundations for experimental study of the second
component of fetal malnutrition, namely the deficiency of placental
transfer. He produced experimental uteroplacental ischemia in rat pups
by occluding the uterine artery for varying time periods. Such ischemia
produced a varying degree of stunting; the individual organs were differentially affected, depending on their growth rate after the time of vascular
occlusion. The brain itself is less affected than the body as a whole.
Similar results have been obtained by Minkowski et al. (1974), Oh and Guy
(1971), and Winick (1971); in rat, as well as in rhesus monkey (Hill, Myers,
Holt, Scott, & Cheek, 1971), the total cell number in the cerebrum is not
affected by placental insufficiency (ischemia).

It would be of interest to find an animal model in which ischemia does
produce demonstrable brain underdevelopment, as seems to occur in "small
for date" human infants. To this end we turned to the rabbit which in
many respects may be a better model than the rat for human brain: the
period of the most rapid brain development in the rabbit is around the time
of birth, placing the rabbit in the same "perinatal brain developer" category as the human. We induced experimental ischemia during the last trimester by ligation of spiral arterioles, and determined the effects on fetal
development at term (van Marthens, Harel, & Zamenhof, 1975). We examined specific regions of the brain in terms of wet weight, total cell number
(DNA), and total protein content. Highly significant decreases in all these
parameters were found in both the cortex and cerebellum following the
previously mentioned experimental intrauterine growth retardation; these
two organs were affected to a different degree, depending on their individual
growth phase at the time of the vascular insult: cell number is affected more
in the cerebellum, and cell size in the cerebrum.

V. "Supernutrition" and Optimal Brain Development

At the end of Section III we discussed the concept that the *actual* brain development may be, in most cases, below the *optimal*, i.e., below the genetic potential of the individual or the species. According to the recent study by Naeye, Blanc, and Paul (1973), "the larger brain size in newborns of mothers who were best nourished raises the possibility that fetal brain growth may reach its full genetic potential *only* under such circumstances of full nutrition" (p. 502). In addition to the more obvious question of what constitutes "full nutrition," at present it is difficult to ascertain whether a particular dietary regime, which does not give any symptoms of malnutrition, is also an optimal regime. Differences in strains, intestinal absorption, etc., may play a considerable role here. A diet optimal in one respect or at one time in development may not be so in other respects or at other times. In this section we concern ourselves with the conditions *optimal for prenatal brain development*.

The term "supernutrition" as distinct from "overnutrition" has been used by Williams (1971) to denote "quality above and beyond nutrition as it is ordinarily experienced" to provide "a completely suitable assortment ideally tailored to individual needs". Although this concept as presented here has mainly qualitative connotations, the optimal *quantity* is also a part of supernutrition. For instance, Winick and Noble (1967) reported the increase in cell number of many organs, including brain, by increasing the *quantity* of milk available to rat pups during nursing.

In this section we will summarize the evidence to suggest that the quantity of nutrients normally allocated to a fetus may not be optimal and, within genetic limits, is subject to experimental improvement.

One work concerns the effects of pituitary growth hormone. In case of maternal malnutrition during pregnancy, which results in malnourished fetuses, one may wonder whether the amounts of nutrients the mother is supplying to them is really all she can do for them: after all, she usually has ample nutrient reserves: fat, glycogen, muscle protein. If only she could mobilize them!

The levels of pituitary growth hormone are known to increase during pregnancy and during fasting. Perhaps this mobilizes maternal nutrient reserves, or at least prevents deposition of fat. Thus, mothers of similar genome but different pituitary development might produce offspring with different brain development.

However, in case of maternal malnutrition such natural mobilization is often not sufficient to produce normal offspring. Thus, an attempt was made to stimulate such nutrient mobilization by injecting pregnant females with additional growth hormone (Zamenhof et al., 1971e). Such treatment of malnourished females indeed produced nearly normal offspring.

The improvements in the malnourished animals were highly significant. In addition, treatment of normally nourished females with growth hormone produced a significant increase in cerebral weight over and above the normal; this increase was due not to water but to increased content of cerebral protein. As already explained, the primary action of this hormone might have been on the mother, by mobilization of maternal nutrient reserves, especially fat deposits. Thus, conceivably, each fetus received more nutrients which stimulated its prenatal brain development.

It has also been demonstrated that growth hormone administered during gestation and lactation restores the levels of catecholamines and of tyrosine hydroxylase that are otherwise lowered by malnutrition (Lee & Dubos, 1972).

The improvement of early brain development upon administration of growth hormone has been also demonstrated in the past (in tadpoles: Hunt & Jacobson, 1970; Zamenhof, 1941; in pregnant rats: Clendinnen & Eayrs, 1961; Zamenhof, 1942; Zamenhof, Mosley, & Schuller, 1966), and also more recently (Sara & Lazarus, 1974, 1975; Sara, Lazarus, Stuart, & King, 1974). Behaviorial studies on rats indicate that the treatment of pregnant female with growth hormone results in a significant improvement of learning ability in the offspring (Block & Essman, 1965; Clendinnen & Eayrs, 1961; Croskerry & Smith, 1975; Ray & Hochhauser, 1969; Sara & Lazarus, 1974, 1975; Sara et al., 1974); however various investigators give different interpretations of the cause of such improvement.

Another method to enhance prenatal brain development is to reduce the number of fetuses during pregnancy by surgical means: presumably such a procedure provides more nutrients to the remaining fetuses. One method for achieving this reduction consists in tying one of the two uterine horns (rat) prior to mating (van Marthens & Zamenhof, 1969). Another method, used in rabbits (van Marthens, Grauel, & Zamenhof, 1972) and rats (van Marthens, Grauel, & Zamenhof, 1974), consists in destroying some implantation sites soon after implantation. The result is the significant increase in neonatal body weight, placental weight, cerebral weight, cerebral DNA (cell number), and cerebral protein. In the case of rabbit the increases in placental weight were up to 105%, in neonatal body weight–up to 50%, in cerebral DNA (cell number)—up to 21%, and in cerebral protein—up to 46%.

In rat the increases in placental weights closely followed the degree of reduction of number of fetuses.

The remarkable constancy of neonatal cerebral DNA (cell number) (Zamenhof & van Marthens, 1971, 1974; Zamenhof, van Marthens, & Grauel, 1972b) in *normal* animals is probably the result of stringent regulatory

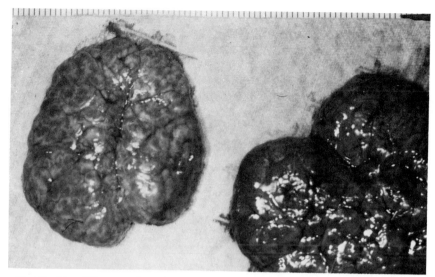

FIG. 5. Size difference of a typical experimental (right) and control (left) rabbit placenta from cesarean sections performed on the 30th day of gestation. Scale 1 graduation = 1mm. From van Marthens *et al.* (1972), reprinted by permission of Pergamon Press, Oxford, Great Britain.

mechanisms. Conceivably, they consist of a multitude of closely over-lapping checks so that if one factor is enhanced, the next one becomes the rate-limiting step, and so on. Nevertheless, cases of enhanced brain development in genetically uniform strains can not only be produced experimentally (as discussed previously) but they also occur naturally: possibly in natural cases many factors have changed in concert.

As can be seen from Fig. 6, in a genetically uniform population, sporadically, animals from the same litter can be found which have brain DNA well above the range of others (more than two standard deviations; Zamenhof & van Marthens, 1974). Such spontaneous occurrences are rare: approximately 2% of cases in the rat. The causes of such high DNA are completely unknown, but their occurrence indicates that the mechanisms of regulation of DNA synthesis and cell number in parental brain are not completely precise and inviolable.

In a recent study (Zamenhof, Guthrie, & van Marthens, 1976a), newborn rats with parameter values more than two standard deviations above the mean [(outstandingly high (OH)] were identified in a normal population of 720 animals and were studied for correlations between the following parameters: body weight, brain weight, brain DNA (cell number), and brain protein.

It was found that an animal OH on one parameter tends to have values for other parameters higher than the mean for the population. Some of

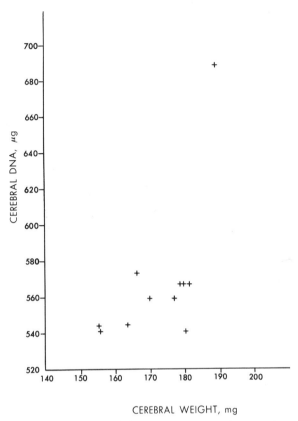

FIG. 6. Individual (+) neonatal rat cerebral weights and neonatal cerebral DNA (cell number): one of the litters in which one fetus has cerebral DNA more than two standard deviations above the mean. From Zamenhof and van Marthens (1974), reprinted by permission of Dr. W. Junk b.v. Publishers, The Hague, The Netherlands.

these animals with OH value of cerebral weight, cerebral DNA, or cerebral protein came from litters whose value on this parameter was also OH ("OH litters"), and the percentages of such animals were significantly higher ($p < .001$) than would be expected if there were no correlations among the parameters. Thus, on a statistical basis, an individual which at birth had an OH cerebral cell number (DNA) is likely to be the one also having a higher than average birth weight, and also to be the one from the litter OH with respect to cerebral cell number. Such findings may facilitate the search for these OH individuals. In the newborn rat, the cerebral cells are mostly neurons, and their number at birth is final or nearly final (see Section III); thus, such an animal may well retain the superiority in neuron number when adult. Other parameters, such as cerebral protein content, may not remain OH in the adult, but nevertheless such superiority at birth may exert beneficial influences during postnatal neuron differentiation.

The normal occurrence of newborns with OH amounts of cerebral DNA (cell number) indicates that the remarkable constancy of this parameter at birth can be circumvented by natural causes. The occurrence of such OH animals has rarely been reported (Zamenhof & van Marthens, 1971, 1974) and the causes are essentially unknown.

It might be hypothesized that the occurrence of OH animals is due to their special genotype. While at present this cannot be totally excluded, it must be pointed out that the rats used in the present study were bred as a closed colony for 33 to 37 generations; thus, *genetic* variability is not very likely to be the explanation of the occurrence of OH animals. It has been often maintained that for many species, including the human, hereditary correlations as such can largely be disregarded as determinants of the size of the newborn, the correlations being here mainly environmental (see review in Widdowson, 1968, p. 3); however, prenatal brain development has not been studied in this respect. The present finding that the newborns OH with respect to brain parameters also have body weights higher than the mean for the population, suggests that for the neonatal brain, too, the causes may be environmental, such as the general optimal intrauterine conditions, including optimal prenatal nutrition. Such conditions might have prevailed for each OH litter, but might have been especially favorable for the OH fetuses within such litters. The improvement of newborn brain parameters by experimental improvements of intrauterine conditions has already been discussed.

VI. Summary and Conclusions

This chapter attempts to assess some of the factors which may affect brain development, in either direction, deterioration or improvement.

The brain starts to develop very early, and its foundations and potential for further development are already partially laid at birth; thus, our considerations have emphasized the prenatal period. The evidence, admittedly very limited, suggests that environmental, rather than genetic factors, are of primary importance in that period. Genetic factors affecting prenatal brain development have not been extensively studied and do not lend themselves to manipulation; this also applies to the factors that determine gene derepression and rerepression and thus start and stop neuronal DNA synthesis and neuron proliferation. On the other hand, there is some information concerning the effects of environmental factors and their manipulation. Of these, embryonal and fetal nutrition has been discussed first.

The maternal nutrient supply to the fetus (embryo) offers an easy target for interference with prenatal brain development. The actual nutrient requirements of the fetus (embryo) are not well known, and a biochemical study of "unknown growth factors" may still yield some surprises. This also applies to the multitude of regulatory factors which control the complex flow of nutrients to the site of synthesis of components in the proliferating neuron (neuroblast). This control is not always for the benefit of the fetus. For example, one of the complex controlling mechanisms described here (resorption of fetuses) has been developed during evolution to protect the mother against organisms of different genomes (fetuses). Evidently, in times of emergency (protein deprivation) it is better to preserve a normal mother than to produce subnormal offspring. Obviously, the evolutionary driving force here was the selection for the features fittest to the species as a whole, rather than the selection of the fittest individual genomes (fetus versus fetus or fetus versus mother).

Other studies presented here indicate the transfer of the effects of prenatal malnutrition on brain development in one generation to the next generation: the mechanism involved is a non-Mendelian, maternal inheritance. These studies reveal the existence of the long-range regulatory mechanisms which, generation after generation, cumulatively adjust the size of individuals and their organs (within genetic limits) to the nutritional opportunities confronting a given strain. Thus, what we consider a deficiency may actually mean an adjustment that has a selective value for survival of an animal species.

The deterioration of prenatal brain development in humans may result in typical mental retardation. More numerous, and therefore more important for society are borderline cases, i.e., *suboptimal* brain development: the non-fulfillment of the genetic potential of the individual.

Deterioration of prenatal brain development caused by a *single* factor, e.g., deficiency of one nutrient, is biochemically easy to understand: this factor (nutrient) soon becomes the rate-limiting step in the synthesis of components of the neuron (neuroblast). Conversely, the removal of this (single) limitation in such cases would lead to improvement toward the optimal state. On the other hand, the deterioration of prenatal brain development, to make it less than optimal, could also be caused by multiple factors acting together. In this case, the improvement toward the optimum is more difficult to achieve: a system as complex as this may consist of a multitude of closely overlapping checks so that if only one factor is enhanced, the next one becomes the rate-limiting step, and so on. Nevertheless, cases of significantly enhanced brain development (admittedly rare), in genetically uniform strains, do occur naturally: possibly, many environmental factors have changed *in concert*, to give an end result that is optimal within genetic limits. Moreover, such enhancement can be produced at will in the laboratory, as has been amply documented in the present chapter. Thus, the limits imposed on prenatal brain development are not completely precise and inviolable.

Acknowledgments

The authors' work has been supported by grants HD-05615 and HD-08927 from the National Institute of Child Health and Human Development and AG-00162 from the National Institute on Aging.

References

Adinolfi, M., Beck, S. E., Haddad, S. A., & Seller, M. J. Permeability of the blood-cerebrospinal fluid barrier to plasma proteins during foetal and perinatal life. *Nature (London)*, 1976, **259**, 140–141.

Alexander, D. P., Britton, H. G., Cohen, N. M., & Nixon, D. A. Foetal metabolism. In G. E. W. Wolstenholme & M. O'Connor (Eds.), *Foetal autonomy*. London: Churchill, 1969. Pp. 95–113.

Altman, J., & Das, G. D. Autoradiographic and histological studies of postnatal neurogenesis. I. A longitudinal investigation of the kinetics, migration and transformation of cells incorporating tritiated thymidine in neonate rats, with special reference to postnatal neurogenesis in some brain regions. *Journal of Comparative Neurology*, 1966, **126**, 337–389.

Angevine, J. B., & Sidman, R. L. Audiographic study of cell migration during histogenesis of cerebral cortex in the mouse. *Nature (London)*, 1961, **192**, 766–768.

Apgar, J. Effects of zinc deficiency on parturition in the rat. *American Journal of Physiology*, 1968, **215**, 160–163.

Babson, G. S., Kangas, J., Young, N., & Bramhall, J. L. Growth and development of twins of dissimilar size at birth. *Pediatrics*, 1964, **33**, 327–334.

Berry, M. Development of the cerebral neocortex of the rat. In G. Gottlieb (Ed.), *Aspects of neurogenesis*. New York: Academic Press, 1974. Pp. 7–67.

Berry, M., & Rogers, A. W. The migration of neuroblasts in the developing cortex. *Journal of Anatomy*, 1965, **99**, 691–709.

Berry, M., Rogers, A. W., & Eayrs, J. T. Pattern of cell migration during cortical histogenesis. *Nature (London)*, 1964, **203**, 591–593.

Blaxter, K. L. Protein metabolism and requirements in pregnancy and lactation. In H. N. Munro & J. B. Allison (Eds.), *Mammalian protein metabolism* (Vol. 2). New York: Academic Press, 1964.

Block, J. B., & Essman, W. B. Growth hormone administration during pregnancy: A behavioural difference in offspring rats. *Nature (London)*, 1965, **205**, 1136–1137.

Brasel, J. A. Cellular changes in intrauterine malnutrition. In M. Winick (Ed.), *Nutrition and fetal development*. New York: Wiley, 1974. Pp. 13–25.

Bressler, D., Ellison, G., & Zamenhof, S. Learning deficits in rats with malnourished grandmothers. *Developmental Psychobiology*, 1975, **8**, 315–323.

Caldwell, D. F., & Churchill, J. A. Learning ability in the progeny of rats administered a protein deficient diet during the second half of gestation. *Neurology*, 1967, **17**, 95–99.

Caldwell, D. F., & Oberleas, D. Effects of protein and zinc nutrition on behavior of the rat. In *Perinatal factors affecting human development*. Sci. Publ. No. 185. Washington, D.C.: Pan Am. Health Organ., 1969. Pp. 2–8.

Chase, H. P., Dabiere, S. C., Welch, N. N., & O'Brien, D. Intrauterine under-nutrition and brain development. *Pediatrics*, 1971, **47**, 491–500.

Chase, H. P., & Jansen, G. R. Effect of feeding lysine and threonine fortified bread during gestation and lactation on growth of the brain of rats. *Journal of Nutrition*, 1976, **106**, 41–47.

Chesters, J. K. Biochemical functions of zinc with emphasis on nucleic acid metabolism and cell division. In W. G. Hoekstra, J. W. Suttie, H. E. Ganther, & W. Mertz (Eds.), *Trace element metabolism in animals* (Vol. 2). Baltimore: University Park Press, 1974. Pp. 39–50.

Clark, G. M., & Zamenhof, S. Correlations between cerebral and cortical parameters in the developing and mature rat brain. *International Journal of Neuroscience*, 1973, **5**, 223–229.

Clark, G. M., Zamenhof, S., van Marthens, E., Grauel, L., & Kruger, L. The effect of prenatal malnutrition on dimensions of cerebral cortex. *Brain Research*, 1973, **54**, 397–402.

Clendinnen, B. G., & Eayrs, J. T. The anatomical and physiological effects of prenatally administered somatotropin on cerebral development in rats. *Journal of Endocrinology*, 1961, **22**, 183–193.

Cowley, J. J., & Griesel, R. D. Some effects of a low protein diet on a first filial generation of white rats. *Journal of Genetic Psychology*, 1959, **95**, 187–201.

Cowley, J. J., & Griesel, R. D. The development of second-generation low-protein rats. *Journal of Genetic Psychology* 1963, **103**, 233–242.

Cowley, J. J., & Griesel, R. D. The effect on growth and behavior of rehabilitating first and second generation low protein rats. *Animal Behavior*, 1966, **14**, 506–517.

Croskerry, P. G., & Smith, G. K. Prolongation of gestation by growth hormone: A confounding factor in the assessment of its prenatal action. *Science*, 1975, **189**, 648–650.

Dancis, J., & Schneider, H. Physiology: Transfer and barrier function. In P. Gruenwald (Ed.), *The placenta*. Baltimore: University Park Press, 1975. Pp. 97–124.

Davis, S. D., Nelson, T., & Shepard, T. H. Teratogenicity of vitamin B_6 deficiency: Omphalocele, skeletal and neural defects, and splenic hyperplasia. *Science*, 1970, **160**, 1329–1330.

Dawes, G. M. *Foetal and neonatal physiology*. Chicago: Year Book Medical Publ., 1968. Pp. 213—219.

Dickerson, J. W. T., Dobbing, J., & McCance, R. A. The effect of undernutrition on the postnatal development of the brain and cord in pigs. *Proceedings of the Royal Society, Series B*, 1967, **166**, 396–407.

Dobbing, J. Prenatal nutrition and neurological development. In J. Cravioto, L. Hambraeus, & J. B. Allison (Eds.), *Early malnutrition and protein metabolism*. Symp. No. 12, Uppsala: Swedish Nutr. Found., 1974. Pp. 96–110.

Dobbing, J., & Sands, J. Timing of neuroblast multiplication in developing human brain. *Nature (London)*, 1970, **226**, 639–640.

Dobbing, J., & Sands, J. Quantitative growth and development of human brain. *Archives of Disease in Childhood*, 1973, **48**, 757–767.

Dobbing, J., & Widdowson, E. M. The effect of undernutrition and subsequent rehabilitation on myelination of rat brain as measured by its composition. *Brain*, 1965, **88**, 357–366.

Dodge, P. R., Prensky, A. L., & Feigin, R. D. *Nutrition and the developing nervous system*. St. Louis: Mosby, 1975.

Drillen, C. M. The small-for-date infant: Etiology and prognosis. *Pediatric Clinics of North America*, 1970, **17**, 9–24.

Driskell, J. A., & Kirksey, A. The cellular approach to the determination of pyridoxine requirements in pregnant and nonpregnant rats. *Journal of Nutrition*, 1971, **101**, 661–668.

Eckhert, C. D., & Hurley, L. S. Fetal brain development in zinc deficient rats. *Federation Proceedings*, 1976, **35**, 658.

Giroud, A. *The nutrition of the embryo*. Springfield, III: Thomas, 1970.

Goss, R. J. Theories of growth regulation. In R. J. Goss (Ed.), *Regulation of organ and tissue growth*. New York: Academic Press, 1972. Pp. 1–11.

Habicht, J. P., Yarbrough, C., Lechtig, A., & Klein, R. E. Relationships of birth weight, maternal nutrition and infant mortality. *Nutrition Reports International*, 1973, **7**, 533–546.

Hahn, P. Lipid metabolism and nutrition in the prenatal and postnatal period. In M. Winick (Ed.), *Nutrition and development*. New York: Wiley, 1972. Pp. 99–134.

Hall, S. M., & Zeman, F. J. Kidney function of the progeny of rats fed a low protein diet. *Journal of Nutrition*, 1968, **95**, 111–116.

Hambridge, K. M. Zinc deficiency in children. In W. G. Hoekstra, J. W. Suttie, H. E. Ganther, & W. Mertz (Eds.), *Trace element metabolism in animals* (Vol. 2). Baltimore: University Park Press, 1974. Pp. 171–183.

Herman, C. J., & Lapham, L. W. Neuronal polyploidy and nuclear volumes in cat central nervous system. *Brain Research*, 1969, **15**, 35–48.

Herschkowitz, N., & Rossi, E. Critical periods in brain development. In *Lipids, malnutrition & the developing brain*. Ciba Found. Symp. Amsterdam: Elsevier, 1972. Pp. 107–119.

Hibbard, B. M., Hibbard, E. D., & Jeffcoate, T. N. A. Folic acid and reproduction. *Acta Obstetrica et Gynecologica Scandinavica*, 1965, **44**, 375–400.

Hill, D. E., Myers, R. E., Holt, A. B., Scott, R. E., & Cheek, D. B. Fetal growth retardation produced by experimental placental insufficiency in the rhesus monkey. *Biology of the Neonate*, 1971, **19**, 68–82.

Hohenauer, L. Prenatal nutrition and subsequent development. *Lancet*, 1971, **2**, 644–645.

Holloway, R. L. The evolution of the primate brain: Some aspects of quantitative relations. *Brain Research*, 1968, **7**, 121–172.

Huber, A. M., & Gershoff, S. N. Some effects of vitamin B_6 deficiency on rat pituitary glands. *Journal of Nutrition*, 1965, **87**, 407–411.

Hunt, R. K., & Jacobson, M. Brain enhancement in tadpoles: Increased DNA concentration after somatotropin or prolactin. *Science*, 1970, **170**, 342–344.

Johnson, E. M. Nutritional factors in mammalian teratology. In J. G. Wilson & J. Warkany (Eds.), *Teratology*. Chicago: University of Chicago Press, 1965.

Johnson, H. A., & Erner, S. Neuron surviving in the aging mouse. *Experimental Gerontology*, 1972, **7**, 111–117.

Kaelber, C. T., & Pugh, T. F. Influence of intrauterine relations on the intelligence of twins. *New England Journal of Medicine*, 1969, **280**, 1030–1034.

Kalter, H. *Teratology of the central nervous system*. Chicago: University of Chicago Press, 1968.

Kaminetzky, H. A., Baker, H., Frank, O., & Langer, A. The effects of intravenously administered water-soluble vitamins during labor in Normovitaminemic and Hypovitaminemic gravidas on maternal and neonatal blood vitamin levels at delivery. *American Journal of Obstetrics and Gynecology*, 1974, **120**, 697–703.

Kitay, D. Z. Folic acid deficiency in pregnancy. On the recognition, pathogenesis, consequences, and therapy of the deficiency state in human reproduction. *American Journal of Obstetrics and Gynecology*, 1969, **104**, 1067–1107.

Kurtz, D. J., Levy, H., & Kanfer, J. N. Cerebral lipids and amino acids in the vitamin B_6 deficient suckling rat. *Journal of Nutrition*, 1972, **102**, 291–298.

Langman, J., & Welch, G. W. Excess vitamin A and development of the cerebral cortex. *Journal of Comparative Neurology*, 1967, **131**, 15–26.

182 S. ZAMENHOF AND E. VAN MARTHENS

Lapham, L. W. Tetraploid DNA content of Purkinje neurons of human cerebellar cortex. *Science*, 1968, **159**, 310–312.
Lee, C. J., & Chow, B. F. Metabolism of proteins by progeny of underfed mother rats. *Journal of Nutrition*, 1968, **94**, 20–26.
Lee, C. J., & Dubos, R. Lasting biological effects of early environmental influences. VIII. Effects of neonatal infection, perinatal malnutrition, and crowding on catecholamine metabolism of brain. *Journal of Experimental Medicine*, 1972, **136**, 1031–1042.
Lentz, R. D., & Lapham, L. W. A quantitative cytochemical study of the DNA content of neurons of rat cerebellar cortex. *Journal of Neurochemistry*, 1969, **16**, 379–384.
Leslie, I. The nucleic acid content of tissues and cells. In E. Chargaff & J. N. Davidson (Eds.), *The nucleic acids*. New York: Academic Press, 1955. Pp. 1–50.
Loeb, L. A. Eucaryotic DNA polymerases. In P. D. Boyer (Ed.), *The enzymes* (3rd ed., Vol. 10). New York: Academic Press, 1974. Pp. 173–209.
Margolis, F. L. DNA and DNA-polymerase activity in chicken brain regions during ontogeny. *Journal of Neurochemistry*, 1969, **16**, 447–456.
McCullough, M. L., & Blackman, D. E. The behavioral effects of prenatal hypoxia in the rat. *Developmental Psychobiology*, 1976, **9**, 335–342.
McFarlane, I. G., & von Holt, C. Metabolism of amino acids in protein-calorie-deficient rats. *Biochemical Journal*, 1969, **111**, 557–563.
McKenzie, J. M., Fosmire, G. J., & Sandstead, H. H. Zinc deficiency during the latter third of pregnancy: Effects on fetal rat brain, liver and placenta. *Journal of Nutrition*, 1975, **105**, 1466–1475.
McKeown, T., & Record, R. G. Observations on foetal growth in multiple pregnancy in man. *Journal of Endocrinology*, 1952, **8**, 386–401.
Metcoff, J. Biochemical markers of intrauterine malnutrition. In M. Winick (Ed.), *Nutrition and fetal development*. New York: Wiley, 1974, Pp. 27–44.
Metcoff, J., Mameesh, M., Jacobson, P., Costiloe, P., Crosby, W., Sandstead, H., & McClain, P. Fetoplacental growth related to maternal nutritional status and leukocyte metabolism at mid pregnancy. *Federation Proceedings*, 1976, **35**, 422.
Miller, S. A. Nutrition in the neonatal development of protein metabolism. *Federation Proceedings*, 1970, **29**, 1497–1502.
Minkowski, A., Roux, J. M., & Tordet-Caridroit, C. Pathophysiologic changes in intrauterine malnutrition. In M. Winick (Ed.), *Nutrition and fetal development*. New York: Wiley, 1974. Pp. 45–78.
Moon, W. H. Y., & Kirksey, A. Cellular growth during prenatal and early postnatal periods in progeny of pyridoxine-deficient rats. *Journal of Nutrition*, 1972, **102**, 123–133.
Naeye, R. L., Blanc, W., & Paul, C. Effects of maternal nutrition on the human fetus. *Pediatrics*, 1973, **52**, 494–503.
Newberne, P. M. Effect of vitamin B_{12} deficiency and excess on the embryonic development of the rat. *American Journal of Veterinary Research*, 1963, **24**, 1304–1312.
Newberne, P. M., Ahlstrom, A., & Rogers, A. E. Effects of maternal dietary lipotropes on prenatal and neonatal rats. *Journal of Nutrition*, 1970, **100**, 1089–1098.
Newberne, P. M., & Young, V. R. Marginal vitamin B_{12} intake during gestation in the rat has long term effects on the offspring. *Nature (London)*, 1973, **242**, 263–264.
Oh, W., & Guy, J. A. Cellular growth in experimental intrauterine growth retardation in rat. *Journal of Nutrition*, 1971, **101**, 1631–1634.
Ounsted, M. Familial factors affecting fetal growth. In *Prenatal factors affecting human development*. Sci. Publ. No. 185. Washington, D.C.: Pan Am. Health Organ., 1969. Pp. 60–67.

Picon, L. Effect of insulin on growth and biological composition of the rat fetus. *Endocrinology*, 1967, **81**, 1419–1421.

Rakic, P. Neurons in Rhesus monkey visual cortex: Systematic relation between time of origin and eventual disposition. *Science*, 1974, **183**, 425–427.

Ray, O. S., & Hochhauser, S. Growth hormone and environmental complexity effects on behavior in the rat. *Developmental Psychology*, 1969, **1**, 311–317.

Rosenthal, W. S., Tanaka, N., & Glass, G. B. J. Influence of growth hormone (GH) on serum B_{12} levels. *Federation Proceedings*, 1969, **28**, 627.

Sara, V. R., & Lazarus, L. Prenatal action of growth hormone on brain and behaviour. *Nature (London)*, 1974, **250**, 257–258.

Sara, V. R., & Lazarus, V. Maternal growth hormone and growth and function. *Developmental Psychobiology*, 1975, **8**, 489–502.

Sara, V. R., Lazarus, L., Stuart, M. C., & King, T. Fetal brain growth: Selective action by growth hormone. *Science*, 1974, **186**, 446–447.

Scarr, S. Effects of birth weight on later intelligence. *Social Biology*, 1969, **16**, 249–256.

Schwarz, K. An agent promoting growth of rats fed amino acid diets. *Journal of Nutrition*, 1970, **100**, 1487–1499.

Schwarz, K. New essential trace elements (Sn, V, F, Si): Progress report and outlook. In W. G. Hoekstra, J. W. Suttie, H. E. Ganther, & W. Mertz (Eds.), *Trace element metabolism in animals* (Vol. 2). Baltimore: University Park Press, 1974. Pp. 355–380.

Siassi, F., & Siassi, B. Differential effects of protein-calorie restriction and subsequent repletion on neuronal and nonneuronal components of cerebral cortex in newborn rats. *Journal of Nutrition*, 1973, **103**, 1625–1633.

Sinclair, A. J., & Crawford, M. A. Low-fat diets and the survival of the newborn rats. *Proceedings of the Biochemical Society*, November 1971, p. 18.

Sinclair, J. C., Saigal, S., & Yeung, C. Y. Early postnatal consequences of fetal malnutrition. In M. Winick (Ed.), *Nutrition and fetal development*. New York: Wiley, 1974. Pp. 147–171.

Steinberg, A. B., Clarke, G. B., & Ramwell, P. W. Effects of maternal essential fatty-acid deficiency on neonatal rat brain. *Developmental Psychobiology*, 1968, **1**, 225–229.

Stephan, J. K., Chow, B., Frohman, L. A., & Chow, B. F. Relationship of growth hormone to the growth retardation associated with maternal dietary retardation. *Journal of Nutrition*, 1971, **101**, 1453–1458.

Sturman, J. A., Gaull, G., & Raiha, N. C. R. Absence of cystathionase in human fetal liver: Is cystine essential? *Science*, 1970, **169**, 74–76.

Svennerholm, L., Alling, C., Bruce, Å., Karlsson, I., & Sapia, O. Effects on offspring of maternal malnutrition in the rat. In *Lipids, malnutrition and the developing brain*. Ciba Found. Symp. Amsterdam: Elsevier, 1972, Pp. 141–157.

Towbin, A. Mental retardation due to germinal matrix infarction. *Science*, 1969, **164**, 156–161.

Towbin, A. Central nervous system damage in the human fetus and newborn infant. *Diseases of Children*, 1970, **119**, 529–542.

Usher, R. H. Clinical and therapeutic aspects of fetal malnutrition. *Pediatric Clinics of North America*, 1970, **17**, 169–183.

van Marthens, E., Grauel, L., & Zamenhof, S. Enhancement of prenatal development by operative restriction of litter size in the rabbit. *Life Sciences*, 1972, **11**(P. I), 1031.

van Marthens, E., Grauel, L., & Zamenhof, S. Enhancement of prenatal development in the rat by operative restriction of litter size. *Biology of the Neonate*, 1974, **25**, 53–56.

van Marthens, E., Harel, S., & Zamenhof, S. Experimental intrauterine growth retardation:

A new animal model for the study of altered brain development. *Biology of the Neonate*, 1975, **26**, 221–231.

van Marthens, E., & Zamenhof, S. Deoxyribonucleic acid of neonatal rat cerebrum increased by operative restriction of litter size. *Experimental Neurology*, 1969, **23**, 214–219.

Varon, S., & Rainborn, C. W., Jr. Dissociation, fractionation and culture of embryonic brain cells. *Brain Research*, 1969, **12**, 180–199.

Vendrely, C. L'acide desoxyribonucleique du noyau des cellules animales. *Bulletin Biologique de la France et de la Belgique*, 1952, **86**, 1–87.

Venge, O. Maternal influence on birth weight in rabbits. *Acta Zoologica* (*Stockholm*), 1950, **31**, 3–148.

Verma, K., & Wei King, D. Disorders of the developing nervous system of vitamin E-deficient rats. *Acta Anatomica*, 1967, **67**, 623–635.

Welker, W. I., Johnson, J. I., & Pubols, B. H., Jr. Some morphological and physiological characteristics of the somatic sensory systems in raccoons. *American Zoologist*, 1964, **4**, 75–94.

Widdowson, E. M. Growth and composition of the fetus and newborn. In N. S. Assali (Ed.), *Biology of gestation* (Vol. 2). New York: Academic Press, 1968.

Wigglesworth, J. S. Experimental growth retardation in the foetal rat. *Journal of Pathology and Bacteriology*, 1964, **88**, 1–13.

Willerman, L., & Churchill, J. A. Intelligence and birth weight in identical twins. *Child Development*, 1967, **38**, 623–629.

Williams, R. J. "Supernutrition" as a strategy for control of disease. *Proceedings of the National Academy of Sciences, U.S.A.*, 1971, **68**, 2899a.

Williamson, B., & Coniglio, J. G. The effects of pyridoxine deficiency and of caloric restriction on lipids in the developing rat brain. *Journal of Neurochemistry*, 1971, **18**, 267–276.

Winick, M. Changes in nucleic acid and protein content of the human brain during growth. *Pediatric Research*, 1968, **2**, 352–355.

Winick, M. Malnutrition and brain development. *Journal of Pediatrics*, 1969, **74**, 667–679.

Winick, M. Cellular growth in intrauterine malnutrition. *Pediatric Clinics of North America*, 1970, **17**, 69–78. (a)

Winick, M. Nutrition and nerve cell growth. *Federation Proceedings*, 1970, **29**, 1510–1515. (b)

Winick, M. Malnutrition and intrauterine growth. *Nutrition Reports International*, 1971, **4**, 239–244.

Winick, M., & Noble, A. Cellular response during malnutrition at various ages. *Journal Nutrition*, 1966, **89**, 300–306.

Winick, M., & Noble, A. Cellular response during malnutrition at various ages. *Journal Nutri-Nutrition*, 1967, **91**, 179–182.

Woodard, J. C., & Newberne, P. M. Relation of vitamin B_{12} and one-carbon metabolism to hydrocephalus in the rat. *Journal of Nutrition*, 1966, **88**, 375–381.

Yamashita, K., & Ashida, K. Lysine metabolism in rats fed lysine-free diet. *Journal of Nutrition*, 1969, **99**, 267–273.

Yarnell, G. R., Nelson, P. A., & Wagle, S. R. Metabolism of gluconeogenic precursors in embryonic and fetal livers. *Federation Proceedings*, 1966, **25**, 449.

Zamenhof, S. Stimulation of the proliferation of neurons by the growth hormone: I. Experiments on tadpoles. *Growth*, 1941, **5**, 123–139.

Zamenhof, S. Stimulation of cortical cell proliferation by the growth hormone: III. Experiments on albino rats. *Physiological Zoology*, 1942, **15**, 281–292.

Zamenhof, S. Final number of Purkinje and other large cells in the chick cerebellum influenced by incubation temperatures during their proliferation. *Brain Research*, 1976, **109**, 392–394. (a)

Zamenhof, S. Stimulation of brain development in chick embryo by elevated temperature. *Wilhelm Roux' Archiv*, 1976, **180**, 1–8. (b)

Zamenhof, S., Bursztyn, H., Rich, K., & Zamenhof, P. J. The determination of deoxyribonucleic acid and of cell number in brain. *Journal of Neurochemistry*, 1964, **11**, 505–509.

Zamenhof, S., Grauel, L., & van Marthens, E. Study of possible correlations between prenatal brain development and placental weight. *Biology of the Neonate*, 1971, **18**, 140–145. (a)

Zamenhof, S., Guthrie, D., & Clarkson, D. Study of possible correlations between body weights and brain parameters in neonatal and mature rats. *Biology of the Neonate*, 1974, **24**, 354–362. (a)

Zamenhof, S., Guthrie, D., & van Marthens, E. Neonatal rats with outstanding values of brain and body parameters. *Life Sciences*, 1976, **18**, 1391–1396. (a)

Zamenhof, S., Hall, S. M., Grauel, L., van Marthens, E., & Donahue, M. J. Deprivation of amino acids and prenatal brain development in rats. *Journal of Nutrition*, 1974, **104**, 1002–1007. (b)

Zamenhof, S., & Holzman, G. B. Study of correlations between neonatal head circumferences, placental parameters and neonatal body weights. *Obstetrics and Gynecology*, 1973, **41**, 855–859.

Zamenhof, S., Mosley, J., & Schuller, E. Stimulation of the proliferation of cortical neurons by prenatal treatment with growth hormone. *Science*, 1966, **152**, 1396–1397.

Zamenhof, S., & van Marthens, E. Hormonal and nutritional aspects of prenatal brain development. In D. C. Pease (Ed.), *Cellular aspects of neural growth and differentiation*. Berkeley: University of California Press, 1971. Pp. 329–359.

Zamenhof, S., & van Marthens, E. Study of factors influencing prenatal brain development. *Molecular and Cellular Biochemistry*, 1974, **4**, 157–168.

Zamenhof, S., van Marthens, E., & Bursztyn, M. The effect of hormones on DNA synthesis and cell number in the developing chick and rat brain. In M. Hamburgh & E. J. W. Barrington (Eds.), *Hormones in Development*, New York: Appleton-Century-Crofts, 1971. Pp. 101–119.

Zamenhof, S., van Marthens, E., & Grauel, L. DNA (cell number) and protein in neonatal rat brain: Alteration by timing of maternal dietary protein restriction. *Journal of Nutrition*, 1971, **9**, 1265–1270. (b)

Zamenhof, S., van Marthens, E., & Grauel, L. DNA (cell number) in neonatal brain: Alteration by maternal dietary caloric restriction. *Nutrition Reports International*, 1971, **4**, 269–274. (c)

Zamenhof, S., van Marthens, E., & Grauel, L. DNA (cell number) in neonatal brain: Second generation (F_2) alteration by maternal (F_0) dietary protein restriction. *Science*, 1971, **172**, 850–851. (d)

Zamenhof, S., van Marthens, E., & Grauel, L. Prenatal cerebral development: Effect of restricted diet, reversal by growth hormone. *Science*, 1971, **174**, 954–955. (e)

Zamenhof, S., van Marthens, E., & Grauel, L. DNA (cell number) and protein in rat brain. Second generation (F_2) alteration by maternal (F_0) dietary protein restriction. *Nutrition and Metabolism*, 1972, **14**, 262–270. (a)

Zamenhof, S., van Marthens, E., & Grauel, L. Studies on some factors influencing prenatal brain development. In R. J. Goss (Ed.), *Regulation of organ and tissue growth*. New York: Academic Press, 1972. Pp. 41–60. (b)

Zamenhof, S., van Marthens, E., Grauel, L., & Stillinger, R. A. Quantitative determination of DNA in preserved brains and brain sections. *Journal of Neurochemistry*, 1972, **19**, 61–68. (c)

Zamenhof, S., van Marthens, E., & Margolis, F. L. DNA (cell number) and protein in neonatal brain: Alteration by maternal dietary protein restriction. *Science*, 1968, **160**, 322–323.

Zamenhof, S., van Marthens, E., & Shimomaye, S. Y. The effects of early maternal protein deprivation on fetal development. *Federation Proceedings*, 1976, **35**, 422. (b)

Zeman, J. F. Effect on the young rat of maternal protein restriction. *Journal of Nutrition*, 1967, **93**, 167–173.

Zeman, F. J., & Stanbrough, E. C. Effect of maternal protein deficiency on cellular development in the fetal rat. *Journal of Nutrition*, 1969, **99**, 274–282.

INFLUENCE OF EARLY UNDERNUTRITION ON BEHAVIORAL DEVELOPMENT AND LEARNING IN RODENTS

PETER LEATHWOOD

Research Department, Nestlé Products
Technical Assistance Co. Ltd.
Lausanne, Switzerland

I. Introduction

Inadequate nutrition in early life can lead to permanent physical stunting, changes in the composition of certain organs, and lasting modifications in metabolism. It was once thought that the brain was relatively protected as compared to other tissues of the body, but it is now clear that its size, structure, and composition are permanently affected if severe nutritional deprivation occurs during brain growth. In recent years a great deal of animal research in this area has been directed toward studying behavioral effects of early undernutrition, often with the aim of establishing the functional significance, if any, of the observed changes in brain biochemistry.

Unfortunately, this task is not straightforward and many complicating factors must be taken into consideration in experimental design and in interpretation of results. These factors, which include the influence of species and genotype on reaction to undernutrition; the type, severity, and timing of undernutrition; the period and conditions for rehabilitation, and the type of behavioral test, have all been used in so many different permutations and combinations that it is not easy to compare different studies.

It has been suggested (Dobbing, 1968) that the period of most active growth of the brain is a "critical" period, a time of maximum vulnerability to nutritional deprivation when irreversible damage can occur. This chapter will examine the development of ideas on critical or vulnerable periods and will review the evidence for long-term behavioral effects of undernutrition during the brain growth spurt. The behavioral implications of the various methods for producing early undernutrition in experimental animals will be examined and their possible relevance to the human condition will be discussed.

II. Undernutrition and Critical Periods during Growth

The idea that periods exist when a growing organism is particularly susceptible to environmental influences has a long history. From the Jesuit adage "give me the child until he is seven years old and I will give you the man," through Freud's theories about human development, Lorenz' concept of imprinting, and Scott's critical period hypothesis (Scott, 1962), to the current studies on early handling, there is abundant evidence, both anecdotal and experimental, that experiences in early life have profound repercussions on behavioral development.

In the biological sciences too, the idea of critical periods in physical development is not new. Stockard (1920), working with fish embryos, showed that a variety of chemicals could produce teratological changes if exposure occurred at the right stage of organogenesis. Jackson and Stewart (1920) observed that preweaning undernutrition in rats led to permanent deficits in body weight and brain weight, while undernutrition after weaning depressed bodily growth only during the period of food restriction, but had no effect on the ultimate size of body or brain. In spite of the potentially important implications of these last observations, study of the effects of undernutrition on central nervous system growth and function received little attention from nutritionists until the work of McCance and Widdowson (1962), Dobbing (1964, 1968), and Winick and Noble (1966).

Winick and Noble were among the first to identify a possible mechanism by which early undernutrition may have long-term effects on body composition. They studied growth patterns of several organs in young rats and showed how this process could be seen as an initial stage of cell division followed by another of cell growth and differentiation. These stages overlapped and merged into one another and varied in duration within each organ. Undernutrition, whenever its onset, curtailed growth, but the effect was permanent only if the cell-division stage was impaired. If cell growth alone was impeded the effects of undernutrition could be rectified on refeeding.

III. The Vulnerable Period Hypothesis

Several different stages during development have been picked out as possible vulnerable periods. This has sometimes led to confusion as to which version of the vulnerable period hypothesis is being discussed. The one we will deal with here was proposed in 1968 by John Dobbing, who made the first tentative attempt to apply ideas on critical periods to the effects of early undernutrition. Ignoring distinctions between cell growth and cell division, he simply suggested that the period of maximum vulnerability to nutritional insult may be placed at the period of fastest growth, which in terms of the whole brain is called the brain growth spurt. He predicted that if the hypothesis were correct, undernutrition during the brain growth spurt would result in a smaller brain and perhaps behavioral deficits.

He did, however (Dobbing, 1968), insist that this is a hypothesis to be tested and not, as is often thought, a generalization summing up the effects of early undernutrition.

Before considering the detailed evidence for or against this hypothesis it is perhaps worth looking more closely at the idea itself and the difficulties involved in testing it. One must first decide what one means by the expression "brain growth spurt." In this chapter, unless specified, the phrase simply means the period of fastest growth of the whole brain. At first sight the process of testing the vulnerable period hypothesis seems relatively straightforward. One must identify the timing of the growth spurt for the developing brain, establish that physical growth is permanently stunted by undernutrition during the growth spurt, show that undernutrition before and after the growth spurt has less effect, and, finally, look for evidence that the physical deficits so produced also entail behavioral deficits.

The developing brain is, of course, extremely heterogeneous, with different cell groups dividing, migrating, growing, and differentiating, and with each group going through its individual growth spurts at different times.

In other words, there may be almost as many growth spurts (and thus vulnerable periods) as there are parameters to measure in the growing brain.

In the absence of knowledge of the functional significance of the various regional brain growth spurts, Dobbing chose the whole brain growth spurt as the hypothetical "vulnerable period." In man and in the pig this peak occurs perinatally, in the rat and mouse it is postnatal, while the guinea pig's brain growth spurt is prenatal (Dobbing, 1968). Perhaps it is worth recalling that these growth spurts correspond to the peaks of glial cell multiplication and growth. Undernutrition during the whole brain growth spurt may produce permanent deficits in glial cell number but there is no direct evidence that these changes are of any functional significance.

The next step is to establish that undernutrition has a greater effect if imposed during the brain growth spurt than before or after. This raises a problem common to all critical and vulnerable period hypotheses. If it is predicted that a given nutritional (or other environmental) manipulation should have a greater effect if it is experienced during the brain growth spurt, testing the hypothesis depends on the experimenter's ability to equate the relative severity of a given manipulation when it is imposed on animals of different ages. To undernourish a rat before, during, or after the brain growth spurt means prenatal, preweaning, or postweaning undernutrition. Is it really possible, in these three very different environments to impose undernutrition (or any other experience) of equal quality and severity? By what criteria should the quality and severity be judged? These difficulties have not yet been satisfactorily resolved.

Another implication of the vulnerable period hypothesis is that there is no second chance, that once brain growth has finished, nothing can be done to redress the balance for the stunted brain. It then seems pertinent to ask if there is any evidence at all that brain weight, anatomy, or biochemistry can be changed in the adult rat after the brain growth spurt is over. Many aspects of brain structure and chemistry are not fixed in early life and can be influenced by nutritional and other environmental factors. Dietary manipulations can in fact lead to clear-cut behavioral and central nervous system biochemical changes (Fernstrom, Madras, Munro, & Wurtman, 1974; McKean, Schanberg, & Giaman, 1967; Pauling, 1968). Bennett, Rosenzweig, and their colleagues (Bennett, Diamond, Krech, & Rosenzweig, 1964; see also the chapter by Rosenzweig and Bennett, in this volume) have elegantly shown that, compared to standard colony controls, rats exposed to an enriched environment have thicker cerebral cortices (occipital cortex), an increased ratio of glial to neuronal cells, and changes in brain enzyme levels. The influence of these different environments is not age-dependent. The magnitude of brain weight changes in rats given an enriched adolescence is the same as that in year-old rats given similar stimulation (Reige, 1970).

Furthermore, these different environments can induce changes in behavior. Such observations of long-term plasticity tend to restrict the use of the concept of vulnerable or critical periods for development as an explanation for environmental influences on brain development and brain function (see the Introduction to Section 3 and Epilogue for further discussion of this issue).

IV. Undernutrition and Physical Development of the Brain

There is no doubt that undernutrition during the brain growth spurt can lead to permanent stunting of body and brain growth. The results of the many studies on effects of under- and malnutrition during this period are remarkably consistent considering the variety of techniques used.

Jackson and Stewart (1920) observed an 8% deficit in the brain weight of adult rats which had been underfed from birth to 3 weeks then given a high quality stock diet until 1 year old. Winick and Noble (1966), using a similar design, found a persistent 10% deficit in brain weight and DNA content. Dobbing (1968), using large litters to produce undernourishment in the young, obtained similar results. In most studies it has been observed that a 40–60% deficit in body weight at weaning, followed by nutritional rehabilitation until adulthood, produces a 6–10% deficit in brain weight and brain DNA content. Not all brain regions are equally affected. For example, it has been found that undernutrition during the growth spurt has a greater effect on the cerebellum than on the rest of the brain (Altman & McCrady, 1972; Bush & Leathwood, 1975; Culley & Lineberger, 1968; Fish & Winick, 1969; Howard & Granoff, 1968). Other long-lasting physical effects of undernutrition during the growth spurt include a decrease in the quantity of myelin lipids and changes and distortions in the levels of some brain enzymes (Dobbing & Smart, 1973).

Undernutrition after the brain growth spurt is over can also retard growth rate but the deficit can be made up on refeeding (Dobbing, 1968; Jackson & Stewart, 1920). Undernutrition before the brain growth spurt entails, for the rodent, prenatal undernutrition. This topic is dealt with in detail by Zamenhof and van Marthens in the previous chapter in this volume so it will be only briefly covered here.

According to the predictions of the vulnerable period hypothesis, fetal undernutrition in the rat or mouse should have less effect on brain development than underfeeding during lactation (Smart & Dobbing, 1971). Testing this proposition is, however, complicated somewhat by the difficulty of defining "equivalent" degrees of undernutrition at different developmental stages. Smart and Dobbing (1971) and Smart, Dobbing,

Adlard, Lynch, and Sands (1973) defined equivalence of deprivation in terms of the mother's food intake. Mother rats were fed half their normal fare during the greater part of pregnancy and throughout lactation. Prenatal undernutrition had much less effect on reflex ontogeny and adult body and brain weights than did early postnatal undernutrition. The results were interpreted as supporting the vulnerable period hypothesis. In terms of growth restriction, however, prenatal and postnatal food deprivation had very different effects. The body weight at birth of prenatally undernourished pups was 8–10% below that of controls while at weaning (day 21) the postnatally undernourished rats weighed 65% less than controls (Smart & Dobbing, 1971).

Stephan and Chow (1968), Blackwell, Blackwell, Yu, Weng, and Chow (1969), and Bush and Leathwood (1975) found that more severe prenatal deprivation of rodents will produce clear-cut deficits in adult brain and body weights. Bush and Leathwood (1975) fed mice low protein diets during pregnancy and lactation. Prenatal deprivation produced birth weight deficits of 40–50% while postnatal undernutrition led to weaning weight deficits of 50–55%, so in terms of bodily growth restriction the degrees of restriction were approximately equivalent. On this occasion the long-term effects of prenatal deprivation on body weights, regional brain weights, and regional brain DNA contents were greater than those produced by postnatal deprivation.

As an experimental test of the vulnerable period hypothesis these results are important. They show that growth restriction before the brain growth spurt can have as much effect on adult body weight, brain weight, etc., as undernutrition during the growth spurt itself. These results, however, cannot be used as an experimental model of human prenatal undernutrition. The newborn rat has yet to experience its brain growth spurt, whereas the newborn human is in the middle of its growth spurt (Dobbing & Smart, 1973), a factor which must be considered before comparing fetal rats with fetal humans. Observations in animals and humans have shown that undernutrition imposed during the last trimester of pregnancy has more influence on birth weight than undernutrition imposed earlier (Habicht, Lechtig, Yarbrough, & Klein, 1974). The developmental stage of the newborn rat is approximately equivalent to that of a human fetus near the end of the second trimester, thus patterns of intrauterine growth retardation will be quite different. For example, in the fetal rat the peak of neuronal multiplication occurs during the third trimester of pregnancy, so prenatal undernutrition may reduce the final number of neurons in brain. In the human fetus, however, this peak occurs during the second trimester of pregnancy (Dobbing & Sands, 1973), so it is extremely unlikely that neuron number will be significantly affected by growth retardation in the third trimester.

Human longitudinal and retrospective studies testing the significance of birth weight in predicting physical and mental development show that with extremely low birth weights there are grave dangers of neurological damage (Butler, 1974). Small deficits in birth weight seem to influence mental development during the first few months: later on, although an effect may persist, it is rapidly swamped by influences related to social class, family size, etc. (Davie, Butler, & Goldstein, 1972; Elliott & Knight, 1974; Stein, Susser, Saenger, & Marolla, 1975).

In summary, it appears that undernutrition before or during the brain growth spurt can produce permanent deficits in some aspects of brain growth. In other words, rather than there being a clear-cut vulnerable period coincident with the brain growth spurt, physical vulnerability lasts from conception to the end of the growth spurt.

V. Undernutrition and Behavioral Development

It is often assumed that the permanent physical brain deficits caused by early undernutrition must lead to deficits in mental function. In children, early undernutrition is associated with subsequent growth retardation and poor school performance, but undernutrition does not occur in isolation from other factors and it is extremely difficult to separate it from other, psychosocial variables which may affect mental performance. Furthermore, in most human studies children are examined during or shortly after an episode of undernutrition. Follow-up to adulthood is extremely rare and difficult. Researchers have, therefore, turned to animal models in an attempt to answer the question of whether undernutrition in early life has any lasting effect on mental function. Unfortunately, the animal models currently in use are not much more successful in isolating undernutrition from other environmental factors which may influence later behavior (Crnic, 1976; Leathwood, 1973; Levine & Weiner, 1976; Plaut, 1970).

A. Methods for Producing Early Undernutrition

In studies on the effects of early nutritional deprivation in animals, food supply to the young is restricted by one of the following techniques:

1. Allowing pups only limited access to the mother.
2. Increasing the litter size.
3. Restricting maternal food intake.
4. Feeding the mother *ad libitum* amounts of a low protein diet.
5. Artificially feeding the pup either by gastric infusion or by means of a stomach fistula.
6. Extensive resection of mammary tissue of a female prior to mating.

It has been argued that, as areas of agreement do exist among experimental findings using the various different techniques outlined here, the common causal factor is likely to be nutritional deprivation (Dobbing & Smart, 1973). All these methods, although intended principally to affect the pups' nutritional status, also influence other aspects of their early environment (Plaut, 1970), and there is now abundant evidence that subsequent physiology and behavior can be affected by the early environment and particularly by aspects of mother–pup interactions (reviewed in Denenberg, 1964; Hinde, 1970).

Taking the mother away from her pups removes not only their food but also a source of social, thermal, and other sensory stimulation. Separation of the mother and pups for short periods each day (insufficient to lower body weight of the pups) leads to significant changes in adult adrenocortical response and behavior. Koos-Slob, Snow, and De Natris-Mathot (1973) undernourished rat pups by separating them from their mother for 12 hours each day. They tried to control for the loss of the mother by replacing her with a virgin female "aunt" able to display all maternal behaviors except lactation. The expected dramatic and permanent deficits in body weight and retarded appearance of developmental milestones occurred but there were no long-term differences in open-field behavior, discrimination learning, and motor coordination tests. The previously undernourished animals learned to run a maze for a food reward faster and were more active in a residential plus-maze. As Levine and Weiner (1976) have pointed out, it is unfortunate that this experiment did not include an undernourished group with no mother substitute during the daily separation period, because one cannot say whether it was the provision of maternal care by the aunt which eliminated these long-term behavioral changes or whether the changes never existed in the first place.

The large- versus small-litter model for producing early undernutrition is widely used, easy to set up, and capable of giving reliable results. Unfortunately, in this model too, early undernutrition is not the only factor operating to disrupt the early environment. Seitz (1954) reported an inverse relationship between litter size and the attention each pup received. Observations in our laboratory using time-lapse photography demonstrated striking differences in both pup and maternal behavior in comparisons between the large and small litters (Leathwood, unpublished). The pups in small litters suckled and slept while those in large litters were engaged in an almost continual struggle for food. We also noted changes in the circadian rhythm of nest occupation by the mother.

Feeding the mother rat a limited quantity of stock diet has been used as a model to study the effects of prenatal and postnatal undernutrition (Mueller & Cox, 1946). But again there is no doubt that this technique produces marked changes in maternal behavior. The mother is less efficient at nest building, spends less time with her pups, and shows a shift of circadian rhythms of activity centered around feeding time(s) (Simonsen, Sherwin, Anilane, Yu, & Chow, 1969; Smart & Preece, 1973).

Feeding the mother *ad libitum* quantities of a low protein diet at least caters to the last of the objections outlined above but there is still no doubt that the treatment leads to dramatic changes in maternal behavior. Fraňková (1971) observed that mother rats fed on a low protein diet retrieved their young less efficiently than controls, while Massaro, Levitsky, and Barnes (1974) found that the low-protein mothers spent more time with their pups.

Artificially feeding the pup nominally allows the experimenter to define precisely the quantity and quality of diet received by the pup (Dymsza, Czajka, & Miller, 1964). Unfortunately, however, this technique is very difficult, time consuming, and often not very successful. Furthermore, it appears that the lack of maternal care or the trauma of artificial feeding in itself produces marked changes in later behavior (Thoman & Levine, 1968).

The last method, extensive resection of the mother's mammary tissue after weaning her first litter,[1] allows limitation of the milk supply without increase in litter size or starvation of the mother. Preliminary experiments at Stanford and in our laboratory have shown that it is possible to produce early undernutrition comparable in degree to that produced by other techniques and we are now studying how this method of undernourishing the pups influences their later behavior.

B. Reflex Development

Cowley and Griesel (1959) reported that feeding rats on a low protein diet throughout life caused their offspring to be retarded in growth and development and suggested that fetal malnutrition or undernutrition may have been the cause. Bush and Leathwood (1975) followed the behavioral development of mice born to a mother fed on a low protein diet throughout pregnancy and cross-adopted to a well-fed foster mother at birth. They observed significant delays in the appearance of most developmental indices even after 14 days of nutritional rehabilitation.

Two groups have studied reflex ontogeny after feeding the mother rat a restricted stock diet during pregnancy. Simonson *et al.* (1969) found postnatal behavioral development to be severely retarded, while Smart and Dobbing (1971) saw little or no effect. The explanation for this apparent inconsistency probably lies in the severity of undernutrition imposed. Smart

[1] Suggested by Dr. R. Levin from the Department of Psychiatry, Stanford University School of Medicine.

and Dobbing's technique produced a deficit in birth weight of 8% while the Simonson study involved a 25% deficit.

Bush and Leathwood (1975) found that postnatal deprivation of mice by suckling from a mother fed on a low protein diet led to marked physical stunting even at 5 days of age but had no discernible effect on reflex ontogeny until the 14th day. Rearing in litters of 20 produced more severe undernutrition and delays in reflex ontogeny. Stunting was more pronounced and delays in appearance of developmental indices began at 7–9 days of age (Bush & Leathwood, 1975). Unfortunately, behavioral characteristics maturing between 14 and 21 days, the period when the effects of postnatal undernutrition are most marked, were not measured.

The results of Smart and Dobbing (1971), using restriction of stock diet as their technique for undernutrition, were similar to those previously outlined. Physical stunting was obvious at 5–7 days while clear-cut delays in reflex ontogeny did not appear until 11–12 days of age.

In summary, undernutrition before birth or during the early postnatal period can retard reflex development, but in neither case do there appear to be gross permanent deficits.

C. Motor Development

From about the 10th day of life of the laboratory mouse or rat there is a steady growth in motor effectiveness and development of exploratory drive. Altman, Sudarshan, Das, McCormick, and Barnes (1971), Simonson et al. (1969), and Smart and Dobbing (1971) all observed delays in the appearance of different motor skills when rat pups were reared by mothers fed restricted quantities of stock diets. Fraňková and Barnes (1968a) obtained similar results using a low protein diet. However, as Altman et al. (1971) pointed out, the motivational state of these animals is complex, they are starved, physically weak, have low energy reserves, and are usually rather passive, so it is not really possible to say which variables contribute most to these deficits in performance.

These observations of retarded development imply that great care must be taken in interpreting behavioral observations carried out before or shortly after nutritional rehabilitation has begun. This stricture applies equally to both animal and human studies. Thus differences in maze learning ability (Baird, Widdowson, & Cowley, 1971) or in passive avoidance behavior in young rats (Smart & Dobbing, 1972) during nutritional rehabilitation may to some extent reflect lag in development rather than permanent deficits.

Several biochemical studies have shown that growth of the cerebellum (which plays a role in motor coordination) is more severely affected by early undernutrition than are other brain regions (Altman & McCrady, 1972). It has been suggested that animals, or children, who have suffered early under-nutrition may have impaired motor ability. Although motor development is retarded under these circumstances, there is little or no evidence from animal experiments of permanent deficits in motor coordination. Guthrie (1968) found no differences in motor coordination between experimental and control groups of rats undernourished by feeding the mother a low protein diet, and we (Leathwood & Bush, unpublished) obtained similar results with mice reared in large or small litters. Smart *et al.* (1973) undernourished rats by feeding the motor restricted amounts of stock diet and observed no significant deficits in mother coordination.

VI. Undernutrition and Later Behavior

A. *Spontaneous Locomotor Activity*

It is not easy to set up a reliable test of spontaneous exploration in an open field, and there are almost as many methods of open-field testing as there are publications on the subject. The general principle is that an animal is placed in or given access to a new environment (the open field). At first the animal is frightened or excited and remains still, sometimes defecating. Then it explores, sometimes defecating and urinating, perhaps thereby marking out a new territory. Eventually, perhaps bored, it goes to sleep. The original aim of this test was to measure "emotionality." The relevance of open-field testing to the fulfillment of this aim has been critically assessed by Archer (1973) who concluded that the test may reveal differences in emotionality but that the direction and degree of behavioral changes in the open field are closely dependent upon the specific conditions of the test situation.

In 1954, Seitz, using large and small litters, showed that the adult rats originating from large litters were slower to leave their home cages and were less active in the open field. Lat, Widdowson, and McCance (1960) and Fraňková and Barnes (1968a) found no difference in locomotion in the open field between adult rats from large and those from small litters, but both studies observed decreased rearing (standing on the hind legs) by the animals from large litters. They chose rearing as their measure of exploration and concluded that suckling in large litters decreases the intensity of exploration. Guthrie (1968) obtained essentially similar results, i.e., no difference in locomotion but a decrease in rearing, while Semiginovsky, Mysliveček, and Zalud (1970) observed increased locomotor activity in rats from large litters.

If young rats are undernourished by feeding the mother restricted quantities of stock diet, spontaneous locomotor activity may appear to be increased (Smart, 1974), decreased (Simonson, Stephan, Hanson, & Chow, 1971), or unchanged (Ottinger & Tanabe, 1970). It is not really possible to compare these three studies, since the experimental designs varied so markedly. The period of nutritional rehabilitation was 4 weeks in one case (Ottinger & Tanabe, 1968), somewhere between 12 and 24 in the second (Smart), and 18 months in the third. During nutritional rehabilitation the rats were housed individually or in groups and the open-field procedures were quite different.

Levitsky and Barnes (1970) studied open-field behavior of adult rats which had been undernourished from birth to 3 weeks of age or from birth to 7 weeks of age. The rats were given four 10-minute sessions in the open field and, in the middle of the 4th session a loud noise was set off close to the field. All the rats "froze" for a few moments and showed a marked drop in activity for several minutes. The rats which had been undernourished after weaning made a greater response to the noise than control rats. Preweaning undernutrition, however, did not alter the response.

Levitsky and Barnes (1972) also measured the interaction of undernutrition and social isolation or social stimulation on open-field behavior. In this experiment they used rats undernourished from birth to 7 weeks of age. Control animals were housed alone, "stimulated" animals were housed in pairs, handled each day when they were from 3 to 7 weeks old, and then housed alone until the end of the experiment. "Isolated" rats were kept in light-proof sound-attenuated chambers until they were 7 weeks old and then returned to control conditions. When the rats were tested at 17 weeks, Levitsky and Barnes found increased locomotor activity in the previously undernourished group. Isolation had a similar effect and the combination of these treatments was cumulative. Early stimulation completely counteracted the effects of early undernutrition. This sort of experiment is extremely fruitful both in suggesting mechanisms by which undernutrition may influence behavior and by offering an explanation for the inconsistencies in the results of other workers. Since in these experiments the rats were undernourished until they were 7 weeks old, the results cannot be directly compared with studies of preweaning undernutrition.

The results of open-field studies are often interpreted to imply increased emotionality in previously undernourished animals, but the results are too inconsistent to warrant a firm conclusion. Furthermore, postweaning undernutrition or malnutrition is more effective than restriction before weaning, an observation which argues against the existence of a well-defined preweaning critical or vulnerable period for this type of behavior. Comparison and interaction of malnutrition with other environmental variables coupled with appreciation of the sensitivity of open-field behavior to the exact conditions of the test show that changes attributed to early malnutrition may be more directly related to other, nonnutritional, factors in the early environment.

B. Maze Learning

Barnes, Cunnold, Zimmermann, Simmons, MacLeod, and Krook, (1966) reared rats in large litters, weaned them on stock diet, and then tested them at 60–80 days in a Y-shaped water maze. They found no differences in error scores in a position reversal test. When these rats were retested at 6–9 months old on a visual discrimination problem in the water maze there were again no differences in error scores, although the control animals were more excited and agitated in their attempts to get out of the water. Only when rats were malnourished from birth to 80 days (by rearing in large litters and weaning on a 4% casein diet) did long-lasting changes in performance appear. Barnes et al. concluded that there were motivational and emotional differences among the various treatment groups so that it was not possible to separate "drive to learn" from "capacity to learn."

Baird et al. (1971), using a similar technique, observed no effect of litter size on performance in the Hebb-Williams maze. Leathwood (1973), again comparing large with small litters, observed no differences in performance between groups either in the water mace or in a Lashley III maze. D'Amato (1960) found that rats from small litters were slower to learn a brightness discrimination.

Rats malnourished in early life by feeding the mother a low protein diet have been reported to show both deficient (Cowley & Griesel, 1966) and improved (Zimmermann & Wells, 1971) maze learning performance. Restricting the mother's food intake can lower (Giurintano, 1974; Hsueh, Simonson, Chow, & Hanson, 1974; Ottinger & Tanabe, 1968; Simonson & Chow, 1970), improve (Smart, et al., 1973), or not change (Cravens, 1974; Giurintano, 1974; Hsueh et al., 1974) performance in different types of mazes, while malnutrition by separating mother and young (with or without a nonlactating aunt to provide maternal care without food) seems to have no effect on maze learning (Howard & Granoff, 1968).

Perinatal undernutrition or malnutrition has surprisingly little effect on maze performance. Even when differences are observed, measures of performance are profoundly influenced by the variety of treatments and testing procedures used. In several of the preceding studies a hungry animal ran the maze to win food and, as Dobbing and Smart (1973) have pointed out, the use of food as a reward is particularly suspect when testing animals which have experienced food deprivation in early life. There is convincing evidence (reviewed in Bronfenbrenner, 1968) that such animals behave differently toward food, particularly when hungry. In some food reward studies attempts have been made to control for motivation (Levitsky, 1975), and when this is done the differences disappear. In agreement with Levitsky and Barnes (1973), one must conclude that there may be differences in motivation between control and previously undernourished animals but that maze learning studies offer no support for the contention that early under-nutrition affects learning ability.

C. Avoidance Conditioning

In an active avoidance learning test a conditioning stimulus (CS), usually a light or a tone, precedes and is paired with an electric shock. The animal avoids or escapes the electric shock either by running into another compartment (as in the Warner cage), pressing a lever (as in the Skinner box), or by jumping onto a pole or screen (pole-jump or screen-jump). During the first trials the animal jumps, runs, or presses only when it receives the shock but gradually it learns to react to the conditioning stimulus and so avoid the electric shock.

Avoidance conditioning; no less than open-field behavior or maze learning, is a complex behavioral situation in which the specific details of the situation are important determinants of the results. In the one-way active avoidance test, avoidance or escape is always one-way from the same shock chamber into the same safe chamber. The animal, usually a rat or a mouse, rapidly learns to associate the CS and shock so that, within a few trials the response is established. Two-way avoidance in the shuttle-box, where the "safe" and "shock" compartments alternate, presents the animals with a conflict. They are agitated and their performance improves slowly. Two-way avoidance learning is used to study "anxiety" (Sachs, 1965) and is a sensitive test for mild anxiolytic drugs which, in low doses, improve performance (Leathwood, Bush, & Mauron, 1975; Sachs, 1965); one-way avoidance performance is unchanged by such doses of minor tranquilizers (Sachs, 1965).

The results of studies on early undernutrition and active avoidance performance in rats are consistent: undernutrition of the fetus or the young pup has little or no effect on subsequent avoidance performance.

Caldwell and Churchill (1967) examined the effects of prenatal under-nutrition on avoidance performance in a pole-jump test. The mother rats were fed a low protein diet during the second half of pregnancy and returned to the high protein stock diet on the birth of her pups. The offspring were tested when only 50 days old. The rate of learning of the previously mal-nourished rats was unaffected but their latency to jump was longer.

Fränková and Barnes (1968b) fed mother rats a low protein (10% casein) diet throughout lactation. Pups weaned on stock diet and tested on a screen-jump avoidance test at 14 weeks old were no different from controls; others, malnourished from birth until 7 weeks (by weaning on a 3% casein diet and feeding stock diet from the end of the 7th week) had similar learning scores but exhibited stereotypy and hyperexcitation. Three groups have examined avoidance performance in rats reared in large and small litters (Di Benedetta & Cioffi, 1972; Guthrie, 1968; Myslivecek & Hassmannová, 1970). All tested their animals in the shuttle-box avoidance apparatus at 18–20 weeks old and all found no difference in performance between large and small litter animals.

A study of environmental effects (including malnutrition) on avoidance performance in mice is being carried out in our laboratory. In an initial series of experiments we showed that rearing mice in large litters led to marked deficits in avoidance performance. Mice were tested at either 2, 4, 6, or 12 months and those reared in large litters showed consistently low performance (Leathwood, Bush, Berent, & Mauron, 1974). Postweaning malnutrition or undernutrition (feeding a 5% casein diet or restricting stock diet from the 4th to 8th weeks of life) followed by 4 weeks rehabilitation did not affect performance. When the pups were undernourished by feeding the mother a 10% protein diet, it was possible to produce degrees of physical stunting comparable to those found in the large litter pups. Avoidance performance deficits in these animals were not so marked (Leathwood & Mauron, 1974). Shock sensitivity of the control and of previously undernourished groups was identical and we could detect no differences in maze learning performance or motor coordination.

A variety of stresses in early life can alter subsequent behavior and all the techniques used to produce early undernutrition introduce other, non-nutritional stresses into the early environment. During and after the first few active avoidance sessions our previously undernourished mice appeared to be more agitated than were the controls. These observations were sufficient to construct the working hypothesis that lowered avoidance performance may be due to increased anxiety or emotionality under stress, rather than to a deficit in learning ability. If this hypothesis is correct it should be possible to find other, nonnutritional disturbances in early life which can also lower avoidance performance, and avoidance performance should be improved if the emotional response to stress is reduced.

If mouse pups are removed from the lactating dam for only a few minutes, her behavior is disturbed for several hours. Denenberg (1970) showed that daily removal ("handling") during the first 3 weeks of life produced a drop in avoidance performance. Leathwood, Bush, and Mauron (1975) repeated this experiment and obtained a similar result. Daily handling did not affect growth of the pups but it did disturb the mother and, when the pups grew up, their avoidance performance was poor. Early undernutrition, caused either by rearing in large litters or by feeding the mother a low protein diet, produced similar drops in avoidance performance. In combination, i.e., handling and rearing in large litters, the treatments were additive, and the performance deficit doubled.

The minor tranquilizer, chlordiazepoxide, improves two-way avoidance in mice and rats (Leathwood *et al.*, 1975; Sachs, 1965) and it has been suggested that it does so by reducing anxiety (Sachs, 1965). Treatment with chlordiazepoxide did improve performance in all groups and the effect was proportionately greatest in the previously "undernourished," handled mice (Fig. 1). The distributions of avoidance performances of the drug-treated groups were too skewed to satisfy the requirements for analysis of variance based on the raw data, so we used the proportion of mice reaching a level equal to or higher than the mean of the controls as the basis for the cal-

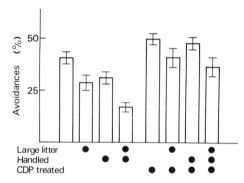

FIG. 1. Avoidance performance of Swiss white mice after early handling, rearing in large litters, and treatment with a minor tranquilizer. Each column represents the total percentage mean avoidance responses (±SEM) of 24 mice. A 2 × 2 × 2 factorial design was used providing 8 possible treatments on a total of 196 mice. The first column shows performance of the "control" group—nonhandled, nondrug treated, and reared in litters of 5. The second column shows the effect of rearing in large litters, the third the influence of early handling. Both treatments lowered avoidance performance by about the same amount. The fourth column shows the effect of combining these two treatments. The treatments were additive. Four more groups of mice were treated as described but prior to each avoidance session they received chlordiazepoxide (columns 5–8). Drug treatment alone produced a slight improvement in performance (column 5 versus column 1). It had a more marked effect on large litter or handled mice (columns 6 and 7 versus 2 and 3); and it produced a dramatic increase in performance of mice subjected to handling and rearing in large litters (column 4 versus column 8).

The results of this experiment show: (a) that early handling and rearing in large litters produce similar and additive effects, suggesting that the performance deficits of mice reared in large litters may well be independent of the concomitant growth stunting, and (b) that treatment with a mild tranquilizer (anti-anxiety drug) improves performance of the handled, previously undernourished mice, suggesting that overresponse to stress may play a role in lowering their avoidance performance (Leathwood *et al.*, 1975).

culation. Handling or rearing in large litters significantly lowered performance while treatment with the tranquilizer improved it. The interaction between handling and litter size was very small confirming that the effects were additive. Of the other two interactions, one (handling versus drug treatment) was significant at the $p < .05$ level, while for the other (litter size versus drug treatment) $p < .07$.

These results suggest that early handling and early "undernutrition" operate to lower avoidance performance by the same mechanism. In other words, the apparent deficit in avoidance learning ability after undernutrition would seem to be due to disturbance of the early environment rather than to early undernutrition per se.

D. Passive Avoidance

In a passive avoidance test the animal is required to withhold a natural response, usually exploratory or appetitive. In the first, the animal is placed in a chamber having access to another chamber. The animal, with its natural inclination to explore, will eventually enter the second chamber. If it receives an electric shock on so doing it may learn to withhold the exploratory urge in subsequent trials. The same test, but with repression of an appetitive response, often referred to as a Conditioned Emotional Response (Leaf & Muller, 1965), introduces a more severe conflict. The animal is trained to drink in a specific place and then is given an electric shock concurrently. On subsequent trials the animal delays drinking in spite of being thirsty.

This sort of one-trial test has been successfully used to study drugs which block learning, but in many other experimental situations results can be ambiguous. We have observed that on the post-shock trials some mice "freeze" and make no movement at all while others appear to be overcome with curiosity and eventually cannot resist exploring, although clearly agitated and nervous. It is difficult to judge which mouse has "learned" a passive avoidance response best.

Levitsky and Barnes (1970) took rat pups suckled by mothers receiving a low protein (10% casein) diet and weaned them on either a 3% casein or 21% casein diet. From 7 weeks old, all animals were fed a 21% casein diet. The animals were tested in a step-down passive avoidance apparatus at 16 weeks old. There was an increase in post-shock latency in the rats undernourished from birth to 3 weeks and a smaller increase in those fed the low protein diet from weaning to 7 weeks of age. Levitsky and Barnes interpreted these results as indicating an increased emotionality or an overresponse to stress in the postnatally malnourished animals.

Smart et al. (1973) also studied this type of passive avoidance behavior (repression of exploratory drive). They, too, found that perinatal under-nutrition increased post-shock latencies. In our laboratory, using a passive avoidance setup similar to Smart's, we found no differences between mice from large and those from small litters in either pre- or post-shock latencies, although the controls defecated less in the post-shock trials (Leathwood, 1973).

Rider and Simonson (1974a, 1974b) have used the conditioned emotional response test to study the effects of prenatal undernutrition on emotionality. They found it led to an increase in both pre- and post-shock latency and they interpreted their results in terms of disruption of brain development.

In summary, passive avoidance experiments appear to give somewhat more consistent results than do other behavioral tests. In most studies, the previously undernourished rats show increased latencies to move, and this finding has been tentatively interpreted as reflecting heightened excitation or emotionality in these animals.

VII. Conclusions

A review of the work on early undernutrition of rodents does allow one to draw some general conclusions. While prenatal and early postnatal undernutrition can lead to permanent deficits and distortions in the physical structure of the brain (see the chapter by Zamenhof and van Marthens, in this volume), behavioral studies, using a range of tasks and assessment procedures, have produced little or no evidence that perinatal under-nutrition per se causes any permanent deficits in brain function. Motor coordination of previously undernourished rodents is indistinguishable from that of controls. Open-field studies suggest differences in emotionality between control and previously undernourished groups, but the results are too inconsistent to warrant a firm conclusion. Maze learning and avoidance tests suggest differences in motivation between control and previously undernourished animals but offer no support for the idea that early under-nutrition affects learning ability. When differences are observed, they appear to be more closely linked to disruption of the early environment rather than to undernutrition. Finally, in several studies, postweaning malnutrition affected later behavior while restriction before weaning did not; an observation which argues against the existence of a well-defined preweaning critical or vulnerable period for the effect of undernutrition on behavior.

One must remember that it is far from certain that early undernutrition per se must have long-term effects on mental function in man (Frisch, 1971). In a retrospective study on the adult (19-year-old) survivors of the Dutch

Hongerwinter of 1944–1945, during which clear deficits in birth weight were documented, no influence of prenatal undernutrition was revealed on performance in five tests of mental ability (Stein *et al.*, 1975). This study showed that a short, acute period of undernutrition during the brain growth spurt did not necessarily lead to detectable mental deficits. The authors did, however, warn that these results should not be lightly generalized to effects of chronic postnatal undernutrition or malnutrition. For example, Richardson (1976) found that if a child grows up in favorable social conditions and with adequate nutrition, then an earlier, acute episode of malnutrition (when the child was less than 2 years old) has a negligible effect on IQ scores at 6–10 years of age. If, however, growth after acute malnutrition occurs in a context of a deprived social background, the two interact and the early acute malnutrition does influence the IQ score. The addition of chronic deprivation to this combination further lowers performance.

It seems one must reject the proposition that a short period of under- or malnutrition during the so-called brain growth spurt invariably leads to permanent mental deficits. Many factors influence mental development and it appears that acute or chronic malnutrition acts to exacerbate the adverse effects of poor social conditions and infection. Richardson's analysis shows how severe malnutrition in early life can be understood only in terms of the child's entire life experience and helps to underline the point that rehabilitation, both nutritional and social, can profitably be undertaken at any stage during juvenile development.

Acknowledgments

I would like to thank the management of Nestlé Products Technical Assistance Co. Ltd., especially Professor J. Mauron and Professor L. Rey, for supporting and encouraging this work. I am grateful to K. Effinger and H. Egli for patient secretarial assistance.

References

Altman, J., & McCrady, B. The influence of nutrition on neural and behavioral development: IV—Effects of infantile undernutrition on the growth of the cerebellum. *Developmental Psychobiology*, 1972, **5**, 111–122.

Altman, J., Sudarshan, K., Das, G. D., McCormick, N., & Barnes, D. The influence of nutrition on neural and behavioral development. III—Development of some motor, particularly locomotor patterns during infancy. *Development Psychobiology*, 1971, **4**, 97–114.

Archer, J. Tests for emotionality in rats and mice: A review. *Animal Behaviour*, 1973, **21**, 205–235.

Baird, A., Widdowson, E. M., & Cowley, J. J. Effects of calorie and protein deficiencies early in life on subsequent learning ability of rats. *British Journal of Nutrition*, 1971, **25**, 391–403.

Barnes, R. H., Cunnold, S. R., Zimmermann, R. R., Simmons, H., MacLeod, R. B., & Krook, L. Influence of nutritional deprivations in early life on learning behaviour of rats as measured by performance in a water maze. *Journal of Nutrition*, 1966, **89**, 399–410.

Bennett, E. L., Diamond, M. C., Krech, D., & Rosenzweig, M. R. Chemical and anatomical plasticity of brain. *Science*, 1964, **146**, 610–619.

Blackwell, B. N., Blackwell, R. Q., Yu, T. T. S., Weng, Y. S., & Chow, B. F. Further studies on growth and feed utilization in progeny of underfed mother rats. *Journal of Nutrition*, 1969, **97**, 79–84.

Bronfenbrenner, U. Early deprivation in mammals: A cross-species analysis. In G. Newton & S. Levine (Eds.), *Early experience and behavior*, Springfield, Ill.: Thomas, 1968, pp. 627–764.

Bush, M., & Leathwood, P. D. Effects of different regimens of early malnutrition on behavioral development and adult avoidance learning in Swiss white mice. *British Journal of Nutrition*, 1975, **33**, 373–385.

Butler, N. R. Risk factors in human intra-uterine growth retardation. In K. Elliott & J. Knight (Eds.), *Size at birth*, Ciba Found. Symp. No. 27, Amsterdam: Elsevier, 1974. pp. 379–382.

Caldwell, D. F., & Churchill, J. A. Learning ability in the progeny of rats administered a protein deficient diet during the second half of gestation. *Neurology*, 1967, **17**, 95–99.

Cowley, J. J., & Griesel, R. D. Some effects of a low protein diet on first filial generation white rats. *Journal of Genctical Pyschology*, 1959, **95**, 187–201.

Cowley, J. J., & Griesel, R. D. The effect on growth and behavior of rehabilitating first and second generation low protein rats. *Animal Behaviour*, 1966, **14**, 506–517.

Cravens, R. W. Effects of maternal undernutrition on offspring: Behavior incentive value of food reward and ability to escape from water. *Developmental Psychobiology*, 1974, **7**, 61–69.

Crnic, L. S. Effects of infantile undernutrition on adult learning in rats: Methodological and design problems. *Psychological Bulletin*, 1976, **83**, 715–728.

Culley, W. J., & Lineberger, R. O. Effect of undernutrition on size and composition of rat brain. *Journal of Nutrition*, 1968, **96**, 375–381.

D'Amato, M. R. Effect of litter size on brightness discrimination and reversal. *Psychological Reports*, 1960, **7**, 91–97.

Davie, R., Butler, N. R., & Goldstein, H. *From birth to 7: The second report of the national child development survey*. London: Longmans, Green, 1972.

Denenberg, V. H. Critical periods, stimulus input and emotional reactivity: A theory of infantile stimulation. *Psychological Reviews*, 1964, **71**, 335–351.

Denenberg, V. H. The mother as a motivator. In W. J. Arnold & M. M. Page (Eds.), *Nebraska Symposium on Motivation*. Lincoln: University of Nebraska Press, 1970. Pp. 69–93.

Di Benedetta, C., & Cioffi, L. A. Early malnutrition, brain glycoproteins and behavior in rats. *Nutrition and Dietetics*, 1972, **17**, 69–82.

Dobbing, J. The influence of early nutrition on the development and myelination of the brain. *Proceedings of the Royal Society of London, Series B*, 1964, **159**, 503–509.

Dobbing, J. Vulnerable periods in developing brain. In A. N. Davison & J. Dobbing (Eds), *Applied neurochemistry*, Oxford Blackwell, pp. 287–316.

Dobbing, J., & Sands. Quantitative growth and development of human brain. *Archives of Disease in Childhood*, 1973, **48**, 757–767.

Dobbing, J., & Smart, J. L. Early undernutrition, brain development and behavior. In S. A. Barnett (Ed.), *Ethology and development*. London: Heinemann, 1973. Pp. 16–32.

Dymsza, H. A., Czajka, D. M., & Miller, S. A. Influence of artificial diet on weight gain and body composition of the neonatal rat. *Journal of Nutrition*, 1964, **84**, 100–106.

Elliott, K., & Knight, J. (Eds.) *Size at birth*. Ciba Found. Symp. No. 27. Amsterdam: Elsevier, 1974.

Fernstrom, J. D., Madras, B. K., Munro, H. N., & Wurtman, R. J. Nutritional control of the synthesis of 5-hydroxytryptamine in the brain. In G. E. W. Wolstenholme & D. Fitzsimmons (Eds.), *Aromatic amino acids in the brain*. Amsterdam: North-Holland Publ., 1974, Pp. 166–174.

Fish, I., & Winick, M. Effect of malnutrition on regional growth of the developing rat brain. *Experimental Neurology*, 1969, **25**, 534–540.

Franková, S. Relationship between nutrition during lactation and maternal behaviour of rats. *Activitas Nervosa Superior*, 1971, **13**, 1–8.

Franková, S., & Barnes, R. H. Effect of malnutrition in early life on avoidance conditioning and behavior in adult rats. *Journal of Nutrition*, 1968, **96**, 485–493. (a)

Franková, S., & Barnes, R. H. Influence of malnutrition in early life on exploratory behavior in rats. *Journal of Nutrition*, 1968, **96**, 477–483. (b)

Frisch, R. E. Does malnutrition cause permanent retardation in human beings? *Psychiatria, Neurologia, Neurochirurgia*, 1971, **74**, 463–479.

Giurintano, S. L. Effects of protein-calorie deficiencies on the learning ability of the Wistar rat. *Physiology and Behavior*, 1974, **12**, 55–59.

Guthrie, H. A. Severe undernutrition in early infancy and behavior in rehabilitated albino rats. *Physiology and Behavior*, 1968, **3**, 619–623.

Habicht, J. P., Lechtig, A., Yarbrough, D., & Klein, R. E. Maternal malnutrition birth weight and infant mortality. In K. Elliott & J. Knight (Eds.), *Size at birth*, Ciba Found. Symp. No. 27. Amsterdam: Elsevier, 1974. Pp. 353–369.

Hinde, R. A. *Animal behaviour*. New York: McGraw-Hill, 1970. Pp. 425–656.

Howard, E., & Granoff, D. M. Effect of neonatal food restriction in mice on brain growth, DNA and cholesterol, and on adult delayed response learning. *Journal of Nutrition*, 1968, **95**, 111–121.

Hsueh, A. M., Simonson, M., Chow, B. F., & Hanson, H. M. The importance of the period of dietary restriction of the dam on behavior and growth in the rat. *Journal of Nutrition*, 1974, **104**, 37–46.

Jackson, C. M., & Stewart, C. A. The effects of inanition in the young upon the ultimate size of the body and various organs of the albino rat. *Journal of Experimental Zoology*, 1920, **30**, 97–106.

Koos-Slob, A., Snow, C. E., & De Natris-Mathot, E. Absence of behavioral deficits following neonatal undernutrition in the rat. *Developmental Psychobiology*, 1973, **6**, 177–186.

Lat, J., Widdowson, E. M., & McCance, R. A. Some effects of accelerating growth. III— Behaviour and nervous activity. *Proceedings of the Royal Society of London, Series B*, 1960, **153**, 347–356.

Leaf, R. C., & Muller, S. A. Simple method for conditioned emotional response (C.E.R.) conditioning and measurement. *Psychological Reports*, 1965, **17**, 211–217.

Leathwood, P. D. Early undernutrition and behaviour. In C. Boella (Ed.), *Nestlé research news*. Lausanne: Nestlé Products Technical Assistance Co. Ltd., 1973. Pp. 36–51.

Leathwood, P. D., Bush, M. S., Berent, C. D., & Mauron, J. Effects of early malnutrition on Swiss white mice: Avoidance performance after rearing in large litters. *Life Sciences*, 1974, **14**, 157–168.

Leathwood, P. D., Bush, M. S., & Mauron, J. Effects of Chlordiazepoxide on avoidance performance of mice subjected to undernutrition or handling stress in early life. *Psychopharmacologia*, 1975, **41**, 105–109.

Leathwood, P. D., & Mauron, J. Effects of early undernutrition on avoidance learning in mice. *Proceedings of the Nutrition Society*, 1974, p. 20A.

Levine, S., & Weiner, S. A critical analysis of data on malnutrition and behavioral deficits. *Advances in Pediatrics*, 1976, **22**, 113–135.

Levitsky, D. A. Malnutrition and animal models of cognitive development in nutrition and mental functions. In G. Serban (Ed.), *Advances in behavioral biology*. New York: Plenum, 1975. Pp. 75–89.

Levitsky, D. A., & Barnes, R. H. Effect of early malnutrition on the reaction of adult rats to aversive stimuli. *Nature (London)*, 1970, **225**, 468–469.

Levitsky, D. A., & Barnes, R. H. Nutritional and environmental interactions in the behavioral development of the rat: Long-term effects. *Science*, 1972, **176**, 68–71.

Levitsky, D. A., & Barnes, R. H. Malnutrition and animal behavior. In D. J. Kallen (Ed.), *Nutrition, development and social behavior*. N.I.H. Publ. No. 73–242. Washington D.C.: U.S. Gov. Printing Office, 1973.

Massaro, T. F., Levitsky, D. A., & Barnes, R. H. Protein malnutrition in the rat: Its effects on behavior and pup development. *Developmental Psychobiology*, 1974, **7**, 551–561.

McCance, R. A., & Widdowson, E. M. Nutrition and growth. *Proceedings of the Royal Society of London, Series B*, 1962, **156**, 326–337.

McKean, C. M., Schanberg, S. M., & Giaman, N. J. Aminoacidaemias: Effects on maze performance and cerebral serotonin. *Science*, 1967, **157**, 213–215.

Mueller, A. J., & Cox, W. The effect of changes in diet on the volume and composition of rat milk. *Journal of Nutrition*, 1946, **31**, 249–259.

Myslivecek, I., & Hassmannová, J. Level of nutrition in early postnatal period and higher nervous functions. *Activitas Nervosa Superior*, 1970, **12**, 160.

Ottinger, D. R., & Tanabe, G. Maternal food restriction: Effects on offspring behavior and development. *Developmental Psychobiology*, 1968, **2**, 7–9.

Pauling, L. Orthomolecular psychiatry. *Science*, 1968, **160**, 265–271.

Plaut, S. M. Studies of undernutrition in the young rat: Methodological considerations. *Developmental Psychobiology*, 1970, **3**, 157–167.

Reige, W. H. Environmental influences on brain and behavior of year old rats. *Developmental Psychobiology*, 1970, **4**, 157–168.

Richardson, S. A. The relation of severe malnutrition in infancy to the intelligence of school children with differing life histories. *Pediatrics Research*, 1976, **10**, 57–61.

Rider, A. A., & Simonson, M. Characteristics of very young mother rats and their pups on low protein diets. *Nutrition Reports International*, 1974, **10**, 345–356.(a)

Rider, A. A., & Simonson, M. The relationships between maternal diet, birth weight, and behavior of the offspring in the rat. *Nutrition Reports International*, 1974, **10**, 19–24.(b)

Sachs, E. Dissociation of learning in rats and its similarities to dissociative states in man. *Proceedings of the American Psychopathological Association*, 1965, **55**, 249–304.

Scott, J. P. Critical periods in behavioral development. *Science*, 1962, **138**, 949–958.

Seitz, P. F. D. The effects of infantile stimulation upon adult behavior in animal subjects: I—Effect of litter size during infancy on adult behavior in the rat. *Americal Journal of Psychiatry*, 1954, **110**, 916–927.

Semiginovsky, B., Myslivecek, J., & Zalud, V. Spontaneous exploratory activity in rats with different nutrition in the early postnatal period. *Activitas Nervosa Superior*, 1970, **12**, 158–159.

Simonson, M., & Chow, B. F. Maze studies on progeny of underfed mother rats. *Journal of Nutrition*, 1970, **100**, 685–690.

Simonson, M., Sherwin, R. W., Anilane, J. K., Yu, W. Y., & Chow, B. F. Neuromotor development in progeny of underfed mother rats. *Journal of Nutrition*, 1969, **98**, 18–24.

Simonson, M., Stephan, J. K., Hanson, H. M., & Chow, B. F. Open field studies in offspring of underfed mother rats. *Journal of Nutrition*, 1971, **101**, 331–335.

Smart, J. L. Activity and exploratory behavior of adult offspring of undernourished mother rats. *Developmental Psychobiology*, 1974, **7**, 315–322.

Smart, J. L., & Dobbing, J. Vulnerability of developing brain. VI–Relative effects of foetal and early postnatal undernutrition on reflex ontogeny and development of behavior in the rat. *Brain Research*, 1971, **33**, 303–314.

Smart, J. L., & Dobbing, J. Vulnerability of developing brain. IV—Passive avoidance behavior in young rats following maternal undernutrition. *Developmental Psychobiology*, 1972, **5**, 129–136.

Smart, J. L., Dobbing, J., Adlard, B. P. F., Lynch, & Sands. Vulnerability of developing brain: Relative effects of growth restriction during the fetal and suckling periods on behavior and brain composition in adult rats. *Journal of Nutrition*, 1973, 103, 1327–1328.

Smart, J. L., & Preece, J. Maternal behavior of undernourished mother rats. *Animal Behaviour*, 1973, **21**, 613–619.

Stein, Z., Susser, M., Saenger, G., & Marolla, F. *Famine and human development*. London and New York: Oxford University Press, 1975.

Stephan, J. K., & Chow, B. F. Growth of progeny from rats underfed during gestation only. *Federation Proceedings*, 1968, **27**, 728.

Stockard, C. R. Developmental rate and structural expression: An experimental study of twins (double monsters and single deformities and their interaction among embryonic organs during their origin and development). *American Journal of Anatomy*, 1920, **28**, 115–278.

Thoman, E. B., & Levine, S. Incubator rearing of infant rats without the mother: Effects on adult emotionality and learning. *Developmental Psychobiology*, 1968, **1**, 219–222.

Winick, M., & Noble, A. Cellular response in rats during malnutrition at various ages. *Journal of Nutrition*, 1966, **89**, 300–306.

Zimmermann, R. R., & Wells, A. M. Performance of malnourished rats on the Hebb-Williams closed-field maze learning test. *Perceptual and Motor Skills*, 1971, **33**, 1043–1049.

Section 3

SENSORY EXPERIENCE, OVERLOAD, ENRICHMENT

INTRODUCTION

The final section describes both the helpful and the harmful effects of sensory experience on the development of the nervous system and behavior.

In the first chapter, Charlotte Mistretta and Robert Bradley describe the developmental course of the auditory, gustatory, olfactory, tactile, and visual senses in the absence of sensory input and with modifications of normal sensory experience. Although the visual system has long been by far the most extensively studied, there has been some research on all the other systems. Since the research on the visual system has been repeatedly reviewed in recent years, Dr. Mistretta and Dr. Bradley focus on the development of the other sensory systems, both prenatally and postnatally. They also raise an interesting and valuable conceptual question, the discussion of which is taken up again in the final chapter by Mark Rosenzweig and Edward Bennett. Namely, should the effects of rather precise and narrow sensory deprivation and modification procedures during early development (described by Mistretta and Bradley) be conceptualized along the same neural, behavioral, and psychological dimensions as the more global "environmental enrichment" studies described by Dr. Rosenzweig and Dr. Bennett? This is a very important issue which has not heretofore been aired to any extent in the literature. In light of the paucity of theoretical issues in the area, it could prove beneficial if the current controversy—Mistretta and Bradley and Rosenzweig and Bennett have a friendly but firm disagreement—sparks a wider and more frequent discussion of the matter.

In an era in which we have come to think of sensory experience during early development as "good" and necessary, it is important to realize that such stimulation, if sufficiently intense and occurring at a vulnerable time during the early structural maturation of a sensory system, can have quite harmful consequences. This theme is spelled out rather specifically by James Saunders and Gregory Bock in their chapter in this section, in which they describe how an otherwise nontraumatic auditory experience, when it occurs during a particular period of auditory development, can make the young animals prone to seizures at a later date. (The young animals do not have seizures at the time of the original experience.) If the same auditory experience occurs either before or after the relatively delimited vulnerable period, the animals do not become seizure prone. The authors present a very intriguing neural theory to account for the "priming" effect of the early auditory trauma.

Finally, Mark Rosenzweig and Edward Bennett review the highlights of the Berkeley group's widely known and highly influential 20-year experimental program on "environmental enrichment" effects on the brain and behavior. As indicated earlier, the conceptually oriented treatment of neuroplasticity, learning, and memory will inevitably provoke wider discussion that will ultimately help us to gain a better abstract understanding of the role of normally occurring early (and late) experience in the development of behavior and the nervous system.

EFFECTS OF EARLY SENSORY EXPERIENCE ON BRAIN AND BEHAVIORAL DEVELOPMENT

CHARLOTTE M. MISTRETTA and ROBERT M. BRADLEY

Department of Oral Biology
School of Dentistry
University of Michigan
Ann Arbor, Michigan

I. Introduction

Through sensory function an organism becomes aware of the environment in which it lives. Sensation and perception gradually develop as the nervous system is established through gene interaction with internal and external environmental factors. Among the external environmental influences that can modify neural development are the various types of sensory stimuli that the organism experiences. In this chapter we discuss several ways in which early sensory experience has been manipulated, from total removal of sensory input to modification of stimulus quality, and the effects

215

of such manipulations on the auditory, gustatory, olfactory, tactile, and visual systems. Experimental evidence of changes in neural structure, neural function, and behavior is discussed.

Since the chapter is not intended to be an all-inclusive review or to provide historical perspective, some subjects will get only a cursory treatment and many references that the reader may find relevant will not appear. Further, our emphasis is limited to mammals, with only occasional references to other vertebrates and invertebrates. What can be provided in this chapter is a broad overview of the various experimental approaches and most significant findings in each of the sensory systems, and this is our intent. Although more research has been published on the role of early experience in the development of vision than any other sensory system, we will give only an extremely brief indication of the findings in this area. Since this research has been reviewed in several recent papers (Barlow, 1975; Blakemore, 1974a, 1974b; Daniels & Pettigrew, 1976; Grobstein & Chow, 1976; Riesen, 1966), we chose to discuss other sensory systems in more detail.

The work reviewed in this chapter represents the efforts of investigators interested in diverse areas, with very different theoretical approaches. We hope that this diversity will not be a source of diffuseness for the reader, but will rather provide a broader perspective for understanding the various functions of experience in development.

II. Early Auditory Experience

Although much is known about the structure and function of auditory receptors and central pathways in adult (Keidel & Neff, 1974) and developing mammals (chapter by Saunders & Bock, in this volume), there are relatively few studies on the effects of early experience on the immature auditory system. Existing information comes principally from behavioral experiments, with fewer electrophysiological studies (Clopton & Winfield, 1974; Moore & Aitkin, 1975).

In the adult mammal (Powell & Erulkar, 1962) and embryonic chick (Levi-Montalcini, 1949), transneuronal degeneration in auditory relay nuclei has been demonstrated after surgical destruction of the periphery. Experimental techniques have also been devised to alter the early auditory environment and yet leave peripheral receptors intact. In nearly all mammalian experiments the animal is deprived of sound either by the use of ear plugs or by being placed in a soundproof environment or by both measures. However, total sound deprivation should prevent the animal from hearing not only noises generated from the environment but also self-produced noises, both of which may be important for normal auditory development (Gottlieb, 1971a). This is virtually impossible to achieve since sound can be transmitted to the auditory receptors via bone conduction. In experiments on avian species, in addition to rearing hatchlings in sound-proof environments, chicks and ducklings have also been surgically deafened or muted. The use of all these techniques has produced convincing evidence that auditory experience can influence subsequent behavior.

In an early study, Wolf (1943) deprived one group of rats of auditory stimuli by plugging the ears during 10–15 days of infancy and deprived another group of visual experience during the same period. After a 40-day training period, he placed rats from each group in competition for food, with either a light or a buzzer used to signal food. Rats deprived of audition were more successful in obtaining food when the signal was a light, and light-deprived rats were more successful when the signal was a buzzer. This study was repeated with some procedural modifications by Gauron and Becker (1959), and they confirmed Wolf's results, concluding that each form of deprivation had limited the sensory ability of the animals. Objections may be raised to the type of auditory deprivation used in these experiments since the precise effectiveness of the ear plugs in excluding sound was not evaluated, the ear plugs may have caused irritation or infection, and the behavioral methods were not designed to test auditory acuity. Tees (1967), also using ear plugs, deprived rats of auditory stimulation for 60 days starting 3–5 days after birth. He routinely checked the auditory canal of each rat and eliminated animals with signs of irritation or infection. The rats were raised in soundproof boxes, initially with their mothers, and then following weaning, in isolation. Behavioral tests for auditory frequency and pattern discrimination were then conducted. Deprived rats were not different from controls in ability to learn frequency discriminations, but were deficient when tested for pattern discrimination.

It is still possible that rats in Tees' study received auditory stimulation, even though they were fitted with ear plugs and placed in soundproof boxes. While eating or grooming, noises may have reached receptors, owing to an ill-fitting ear plug or bone conduction, and maternal vocalizations may have been heard. Batkin and co-workers (Batkin, Groth, Watson, & Ansberry, 1970) tried to eliminate some of these sources of sound by raising rats with muted mothers and clipping their toes. After weaning they were individually housed in soundproof boxes for 8 months. When the thresholds of auditory-evoked responses were measured at the cortex, values for deprived rats were higher than those for control littermates. Some indication of more specific neural changes is suggested by the preliminary findings of Clopton and Win-field (1974). They exposed rats from birth for 4 months, 5 hours daily, to a specific temporal auditory pattern. Subsequently, the selectivities of units in the inferior colliculus were shifted toward the pattern experienced from birth. The mothers of these rat pups did not show this change, although they were exposed at the same time. But when kittens were exposed during the first 50–75 days after birth to a continuous pure tone stimulus of 1000 Hz for 5–8 hours daily (Moore & Aitkin, 1975), response characteristics of inferior colliculus units were not significantly altered. Responses were recorded either immediately after, or 100 days after, the early exposure period; unit tuning curves and tonotopic collicular organization were similar to those of the adult cat. The thresholds for units in kittens tested immediately after the exposure period were, however, substantially lower than adult values or values from kittens tested 100 days after the exposure. Since the stimulus parameters were different in the latter two experiments, it is not possible to directly compare the results; more neurophysiological studies of this type would elucidate critical stimulus and response characteristics.

These experiments in mammals indicate that elimination or alteration of early auditory stimulation can affect later auditory behavior. Other evidence is found in work on priming of auditory seizures (chapter by Saunders & Bock, in this volume); mice normally resistant to auditory seizure can be made susceptible by exposing them to a noise early in life (Henry, 1967). It is also well known that environmental noise can permanently damage the auditory system, and the extent to which this is true in young mammals is reviewed by Saunders and Bock (in this volume).

Much progress has been made in evaluating the role of early auditory experience in behavioral development in avian species. This work has recently been comprehensively reviewed (Gottlieb, 1971a; 1976a, 1976b) and, therefore, will not be discussed here. An important role of prehatching self-stimulation and parental auditory stimulation in synchronizing hatching (Vince, 1973), and in the ability of the newly hatched gull chick (Tschanz, 1968) and duckling (Gottlieb, 1976a, 1976b) to recognize parental calls has been shown. Post-hatching sound stimulation is also important. When a young male white-crowned sparrow is deafened it subsequently develops a very abnormal song (Konishi, 1965). Similarly, a sparrow raised in social isolation from 5 days of age develops an abnormal song (Marler & Tamura, 1962). Hearing oneself and others is also important in the development of human speech (Lenneberg, 1969), as evidenced by the difficulty with which congenitally deaf children learn to speak.

In summary, then, it has been demonstrated in several species that responses to auditory stimuli are modified after early auditory deprivation. These results should be expanded to elucidate further the anatomical and neurophysiological substrates of the behavioral changes. Also, auditory stimulus parameters should be manipulated in different ways as, for example, in studies of the effects of early exposure to predominant frequencies. Finally, the effects of early monaural versus binaural deprivation, an approach that has yielded striking results in the visual system, should be studied at anatomical, neurophysiological, and behavioral levels.

III. Early Gustatory Experience

Most vertebrate species prefer sweet substances, which are usually nutritious, and avoid bitter substances, which are often poisonous. Since these taste preferences and aversions would be advantageous to the individual searching for food, it is reasonable to assume that they have been selected for during evolutionary history. This would, then, suggest a genetic basis of preferences and aversions, and indeed a genetic component for some taste behaviors has been demonstrated (Kalmus, 1971; Nachman, 1959; Stockton & Whitney, 1974). But experience can begin to exert an influence early in development. From the first feeding, alterations of the natural food may occur. For example, milk can easily absorb extraneous chemicals that the lactating mother eats, changing the taste and odor of milk (Ling, Kon, & Porter, 1961). At weaning the opportunities for varied taste experience are multiplied, and observations on animals and humans suggest that this experience can influence later feeding behavior (Arnold, 1964; Jerome, 1977; Moskowitz, Kumaraiah, Sharma, Jacobs, & Sharma, 1975).

Experimental studies on the influence of early taste experience on later taste preferences and aversions are difficult to design, and negative results are not easily interpreted. Two important experiments in this area were on invertebrates. Evans (1961) and Dethier and Goldrich (1971) found that the chemical composition of food ingested by blowfly larvae affected the behavioral taste responses of the adults. Specific sugars were added to a basic larval diet that lacked all sugars except lactose. After eclosion, the taste sensitivity of the adult blowflies to sugars was tested. In both studies changes in adult sugar sensitivity were reported as a result of the larval exposures to special diets. This implied an alteration in the nervous system that was transmitted through metamorphosis into adult life.

Vertebrate experiments have been focused on two different manipulations: (1) adding a specific chemical to the maternal diet during pregnancy and/or lactation; or (2) adding a specific chemical to the offspring's diet at birth or weaning, and subsequently measuring food preferences. Most of the manipulations of maternal diets have been made in rodents, but Burghardt (1971) tested the hypothesis that cues from the maternal diet may be detected prenatally in viviparous species of snakes. In his results there were no significant differences in responses to food extracts by newborn snakes whose mothers had been fed different diets; Burghardt concluded that maternal feeding experience does not influence the chemical preferences of young snakes. Comparable experiments have not yet been reported in mammals.

Attempts to transmit cues to the young of lactating rodents via the flavor of milk have met with varying degrees of success. A relatively direct approach was made by LeMagnen and Tallon (1968) who injected citral subcutaneously near the nipples of lactating rats for the first 10 or 30 days after birth. All pups were weaned at 30 days and fed *ad libitum* on laboratory chow. During subsequent 24-hour test periods at 40 and 60 days a weak preference for the citral diet was exhibited; but by 120 days such effects disappeared. In a similar type of experiment, rat pups were tested *during weaning* to establish whether they would prefer a diet fed to their mothers during lactation (Galef & Henderson, 1972). Nursing females were fed one of two diets distinctly different in taste, smell, color, and texture. When tested during weaning Days 17–23 to determine their preferred diet, pups chose to eat more of the diet fed to their mothers during lactation. Pups were not tested several weeks or months later to establish whether the effect was lasting. Capretta and Rawls (1974) designed an experiment to determine the relative importance of nursing versus postweaning taste experience. Rats were exposed to garlic via their mother's milk and/or their drinking water, after weaning. Exposure to a taste stimulus during nursing *and* weaning proved to be more effective in influencing later taste behavior than nursing or weaning exposure alone.

In other experiments only early postnatal taste experience has been manipulated and the role of possible indirect influences via the maternal diet has been ignored. Snapping turtles (Burghardt & Hess, 1966) and chicks (Rabinowitch, 1968) preferred the food they had ingested for the first several days after hatching when offered a choice of foods. The turtles continued to prefer their original food even after intervening experience with a different diet, but in the chick experiments no attempt was made to determine how lasting this effect might be.

In the experiments on turtles and chicks, hatchlings were exposed to foods that would be characteristically encountered by the species. In contrast to this work are some experiments on rats in which early exposure to highly unusual chemicals was used in attempts to influence the formation of adult food preferences. For example, Bronson (1966) fed rats pellets, mashed and soaked in wine vinegar, from the time of weaning for 48 days. Hilker, Hee, Higashi, Ikehara, and Paulsen (1967) fed weanling rats diets containing spices for periods of 3 weeks, 5 weeks, or 4 months. Although the rats ate and grew well on the special diets, when tested over several days after the exposure periods they chose a plain diet. These experiments could be interpreted as evidence that early diet does *not* influence later food preference, but the diets contained chemicals far removed from a rat's usual repertoire. On the other hand, Warren and Pfaffmann (1959) were able to change the guinea pig's normal aversion for an unusual, bitter chemical through early exposure, although the effect was short-lived. From 2 or 3 days of age guinea pigs were given a solution of the nontoxic, intensely bitter chemical sucrose octaacetate (SOA) as their only available fluid for periods of 2–3 weeks. This chemical is aversive to adult guinea pigs. In subsequent preference tests extending over several days, guinea pigs with the bitter experience drank significantly more SOA at higher concentrations than did the controls; the experimental subjects accepted SOA almost equally with tap H_2O. After 3 to 4 months of intervening experience with plain water, though, there was no significant difference in preference between SOA-fed and control guinea pigs.

As well as trying to influence the acquisition of one particular taste or food preference, it is also of interest to determine whether rats given several distinctive flavors early in life will be more likely to accept a novel flavor later than rats experiencing a more homogeneous early diet (Capretta, Petersik, & Stewart, 1975). Four groups of immature rats were given either plain water, or water flavored with either black walnut, rum, or vanilla from 25 to 36 days of age. Another group had sequential exposure to all three flavors, one at a time, during the same period. After the exposure period the rats were preference-tested for 10 days with a new flavor, chocolate, versus plain water. At 80–85 days of age, rats were tested again. At both testing periods, the group that had sequential experience with all three flavors consumed the most chocolate relative to plain water. All groups that had experience with only a single flavor had significantly lower chocolate preferences. In a similar experiment on mature rats there was no effect of varied experience on subsequent chocolate preference. So experience with several flavors early in life will predispose rats to accept novel foods.

Discussion. It is difficult to evaluate why some studies have demonstrated an influence of early taste experience on later feeding preference whereas others have failed to show such an effect. Several factors may have been critical, and there are as yet few experiments that test the influence of these factors. First, since taste and feeding behavior determine intake, and thereby directly affect the organism's internal physiological state, the choice of stimulus or early exposure chemical is crucial. The influence of the specific taste of some food or fluid must be distinguished from possible positive or harmful physiological effects of the food. Presumably, if something highly unpalatable or potentially harmful is used as the early exposure chemical, i.e., vinegar or spices, it will be more difficult to substantially alter the organism's aversion and change it to acceptance or preference.

Not only is the quality of the chosen stimulus important but the concentration chosen for exposure and later testing may also be critical. Exposure to a relatively low concentration of a specific chemical may be more effective in altering later choice behavior than experience with very high and potentially more aversive concentrations. In experiments that involve feeding a lactating female a "tainted" diet, the assumption is made that a flavor is transmitted into the milk. But thus far no assays have been made for these chemicals and therefore the exposure concentration is unknown. Further, effects that do occur may be subtle. Tests of possible threshold shifts might be necessary to demonstrate effects in some experiments, in addition to the commonly used preference tests.

The timing of the onset and termination of exposure and the overall length of the total early experience period are also important. The relation of the stage of development of the taste system to the time of presentation of the early taste experience is referred to only cursorily, if at all, in these studies. In rats, although the taste receptors do not acquire adult morphological characteristics until about 12 days after birth, the receptors begin to form prenatally (Farbman, 1965; Mistretta, 1972). In mammals with comparatively lengthy gestations, on the other hand, taste buds undergo major structural and functional development *in utero* (Bradley & Mistretta, 1975). Unfortunately, there are no data on the time course of the structural development of the taste pathways, so it is presently impossible to choose optimal periods for these experiments. Species that undergo a major part of development postnatally might be more readily influenced by changes in the lactating mother's diet. Further, vertebrates that are hatched in a precocial state, ready to feed, may be less flexible and therefore less susceptible to attempts to drastically alter food choice; but their very first intake is perhaps critical. The testing period should also be carefully timed. In many of the experiments cited here the onset of testing coincided with weaning and physical separation from the mother. These attendant environmental changes may serve to mask other behaviors that would be apparent in more stable conditions. The only experimental evidence related to any of these questions of timing indicates that for rats, exposure during nursing *and* weaning is more effective than during nursing or weaning alone (Capretta *et al.*, 1975).

The possible influence of novelty in preference tests is frequently ignored in discussions of early experience effects. When offered a new food in familiar surroundings rats will explore and sample the novel diet but their first sampling behavior may bear no relation to subsequent preferences (Barnett, 1956). Only after 1 or 2 days will preferences be clearly expressed. Domjan (1976) and Green and Parker (1975) have shown that if after initial ingestion of a small quantity of food there are no adverse physiological effects, rats will gradually increase their consumption of a novel diet. Therefore, to clearly establish whether early experience has significantly influenced later taste preferences and aversions and to avoid the effects of novelty *per se*, testing should continue over several days.

All of these factors—stimulus quality and concentration, method of testing, timing of the early exposure, choice of species, novelty effects— can have significant influences on the outcome of the experiments described in this section. Some of the factors, such as concentration and timing, are infinitely variable. Since we lack detailed baseline data on development of feeding behavior and of the sensory systems underlying the behavior in any species, correct interpretation of results is made even more difficult. As in the auditory system, the anatomical and neurophysiological substrates underlying the behavioral changes should be explored. Yet some alterations in taste preferences and aversions have certainly been demonstrated, even though in many instances the effects of early experience were reversible. But the reversibility, rather than implying negative results, may just further reflect the plasticity of the system and be a normal feature of development, contrary to the more classical connotation of "food imprinting".

IV. Early Olfactory Experience

Studies of the effects of early olfactory experience on the nervous system encompass anatomical and behavioral experiments, but there have been no attempts to use electrophysiological techniques to detect functional changes in the mammalian nervous system. In addition to the studies that will be discussed here, there is an extensive literature on the role of olfaction in the phenomenon of fish migration to home streams. This work will not be discussed; the interested reader is referred to Hasler (1960) and Madison, Scholz, Cooper, Horrall, Hasler, and Dizon (1973).

Dependence of neural elements in the olfactory bulb on the integrity of peripheral receptors has been demonstrated in light- and electron-microscopic studies (Matthews & Powell, 1962; Pinching & Powell, 1971). After unilateral destruction of the olfactory mucosa in young rats and rabbits (35–56 days), a variety of cellular effects were observed in the olfactory bulb. These effects, the authors hypothesized, were related to the extent of loss of afferent olfactory fibers. Although many cells lost most of their afferent excitatory input, they probably retained other excitatory and inhibitory inputs (Pinching & Powell, 1971). All layers of the bulb, except the periventricular, were shrunken. Individual periglomerular, tufted, mitral, and granule cells showed evidence of shrinkage, concentration of cytoplasmic and nuclear contents, alteration in the organization of nucleic acid material, and swelling of membrane bound systems (Matthews & Powell, 1962; Pinching & Powell, 1971). Since some features of cytological organization were retained, the authors thought that cell death was not occurring.

Not only receptor destruction, but drastic changes in the olfactory environment also affect the olfactory bulb. Selective degeneration of olfactory bulb neurons was noted after exposure of young rats to specific odors (Døving & Pinching, 1973; Pinching & Døving, 1974). Rats at about 2 weeks of age were continuously exposed to odors for periods of 2 weeks to several months. Chemicals representing a variety of odor qualities and physicochemical properties were blown into the home cages from a common source with previously filtered room air. After exposure to odors, degenerative changes were observed by light- and electron-microscopic methods in mitral and tufted cells in distinct zones of the olfactory bulb. The zones were consistent for a particular odor in all rats, even though groups of rats were exposed for varying lengths of time. There were no signs of degeneration in olfactory nerve terminals in any part of the bulb, and the authors concluded that the observed changes resulted from functional alterations in the second order cells. They emphasized that they did not mean to imply cell death by using the term degeneration. A consistent and distinct pattern of degeneration was observed in the olfactory bulbs of control rats, also; the authors suggested that this may have been caused by the odor originating from the lucite cages in which the rats were housed.

There have been many behavioral experiments to determine whether exposure of young mice, rats, hamsters, and guinea pigs to olfactory stimuli leads to a preference for the odor. In some studies preferences for natural or artificial home-bedding odors were measured (Cornwell, 1975; Devor & Schneider, 1974; Gregory & Pfaff, 1971; Leon & Moltz, 1972). After varying lengths of exposure, pups were found to prefer home odors. Even when pups were reared on bedding with a normally aversive odor, later acceptance of the odor was shown (Cornwell, 1975). Porter and Etscorn (1974) reported that if spiny mice, 2–12 hours old, were exposed to bedding odorized with either cumin or cinnamon for only 1 hour, these precocial rodents would subsequently prefer bedding that smelled of cumin or cinnamon. Since in many of these experiments pups were tested for odor preference over several days, it would seem that they are not simply avoiding novel odors. Various authors hypothesize that pups develop a preference for home odors and thereby stay close to the nest. The preference for natural home-bedding and maternal odors was found to wane after about 10 days in hamsters (Devor & Schneider, 1974) and 21 days in rats (Leon & Moltz, 1972), coincident with weaning.

In related experiments, all members of guinea pig or rat litters, including the mother, were rubbed daily with an artificial odor for varying exposure periods (Carter & Marr, 1970; Marr & Gardner, 1965; Marr & Lilliston, 1969). On subsequent testing pups were observed to spend more time near a stimulus animal treated with the appropriate early exposure odor than a natural-odor animal. Marr and Gardner (1965) also reported that rearing rats with artificial odors interfered with later sexual responsiveness to normal, opposite-sexed rats.

Early exposure to a specific odor can also alter later food preference (Drickamer, 1972). Young mice, 21 days old, and adult mice of two different species were presented with food containing either oil of anise, wintergreen, or pine odor for 2 weeks. Mice were tested at the end of the exposure period and 1 month later. Young *Peromyscus m. bairdi* mice preferred food containing the exposure odor on both tests. Adults of this species were not influenced by the exposure. Both young and old *P. leucopus* mice were affected, but on the first test only. Drickamer concluded that *P. leucopus* showed more flexibility in feeding behavior and related this flexibility to their varied ecological habitats; *P. m. bairdi* occupies a more restricted habitat.

Invertebrates have also been found to be sensitive to early food odors. Manning (1967) reared *Drosophila* larvae on a medium containing 0.5% geraniol by volume and tested the adult flies for odor preference within several hours after hatching. The test concentration of geraniol was normally aversive to *Drosophila*. Flies reared on geraniol medium were significantly less aversive to geraniol than those reared on plain medium. In these experiments, and in the Evans (1961) and Dethier and Goldrich (1971) experiments on taste preferences in blowflies, neurophysiological modifications that may have occurred in the larvae were presumably transmitted through metamorphosis to the adult organism.

Discussion. As in the studies on early taste experience, there is frequently no attempt to relate the results of these behavioral experiments to the neuroanatomical and neurophysiological development of the sense of smell. Sensory cells begin to differentiate prenatally in the olfactory mucosa of the mouse on the 10th day of gestation, and the central ends of the olfactory axons make contact with the developing olfactory bulb on the 11th day (Cuschieri & Bannister, 1975a, 1975b). Young neurons are first identified in the mouse olfactory bulb on the 12th day of gestation (Hinds, 1972a, 1972b). The final stages of peripheral receptor differentiation begin on about the 17th day prenatally; however, there are still immature receptors in the base of the epithelium after birth (Cuschieri & Bannister, 1975a, 1975b).

Electrical activity was first recorded from the rat olfactory bulb on postnatal Day 3 by Salas, Guzman-Flores, and Schapiro (1969) and on Day 2 by Schönfelder and Schwartze (1971). Salas *et al.* reported a mature pattern of olfactory bulb activity by Day 24, but Schönfelder and Schwartze not until approximately 42 days of age. Although numerous mature synapses were observed in the rat's olfactory cortex at birth, the cortex did not closely resemble adult tissue until the age of 14 days (Westrum, 1975).

At birth, then, in the mouse and rat, an immature sensory system is present that gradually matures over the first few weeks of postnatal life. Therefore, in most of the behavioral experiments on rats and mice discussed here, exposure to environmental odors took place at times when the olfactory system was far from mature. However, the studies of transneuronal degeneration after olfactory mucosa destruction were initiated at a period when the rat olfactory system was structurally and possibly neurophysiologically mature. Similarly, the rabbit transneuronal degeneration experiments were performed after the olfactory bulb activity had attained an adult pattern of burst frequency and amplitude (achieved by postnatal Day 8, see Schwartze, 1967). Since transneuronal effects are usually less pronounced if deafferentation takes place after synaptic continuity has been achieved (Globus, 1975), it would be interesting to study transneuronal degeneration in younger animals.

All of the factors that were mentioned as important in the design of experiments on early exposure to taste stimuli apply also to olfaction experiments. As in the taste studies, stimulus concentration and novelty effects are often not discussed, but more attention is given to the timing and duration of odor stimulus presentation. Also, there is emphasis throughout this literature on exposure of neonates to both natural and experimental odors. It is interesting to speculate on why it has apparently proved easier to demonstrate behavioral changes as a result of early olfactory exposure than changes related to early taste experience. It may be that since olfaction plays an important role in attachment, the neonate's nervous system must be ready to "imprint on" odors associated with the nest. Also, since olfactory stimuli are not ingested, possible confounding metabolic effects are less direct than after exposure to gustatory stimuli.

V. Early Tactile Experience

Study of the role of early somesthetic experience in neural development has centered upon the effects of peripheral receptor destruction on central nervous structure and on behavior. One system ideally suited to examination of the effects of receptor destruction is that of the mouse vibrissae and their central connections (Van der Loos & Woolsey, 1973; Weller & Johnson, 1975). Each discrete vibrissa on the mouse vibrissal pad projects to a distinct anatomical location, termed a barrel, in the contralateral somatosensory cortex. The cortical barrels are organized in an arrangement that is topologically similar to that of the vibrissae. If the vibrissae and their receptor organs are destroyed at birth, there is a subsequent disruption of barrel organization in the contralateral cortex (Van der Loos & Woolsey, 1973). For each missing vibrissa and receptor, the corresponding barrel is also missing.

If, however, the receptors are not destroyed until postnatal Day 5, no such cortical changes are apparent at the light-microscopic level in the mouse (Weller & Johnson, 1975). Since rudimentary barrels are normally seen by the 5th postnatal day, it seems that the peripheral influence is exerted only during the period of barrel morphogenesis (Weller & Johnson, 1975). Globus (1975) has noted that generally there is a much less pronounced transneuronal effect if the periphery is disturbed after the period during which synaptic continuity is achieved. There is, then, presumably synaptic continuity in the vibrissae pathways in the mouse by 5 days, but not at birth. This assumption has not been neurophysiologically verified, however.

Ryugo, Ryugo, and Killackey (1975) measured dendritic spine loss on layer V pyramidal cells of barrel fields after vibrissae receptor damage in newborn rats. Their lesioning procedure did not result in permanent loss of vibrissae, and by 15 days of age a variable number of misshapen vibrissae were present. The pups were sacrificed at 25 days postnatally. There was a significant reduction in spine density on deep layer V pyramidal cells but not on cells in superficial layers. The authors suggest that these spine losses may reflect alterations in synaptic organization.

Weller and Johnson (1975) were interested not only in the effects of receptor destruction but also in possible central alterations after simply removing the vibrissae while the receptors remained intact. Each day for 10 days after birth vibrissae were removed with a depilatory; there were no subsequent alterations in cortical barrel structure. The authors concluded that lack of sensory stimulation alone could probably not produce cortical alterations. But Weller and Johnson's technique of daily depilitation would, itself, provide stimulation to the receptors; also, even though the hairs were removed, the vibrissae organs may still have been stimulated whenever a pup's face was touched. Nevertheless, it is clear that the quality of the sensory stimulation during the period of depilitation would have been vastly changed.

Behavioral changes were reported in kittens as a result of clipping the vibrissae off at 1 day after birth and reclipping at intervals thereafter (Turkewitz, Gilbert, & Birch, 1974). During a period of daily testing, kittens with clipped vibrissae chose the shallow side of a visual cliff 4 days earlier than kittens with intact vibrissae. It was concluded that reduced input in the tactile system accelerated the development of visual function. But these conclusions seem unwarranted on the basis of this experiment alone. It is just as likely that the kitten's behavior resulted from sole use of vision, rather than both vision and touch, when performing on the cliff apparatus. When using tactile information and vision a kitten may touch both sides of the cliff with its vibrissae and subsequently step on either the visually deep or visually shallow side. This possibility is supported by the finding that while adult rats with clipped vibrissae choose the shallow side of a visual cliff, controls using vibrissae input and vision do not show a preference for either side (Schiffman, Lore, Passafiume, & Neeb, 1970).

In addition to studies on the central effects of vibrissae removal and receptor destruction, there are several studies on the influence of somesthetic stimulation via the limbs on neural organization and behavior. When the hind leg or foot was amputated in neonatal opposums, 4–5 days old, neurons in that portion of the adult gracile nucleus normally receiving projections from the leg or foot degenerated (Johnson, Hamilton, Hsung, & Ulinski, 1972). By mapping the cuneate–gracile complex electrophysiologically, Johnson et al. determined that mechanosensitive projections still present in the rest of the complex were organized normally. Because the precise timing of hind limb innervation is not known for opossums, it is not clear whether distal processes of dorsal root ganglion cells were severed when the limb was amputated. The authors suggest that disturbance of the peripheral input might have influenced either proliferation and migration of certain second order cells or survival of the cells.

Many studies have attempted to determine whether somatic sensation is necessary for the development of coordinated, voluntary movements. We will not discuss the evidence on motor primacy in chick embryos because the topic has been well reviewed by Hamburger (1973) and by Oppenheim (1974). In brief, chick embryos move before they are capable of responding to sensory stimulation. Thus, the earliest chick movements are not reflex responses but are spontaneously generated. In some species, however, sensory feedback does seem necessary, at least for the development of precise movements.

Berman and Berman (1973), and Taub, Perrella, and Barro (1973), deafferented the forelimbs in monkeys by sectioning dorsal roots C_2 to T_4 at birth or at 6–10 days before birth, and found that postnatal sensory feedback was not necessary for the development of normal ambulatory sequences. Berman and Berman reported that fine motor movements by the distal musculature were severely retarded, but according to Taub et al., although grasp of small objects between thumb and forefinger did not occur spontaneously, the monkeys could be operantly trained to grasp. Mammalian fetuses, however, have considerable tactile experience before birth (Bradley & Mistretta, 1975), so deafferentation at birth cannot preclude any previous stimulation. In subsequent experiments, Taub, Barro, Heitmann, Grier, Boretos, and Cicmanec (1975) deafferented the forelimbs in monkey fetuses when about two-thirds of the gestation period was completed. Two fetuses that survived to 3 months postnatal age used their deafferented limbs for ambulation and climbing but clearly had a motor deficit in fine control and timing of movement. It seems, then, that the role of somatosensory input is to supply precision, accuracy, and smoothness to genetically determined gross patterns of coordination.

Since vibrissae receptor ablation and limb amputation or deafferentation can be accomplished relatively easily, these experimental techniques have been used to evaluate the role of tactile experience in neural development. But structural or functional alterations in the somesthetic nervous system as a result of manipulating stimulus quality have not been demonstrated. It is difficult to deliver a controlled tactile stimulus to a pre- or postnatal mammal, exclusive of, or predominant over, other stimulation. So experiments that provide a particular type of early sensory experience, such as a characteristic tone, taste, odor, or visual pattern are more difficult in the tactile system.

VI. Early Visual Experience

Since the literature on the effects of early visual experience on the developing nervous system is too immense to be effectively covered in this chapter and is comprehensively reviewed elsewhere (Barlow, 1975; Blakemore, 1974a, 1974b; Daniels & Pettigrew, 1976; Grobstein & Chow, 1976; Riesen, 1966), we will restrict this section to discussion of the various experimental approaches used in these studies. Rather than citing specific journal articles, we will often refer instead to a review.

Early investigators used enucleation techniques and found marked effects on the visual pathways. Globus (Table I, 1975) has reviewed the studies on enucleation; the procedure results in reduced dendritic branching, fewer dendritic spines, reduction in the size of the lateral geniculate nucleus, and numerous other morphological and biochemical changes in the deafferented visual pathway. Dark-rearing, which effectively removes visual input without directly interfering with the visual receptors, has been extensively used to alter the early visual environment. Although dark-reared animals have an eye-blink to light stimulation and a pupillary reflex, behavioral deficits including poor spatial coordination, and a lack of visual startle response, visual recognition, and sustained visual fixation, have been observed in monkeys, kittens, rabbits, rats, and chickens (Riesen & Zilbert, 1975). Beginning with the work of Wiesel and Hubel (1963), visual deprivation has been achieved by suturing the eyelids of kittens or fitting kittens with translucent visual occluders. These experiments involved either both eyes (binocular deprivation) or one eye (monocular deprivation). A variation of this technique is alternating occlusion, so that the two eyes are not stimulated at the same time, but reversibly (experiments discussed by Blakemore, 1974a). To test the hypothesis that the effects of visual deprivation in the lateral geniculate nucleus are not simply passive changes, Guillery (1972) coupled monocular deprivation in kittens with a small lesion in the retina of the open eye. Another surgical technique involves cutting one extraocular muscle, thereby artificially deviating one eye to produce strabismus (Hubel & Wiesel, 1965).

The techniques described thus far achieve an experimental situation in which the subject's eyes are either deprived of light, are not stimulated at the same time, or are not stimulated by the same visual space. To manipulate the visual patterns that the developing mammal is exposed to, Blakemore and Cooper (1970) and Hirsch and Spinelli (1970) raised kittens in defined visual environments. In normal cats, neurons in the visual cortex are selective for the orientation of lines and edges in the visual field. Each cortical neuron responds to a particular orientation of slits or lines presented to the eyes, and cells responding to all orientations are present (Hubel & Wiesel, 1962). However, this normal pattern is altered if cats are raised in an environment of either horizontal or vertical stripes. A predominance of visual neurons become responsive to either vertical or horizontal stripes, depending on the particular early environment (Blakemore & Cooper, 1970). A similar result is obtained if cats are reared viewing horizontal stripes with one eye and vertical stripes with the other. In this situation, the eye exposed to vertical stripes drives primarily neurons responding only to vertical stripes, and vice versa (Hirsch & Spinelli, 1970).

Other forms of visual environment have also been shown to modify the response of the cortical neurons. Rearing kittens that view a stroboscopic light (Cynader, Berman, & Hein, 1973; Olson & Pettigrew 1974), an environment of moving stripes (Cynader, Berman, & Hein, 1975; Pettigrew & Garey, 1974; Tretter, Cynader, & Singer, 1975), a visual environment of dots (Pettigrew & Freeman, 1973; Van Sluyters & Blakemore, 1973), or a visual field deviated with prisms (Shlaer, 1971) all result in altered neurophysiological responses in cortical cells. The response characteristics of units in cats reared with these various treatments are not found in normal cortical cells, indicating a marked degree of plasticity in the young kitten's visual cortex.

Morphological and electrophysiological effects of altered early visual environments have been observed in the retina, lateral geniculate nucleus, superior colliculus, and cortex (Blakemore, 1974a). Daniels and Pettigrew (1976, Tables I & II) have summarized the effects of different manipulations of the visual environment at various levels in the kitten's visual system. Although the cat has been most widely used in these experiments, there are also data from mice, rats, rabbits, and monkeys. Behavioral effects have

been observed in humans. Many humans have astigmatism, in which the refractive power of the eye is different for various meridians. Such people
can focus lines in one meridian but not in the perpendicular meridian. In
cases of high astigmatism the refractive error is present shortly after birth
and remains relatively constant throughout life. These people are therefore
exposed during development to a situation reminiscent of the animal experiments of Blakemore and co-workers (Blakemore & Cooper, 1970; Blakemore & Mitchell, 1973), in which cats were raised viewing only horizontal
or vertical stripes. When human astigmatic subjects are tested as adults they
indeed have sensitivity differences in the visual resolution of vertical gratings
as compared with horizontal gratings. The defect is neural rather than
ocular, since optical correction of the lens does not alter visual sensitivity
in behavioral tests (Freeman, Mitchell, & Millodot, 1972; Mitchell,
Freeman, Millodot, & Haegerstrom, 1973). In addition, the visual evoked
responses of astigmatic subjects are decreased for the stimulus orientation
for which these individuals have a reduced resolution (Freeman & Thibos,
1973).

Behavioral studies on monocularly deprived kittens (Dews & Wiesel,
1970) and monkeys (Von Noorden & Dowling, 1970; Von Noorden,
Dowling, & Ferguson, 1970) and on kittens exposed to a restricted visual
pattern (Blakemore & Cooper, 1970) have shown subsequent defects in
visually guided behavior. Active participation with a patterned environment
is also important for development of visuomotor coordination (Hein,
1972).

There are three issues which repeatedly appear in discussions on the role
of early visual experience in neural development. The first concerns the
extent to which cortical neurons are functional before visual experience
begins in the kitten, and whether early experience in normal development
influences the formation of neural connections. In adult cats cortical
neurons selectively respond to certain features of the visual stimulus. There
are cells which respond to: (1) the position of the stimulus, (2) whether the
stimulus is darker or lighter than the background, (3) the direction and
velocity of movement of the stimulus, (4) the size and orientation of the
stimulus, and (5) the disparity or relative positioning of the image in the
two eyes (Barlow, 1975). Neurons with the first three response characteristics
are already present in visually inexperienced kittens, but there is some
debate concerning the presence of the last two types (Blakemore & Van
Sluyters, 1975). The consensus of opinion is that all types exist in kittens
except those units responding to binocular disparity. It remains to be determined whether the kitten units have the same degree of selectivity as those
in adults; experience may contribute to producing refinements in their
responsivity. It is certainly true to say that the visual system of the kitten

continues to mature after eye opening, since the newborn does not have the visual acuity characteristic of the adult (Barlow, 1975). Grobstein and Chow (1976) have extensively discussed the evidence bearing on these questions.

A second issue concerns critical or sensitive periods during which early experience is likely to be most effective in influencing visual development. This question has been studied in cats (Hubel & Wiesel, 1970), monkeys (Baker, Grigg, & Von Noorden, 1974), and humans (Banks, Aslin & Letson, 1975) and is discussed by Blakemore (1974a) and Daniels and Pettigrew (1976). The third issue centers on the extent to which the rabbit visual system is sensitive to alterations of the early visual environment; the reader is referred to discussions by Grobstein and Chow (1976) and Daniels and Pettigrew (1976).

There is a large and growing body of evidence that the early visual environment can influence the development of the mammalian visual system at several levels and in a variety of species. But exactly *how* does experience act in the developing nervous system? Grobstein and Chow (1976) put the question in terms of experience-sensitivity, or the observation that the formation of neural connections is affected by experience, versus experience-dependence, or the extent to which there are critical pieces of ontogenetic information that are provided by experience during development. Experience-sensitive processes have certainly been documented, but are there aspects of neural development that are truly experience-dependent? Only in the visual system are there at present sufficient data to begin to directly test the existence of experience-dependent neural connections.

Much of the progress in understanding how the early environment can modify the developing visual system derives from an extensive knowledge of the anatomy, physiology, and behavior of the adult system, and from use of a variety of technical approaches for manipulating the early visual environment. Many principles are emerging that can be tested in other senses as more information on structural and functional development is acquired and as a greater variety of methods for changing the early environment are used in these senses.

VII. General Discussion

A. *Possible Mechanisms for Structural and Neurophysiological Effects*

Several different levels of neuronal and behavioral plasticity have been described in this chapter, including ultrastructural and light-microscopic anatomical alterations, single-unit and evoked-potential electrophysiological changes, and both highly specific and general behavioral modifications. Although it is hoped that the physiochemical mechanisms related to each of these phenomena will ultimately be understood, at present we can only outline possible neural mechanisms that might underlie the effects of early sensory experience.

During neural development the processes of cell division, migration, growth, differentiation, and death all take place. Depending on when the organism is exposed to a particular modification of its usual early sensory experience, any one of these ongoing processes could be affected. It has often been suggested that one of the least complex ways to modify the developing nervous system would be through the process of cell death. Examples of cell death in the central nervous system after receptor destruction are numerous; loss of neurons has been observed after destruction of auditory (Levi-Montalcini, 1949), tactile (Johnson *et al.*, 1972), and visual (DeLong & Sidman, 1962) receptors. Cell death, however, seemingly does not account for many of the structural and electrophysiological neuronal modifications that result from early experience. In the tactile system, alterations in the usual neuronal proliferation and migration are thought to be the most likely mechanisms to explain the disarrangement of cortical barrels after vibrissae receptor destruction (Van der Loos & Woolsey, 1973; Weller & Johnson, 1975). In the visual system, changes in neurophysiological response characteristics in the cat visual cortex after destruction of the early visual environment could conceivably be attributed to cell death. But during penetration of the visual cortex with microelectrodes, regions of silent cells that have degenerated are not encountered (Blakemore & Cooper, 1970; Pettigrew, Olson, & Hirsch, 1973). It seems more likely, therefore, that neurons are modified in some manner which alters their responsiveness to visual stimulation. Also, in the olfactory system, after exposing rats to a specific odor for a prolonged period, degenerative changes are seen in some neurons in the olfactory bulb but cell death is not thought to occur (Døving & Pinching, 1973).

What specific types of neuronal modification could occur that might explain the structural and functional changes effected by manipulation of early sensory experience? During the complex process of neuron differentiation there are many stages that may be susceptible to modification, including: maturation and growth of the soma; growth of the axon; myelination; axonal branching at nerve terminals involving both collateralization and possibly regression of terminals; growth of dendrites, including dendritic spine formation; and formation of synapses. Through axonal branching, dendritic growth, and synapse formation, whereby presynaptic and postsynaptic neurons interact, the actual circuitry of the nervous system is finally established. Some circuits seem to develop quite autonomously. Saunders and Bock (in this volume) note that the auditory pathway in the kitten is functional before synaptic junctions between the VIIIth nerve and the hair cells are functional. The basic organization and connections of this pathway are established without peripheral input. In the visual cortex of the cat, too, field potentials can be evoked by electrical stimulation of the optic nerve 4–6 days before units respond to flash stimulation of the eyes (Cragg, 1974).

Other neural circuits, however, have been modified through early sensory experience. Among the proposed structural changes that may underlie observed functional plasticity in the cat and monkey visual cortex are changes in dendritic branching and spine density, collateral branching of axon terminals, and alterations in synapses. The first of these, increased dendritic spine density, was reported in the lateral geniculate nucleus and cortex as a result of excess light stimulation in the rat (Parnavelas, Globus, & Kaups, 1973a, 1973b); conversely, light deprivation resulted in decreased spine density and dendritic branching in the visual cortex (Coleman & Riesen, 1968; Globus & Scheibel, 1967). Hubel, Wiesel, and LeVay (1976) hypothesized that the changes in width of monkey cortex ocular dominance columns after monocular deprivation came about through branching of nerve terminals supplying one set of columns, while terminals supplying the other set retracted. A similar phenomenon might take place in the somatosensory cortex. Van der Loos and Woolsey (1973) noted that after vibrissae destruction, in some instances remaining cortical barrels adjacent to a barrelless region appeared larger in size than their controls in the opposite hemisphere. Perhaps an increase in nerve terminals through collateral sprouting resulted in larger barrels.

Another suggestion that Wiesel and Hubel (1965) made, in discussing cortical effects of monocular and binocular deprivation in the kitten, is that afferent terminals *compete* for space on the cortical cell membrane, with more efficient synapses expanding and others shrinking. Synaptic competition is also discussed by Blakemore, Van Sluyters, and Movshon (1976), who propose that inefficient synapses, e.g., those connected to a deprived eye, are silenced but capable of reactivation. Just as it is suggested that inefficiency derives from disuse, the passage of neural activity along used pathways is possibly facilitated (Hebb, 1949). Rutledge (1976) has reported postsynaptic structural changes, including growth in apical dendrites and their spines, as a consequence of increased use.

In summary, several mechanisms including neuronal death, proliferation, migration, collateral branching of axon terminals, competition for synaptic space, and alterations in synaptic efficiency seem to relate to the structural and functional changes described in this chapter. Yet at present we cannot hope to resolve the cellular and molecular mechanisms underlying neural plasticity because there are so many basic questions for which we have no answers. For example, what determines the specificity of new synapses? What factors determine the sites of synaptogenesis? How are the density and topography of transmitter release sites regulated? (For discussion of these and related questions, see Appel, 1975; Strumwasser, 1976.) What is the relation between anatomical and functional maturity in a neuron, or what characterizes the progress from a morphologically differentiated synapse to a functional unit (Appel, 1975)? For experience to have an effect on the developing nervous system, some structure must presumably be functional to interact with experience. A synapse only gradually assumes adult structure (Cragg, 1972). Early synapses are characterized by: short regions of apposed membrane not fully differentiated into dense projections; lack of distinguishing features between pre- and postsynaptic membranes; few synaptic vesicles; and mitochondria that are not yet accumulated in the axon terminal. When, during these gradual morphological changes, is the synapse first functional? And does function gradually progress to the adult form as does structure? Until more of these questions are resolved, we must remain in the realm of speculation concerning the cellular and subcellular bases of neural plasticity.

B. Neural Plasticity, Learning, and Memory

If one adopts a broad definition of plasticity such as Davis's—"a modification of a behavioral or neural output pattern that is acquired because of experience" (Davis, 1976, p. 431)—then the definition encompasses learning and memory as well as the neurophysiological and behavioral changes described in this chapter. The usefulness of evoking traditional concepts of learning to describe the types of modifications discussed here has been questioned (Gottlieb, 1976a), but obviously there can be an advantage in seeking unifying, general concepts. Blakemore (1974b), Globus (1975), and Mark (1974) have suggested that learning and memory are examples or extensions of the mechanisms responsible for the physical changes that occur during interactions between the developing nervous system and the environment. Diamond, Cooper, Turner, and Macintyre (1976) give evidence that axonal branching exists throughout life as a means of continuous regulation of nerve fields—providing an enduring ability to modify neural circuits. The effects of early sensory experience on the developing nervous system may well be examples of a broader neural flexibility encompassing learning and memory.

However, Rosenzweig and Bennett in their chapter in this volume state that brain changes resulting from interactions with an enriched environment are not directly comparable to the modifications effected by manipulation of the visual environment. They state that the effects of visual deprivation or distortion are limited to critical periods early in the life of the animal. On the other hand, Rosenzweig and Bennett maintain that the enriched environment effects which they describe can be obtained throughout the life cycle and are therefore more comparable to the continual process of learning and memory.

But the effects of early modification of the visual environment are not in fact limited to a strict critical period; rather the organism is merely more sensitive during a period of maximum susceptibility. As Blakemore (1974a) points out, effects are pronounced only if the visual environment is altered during the period of about 3 to 15 weeks of age in kittens. However, adult cats exposed to a visual environment of selected orientation also have altered cortical neuronal responses (Creutzfeldt & Heggelund, 1975). "Perhaps there is no finite end to the sensitive period; while modifiability is certainly at its most pronounced early in life, it may persist in some rudimentary fashion even in the adult visual cortex" (Blakemore, 1974a, p. 155).

Similarly, for some of the other effects of early sensory experience reported in this chapter, there does not seem to be a critical period in the strict embryological sense of a very limited time when irreversible changes result from environmental manipulations. Marr and Lilliston (1969) examined the relationship in rats between age of exposure to an unnatural odor and later preference for that odor and found no support for the critical period hypothesis. In studies on guinea pigs (Carter & Marr, 1970), it was found that animals exposed to an odor from 1 to 6 days of age had a greater preference when tested later than did animals exposed at older ages, but guinea pigs exposed at all periods demonstrated an effect. As in the visual system, there seems to be increased sensitivity to environmental changes during a maximally susceptible period. And indeed Rosenzweig and Bennett note that, in their own experiments, responsiveness to enriched and impoverished environments decreased as successively older starting ages were tested, consistent with a period of maximum susceptibility. Thus, a distinction between the effects of interactions with an enriched environment and those of a particular form of sensory stimulation on the basis of critical periods seems unfounded.

C. *Approaches to Studying the Effects of Early Sensory Experience*

At present a variety of methods are being used to study the effects of early experience on the visual system. Table I demonstrates how few of these various approaches have been used in audition, gustation, olfaction, and touch. There are probably two major reasons for this imbalance: the extent of knowledge on development of the visual system and the ability to control visual stimuli. Both will be discussed.

TABLE I

EXPERIMENTAL MANIPULATION OF EARLY SENSORY EXPERIENCE IN AUDITORY, GUSTATORY, OLFACTORY, TACTILE, AND VISUAL SYSTEMS IN MAMMALS AND BIRDS[a]

Experimental manipulation[b]	Effect studied[c]	Sensory system[d]				
		Auditory	Gustatory	Olfactory	Tactile	Visual
1. Surgical destruction of the peripheral receptor	a. Neuroanatomical	+		+	+	+
	b. Neurophysiological				+	+
	c. Behavioral					
2. Elimination of all sensory input	a. Neuroanatomical	+				+
	b. Neurophysiological					+
	c. Behavioral					+
3. Modification of sensory input	a. Neuroanatomical			+	+	+
	b. Neurophysiological	+		+		+
	c. Behavioral	+	+	+		+

[a]This table summarizes the different approaches to the study of the effects of early sensory experience on central nervous system development and behavior. The table is based on references cited in this chapter only.

[b]Three general kinds of experimental manipulations have been used: (1) destruction of the peripheral receptor, e.g., enucleation; (2) elimination of sensory input, e.g., auditory, with ear plugs; tactile, with deafferentation; visual, with eyelid sutures; (3) modification of sensory input, e.g., one predominant taste or odor; vertical stripes.

[c]For each experimental manipulation, three types of neural effects may be studied: neuroanatomical, neurophysiological, or behavioral changes.

[d]The (+) symbol in a column indicates that at least one experiment has been performed; no weighting factor has been included to suggest numbers of studies.

There are detailed data on the structural and functional development of the visual system, especially in cats. Thus a suitable experimental animal is available, as is a baseline against which to compare the effects of early experience. In comparison very little is known in any species about the structural and functional development of the other sensory systems (for a review of prenatal sensory development, see Bradley & Mistretta, 1975; for postnatal, see Gottlieb, 1971b). This paucity of basic developmental knowledge makes it difficult to interpret how early experience might be altering the nervous system. Gottlieb (1976a, 1976c) has recently suggested that early experience could contribute to neural development in three ways: (1) in an inductive manner, by channeling development in one direction rather than another; (2) in a facilitative way, influencing thresholds or the rate at which structural and functional development proceeds; (3) through maintenance of the integrity of an already complete system. Of course all three of these mechanisms could be acting simultaneously, on different neural structures at different stages of development. But to determine what type of influence is acting in a particular experiment, developmental changes and the time at which they occur must be known.

Although it is possible to precisely control the quality and quantity of visual stimulation that is presented to the developing organism, it is not so easy to manipulate other sensory stimuli. Some of the earliest reported and most striking effects in visual experiments resulted from visual deprivation by enucleation, eyelid suturing, and dark-rearing. In other senses, similar experiments can be performed; for example, surgical removal of the organ of Corti and surgical or chemical ablation of the olfactory mucosa and Jacobson's organ. But it is not possible to remove *all* of an animal's taste buds or all tactile receptors. And without surgical ablation, it is difficult to deprive an organism of the experience of taste, smell, touch, or audition. Of course, this is not to say that the quantity of sensory stimulation cannot be radically altered; and certainly qualitative modifications can be introduced.

Until there are more studies of the effects of early sensory experience on the development of sensory systems other than vision, we can only speculate on the extent to which all sensory systems are plastic. Perhaps one should not expect that each sensory system would be equally plastic. Two advantages for plasticity in the visual system have been proposed (Blakemore, 1974a, 1974b). One advantage is that the environment can play a substantial role in establishing a visual system ideally suited to the organism's visual world. It could also be an advantage for other sensory systems to develop specialized "feature detectors" for the organism's particular auditory, taste, smell, or touch world. But plasticity carries inherent dangers as well, and the stakes may be extremely high in, for instance, the taste system. If an animal through early experience developed an extreme sensitivity or very low threshold for detecting a noxious substance, that would be advantageous. But it would be dangerous if an animal developed a preference or lowered aversion for harmful chemicals through early exposure. Since taste and olfaction direct food ingestion, which is directly related to the organism's health, it may be more advantageous to specify basic taste preferences and aversions without opportunity for environmental modification.

The second proposed advantage for visual plasticity relates to binocularity. The ability of cortical neurons to change preferred orientation would ensure that binocular neurons adopt similar preferred orientations on the two retinas; this is important for the role of cortical neurons in binocular fusion and stereopsis. A related argument could possibly apply to the auditory system also, but not to taste, smell, or touch.

As well as considering whether all sensory systems are equally plastic, it is important to discuss whether all species are susceptible to neural modification through early experience. One may expect differences in susceptibility according to how an animal uses a particular sensory system and possibly according to the organism's phylogenetic position. It has been reported that the rabbit's visual system is not as easily modified through early experience as is the cat's (Mize & Murphy, 1973). Blakemore and Van Sluyters (1975) suggest that extreme plasticity in the visual system may occur only in highly binocular animals with well-developed cortical processes for stereoscopic vision. For the taste system, Drickamer (1972) has suggested that small mammals may have different inherent capacities for the extent to which their food habits can be affected by the early environment, depending on whether they occupy broad or narrow habitats.

Globus (1975) has noted that the effects of deafferentation on the nervous system are usually more pronounced the earlier the deafferentation is performed, the more complete it is, and the higher the species' position on the phylogenetic scale. Also, the number and proportion of central nervous system neurons with exclusively local synaptic connections increase according to level in phylogeny, reaching a peak in the human (Schmitt, Dev, & Smith, 1976). It is these neurons, termed microneurons, that form relatively late in development and are hypothesized to be the most susceptible to modification (Altman, 1967; Jacobson, 1974). These data suggest that primates are a highly flexible group. The primates, and especially humans, are also characterized by a long period of immaturity, a time for transmission of culture and learning. If an organism's behavior were rigidly determined, this lengthy period would serve few positive functions and much adaptive flexibility would be lost.

Since the nervous system develops at different rates in different species (and in different regions within the same species), the role of the *postnatal* environment in influencing nervous system development may be very different from species to species. It is odd that the possibility of prenatally modifying mammalian brain and behavioral development through intrauterine sensory stimulation has received so little attention compared to, for example, avian embryos. Auditory, gustatory, olfactory, tactile, and visual stimulation could be altered in quality and intensity using chronic fetal preparations (Bradley & Mistretta, 1975). Also, various surgical manipulations could be performed, such as receptor ablation, eyelid suturing, eye rotation, and receptor grafting. Fetal tissues heal rapidly in the warm, sterile, liquid environment of the amniotic fluid. As discussed in the section on early tactile experience, Taub and collaborators have begun to use this type of preparation. Perhaps in the future we will be able to learn more about the relative effectiveness of the intra- versus extrauterine environments in influencing the developing nervous system in different species.

A new understanding of how early sensory experience affects the developing nervous system will certainly emerge with increasing knowledge of basic processes in neural development and function and of the ontogenesis of sensory systems. But this new understanding will probably come more quickly if investigators working in sensory systems other than vision use more varied approaches in manipulating early sensory experience and in analyzing subsequent effects. Further, interrelations among the various levels of effects will be found as more investigators study anatomy, physiology, and behavior in one species, after one particular environmental manipulation. An attempt to compare specific effects, both cellular and behavioral, with broader phenomena should provide additional insights. And finally, an extension of studies into prenatal life may yield a whole new frame of reference from which to consider when sensory experience begins.

VIII. Summary

In this chapter we have discussed a variety of ways in which early sensory experience has been manipulated in attempts to alter development of the auditory, gustatory, olfactory, tactile, and visual systems. Techniques ranging from total elimination of sensory input by surgical removal of receptors to alteration of the quality of sensory stimuli have been used, and structural, neurophysiological, and behavioral effects have been studied. In the auditory and gustatory systems most investigations have been focused on assessing behavioral changes after modifying early sound or taste experience. As well as behavioral effects, there has been an emphasis on examining structural changes subsequent to early experience in the olfactory and tactile systems. In the visual system, structural, neurophysiological, and behavioral effects have been extensively studied; similarly, a variety of manipulations for modifying visual input have been used. From experiments in all five of the sensory systems discussed, it can be concluded that early sensory experience has an effect on developing neural structure, physiology, and behavior. But without more experiments in systems other than visual, it is not yet possible to assess whether all sensory systems are equally susceptible to manipulations of early experience.

Acknowledgments

The authors held NIH Grant HD07483 and Contract HD-4-2868 while writing this chapter. We thank Miss S. M. Carr for bibliographic assistance.

References

Altman, J. Postnatal growth and differentiation of the mammalian brain, with implications for a morphological theory of memory. In G. Quarton, T. Melnechuk, & F. O. Schmitt (Eds.), *The neurosciences: A study program.* New York: Rockefeller University Press, 1967. Pp. 723–743.

Appel, S. H. Neuronal recognition and synaptogenesis. *Experimental Neurology*, 1975, **48**(3), P. 2, 52–74.

Arnold, G. W. Some principles in the investigation of selective grazing. *Proceedings of Australian Society of Animal Production*, 1964, **5**, 258–271.

Baker, F. H., Grigg, P., & Von Noorden, G. K. Effects of visual deprivation and strabismus on the response of neurons in the visual cortex of the monkey, including studies on the striate and prestriate cortex in the normal animal. *Brain Research*, 1974, **66**, 185–208.

Banks, M. S., Aslin, R. N., & Letson, R. D. Sensitive period for the development of human binocular vision. *Science*, 1975, **190**, 675–677.

Barlow, H. B. Visual experience and cortical development. *Nature (London)*, 1975, **258**, 199–204.

Barnett, S. A. Behaviour components in the feeding of wild and laboratory rats. *Behaviour*, 1956, **9**, 24–43.

Batkin, S., Groth, H., Watson, J. R., & Ansberry, M. Effects of auditory deprivation on the development of auditory sensitivity in albino rats. *Electroencephalography and Clinical Neurophysiology*, 1970, **28**, 351–359.

Berman, A. J., & Berman, D. Fetal deafferentation: the ontogenesis of movement in the absence of peripheral sensory feedback. *Experimental Neurology*, 1973, **38**, 170–176.

Blakemore, C. Development of functional connexions in the mammalian visual system. *British Medical Bulletin*, 1974, **30**, 152–157. (a)

Blakemore, C. Developmental factors in the formation of feature extracting neurons. In F. O. Schmitt & F. G. Worden (Eds.), *The neurosciences: Third study program.* Cambridge, Mass.: MIT Press, 1974. Pp. 105–113. (b)

Blakemore, C., & Cooper, G. F. Development of the brain depends on the visual environment. *Nature (London)*, 1970, **228**, 477–478.

Blakemore, C., & Mitchell, D. E. Environmental modification of the visual cortex and the neural basis of learning and memory. *Nature (London)*, 1973, **241**, 467–468.

Blakemore, C., & Van Sluyters, R. C. Innate and environmental factors in the development of the kitten's visual cortex. *Journal of Physiology (London)*, 1975, **248**, 663–716.

Blakemore, C., Van Sluyters, R. C., & Movshon, J. A. Synaptic competition in the kitten's visual cortex. *Cold Spring Harbor Symposia on Quantitative Biology*, 1976, **40**, 601–609.

Bradley, R. M., & Mistretta, C. M. Fetal sensory receptors. *Physiological Reviews*, 1975, **55**, 352–382.

Bronson, G. Evidence of the lack of influence of early diet on adult food preferences in rats. *Journal of Comparative and Physiological Psychology*, 1966, **62**, 162–164.

Burghardt, G. M. Chemical-cue preferences of newborn snakes: Influence of prenatal maternal experience. *Science*, 1971, **171**, 921–923.

Burghardt, G. M., & Hess, E. H. Food imprinting in the snapping turtle, Chelydra serpentina. *Science*, 1966, **151**, 108–109.

Capretta, P. J., Petersik, J. T., & Stewart, D. J. Acceptance of novel flavours is increased after early experience of diverse tastes. *Nature (London)* 1975, **254**, 689–691.

Capretta, P. J., & Rawls, L. H. Establishment of a flavor preference in rats: Importance of nursing and weaning experience. *Journal of Comparative and Physiological Psychology*, 1974, **86**, 670–673.

Carter, C. S., & Marr, J. N. Olfactory imprinting and age variables in the guinea pig, *Cavia porcellus*. *Animal Behaviour*, 1970, **18**, 238–244.

Clopton, B. M., & Winfield, J. A. Early auditory experience modifies unit responsiveness to temporal auditory patterns in the inferior colliculus. *Journal of the Acoustical Society of America*, 1974, **55**, 468. (Abstract).

Coleman, P. D., & Riesen, A. H. Environmental effects on cortical dendritic fields. I. Rearing in the dark. *Journal of Anatomy*, 1968, **102**, 363–374.

Cornwell, C. A. Golden hamster pups adapt to complex rearing odors. *Behavioral Biology*, 1975, **14**, 175–188.

Cragg, B. G. The development of synapses in cat visual cortex. *Investigative Opthalmology*, 1972, **11**, 377–385.

Cragg, B. G. Plasticity of synapses. *British Medical Bulletin*, 1974, **30**, 141–144.

Creutzfeldt, O. D., & Heggelund, P. Neural plasticity in visual cortex of adult cats after exposure to visual patterns. *Science*, 1975, **188**, 1025–1027.

Cuschieri, A., & Bannister, L. H. The development of the olfactory mucosa in the mouse: electron microscopy. *Journal of Anatomy*, 1975, **119**, 471–498. (a)

Cuschieri, A., & Bannister, L. H. The development of the olfactory mucosa in the mouse: light microscopy. *Journal of Anatomy*, 1975, **119**, 277–286. (b)

Cynader, M., Berman, N., & Hein, A. Cats reared in stroboscopic illumination: Effects on receptive fields in visual cortex. *Proceedings of the National Academy of Sciences U.S.A.*, 1973, **70**, 1353–1354.

Cynader, M., Berman, N., & Hein, A. Cats raised in a one-directional world: Effects on receptive fields in visual cortex and superior colliculus, *Experimental Brain Research*, 1975, **22**, 267–280.

Daniels, J. D., & Pettigrew, J. D. Development of neuronal responses in the visual system of cats. In G. Gottlieb (Ed.), *Studies on the development of behavior and the nervous system* (Vol. 3): *Neural and behavioral specificity*. New York: Academic Press, 1976. Pp. 195–232.

Davis, W. J. Plasticity in the invertebrates. In M. R. Rosenzweig & E. L. Bennett (Eds.), *Neural mechanisms of learning and memory*. Cambridge, Mass.: MIT Press, 1976. Pp. 430–462.

DeLong, G. R., & Sidman, R. L. Effects of eye removal at birth on histogenesis of the mouse superior colliculus. An autoradiographic study with tritiated thymidine. *Journal of Comparative Neurology*, 1962, **118**, 205–224.

Dethier, V. G., & Goldrich, N. Blowflies: Alteration of adult taste responses by chemicals present during development. *Science*, 1971, **173**, 242–244.

Devor, M., & Schneider, G. E. Attraction to home-cage odor in hamster pups: Specificity and changes with àge. *Behavioral Biology*, 1974, **10**, 211–221.

Dews, P. B., & Wiesel, T. N. Consequences of monocular deprivation on visual behaviour in kittens. *Journal of Physiology (London)*, 1970, **206**, 437–455.

Diamond, J., Cooper, E., Turner, C., & Macintyre, L. Trophic regulation of nerve sprouting. *Science*, 1976, **193**, 371–377.

Døving, K. B., & Pinching, A. J. Selective degeneration of neurones in the olfactory bulb following prolonged odour exposure, *Brain Research*, 1973, **52**, 115–129.

Domjan, M. Determinants of the enhancement of flavored-water intake by prior exposure. *Journal of Experimental Psychology: Animal Behavior Processes*, 1976, **2**, 17–27.

Drickamer, L. C. Experience and selection behavior in the food habits of Peromyscus: use of olfaction. *Behaviour*, 1972, **41**, 269–287.

Evans, D. R. Depression of taste sensitivity to specific sugars by their presence during development. *Science*, 1961, **133**, 327–328.

Farbman, A. I. Elecron microscope study of the developing taste bud in rat fungiform papilla. *Developmental Biology*, 1965, **11**, 110–135.

Freeman, R. D., Mitchell, D. E., & Millodot, M. A neural effect of partial visual deprivation in humans. *Science*, 1972, **175**, 1384–1386.

Freeman, R. D., & Thibos, L. N. Electrophysiological evidence that abnormal early visual experience can modify the human brain. *Science*, 1973, **180**, 876–878.

Galef, B. G., Jr., & Henderson, P. W. Mother's milk: A determinant of the feeding preferences of weaning rat pups. *Journal of Comparative and Physiological Psychology*, 1972, **78**, 213–219.

Gauron, E. F., & Becker, W. C. The effects of early sensory deprivation on adult rat behavior under competition stress: An attempt at replication of a study by Alexander Wolf. *Journal of Comparative and Physiological Psychology*, 1959, **52**, 689–693.

Globus, A. Brain morphology as a function of presynaptic morphology and activity. In A. H. Riesen (Ed.), *The developmental neuropsychology of sensory deprivation*. New York: Academic Press, 1975, Pp. 9–91.

Globus, A., & Scheibel, A. B. The effect of visual deprivation on cortical neurons: a Golgi study. *Experimental Neurology*, 1967, **19**, 331–345.

Gottlieb, G. *Development of species identification in birds. An inquiry into the prenatal determinants of perception.* Chicago: University of Chicago Press, 1971. (a).

Gottlieb, G. Ontogenesis of sensory function in birds and mammals. In E. Tobach, L. R. Aronson, & E. Shaw (Eds.), *The biopsychology of development*. New York: Academic Press, 1971. Pp. 67–128. (b)

Gottlieb, G. Conceptions of prenatal development: Behavioral embryology. *Psychological Review*, 1976, **83**, 215–234. (a)

Gottlieb, G. Early development of species-specific auditory perception in birds. In G. Gottlieb (Ed.), *Studies on the development of behavior and the nervous system* (Vol. 3): *Neural and behavioral specificity*. New York: Academic Press, 1976, Pp. 237–280. (b)

Gottlieb, G. The roles of experience in the development of behavior and the nervous system. In G. Gottlieb (Ed.), *Studies on the development of behavior and the nervous system* (Vol. 3): *Neural and behavioral specificity*. New York: Academic Press, 1976, Pp. 25–54. (c).

Green, K. G., & Parker, L. A. Gustatory memory: Incubation and interference. *Behavioral Biology*, 1975, **13**, 359–367.

Gregory, E. H., & Pfaff, D. W. Development of olfactory-guided behavior in infant rats. *Physiology and Behavior*, 1971, **6**, 573–576.

Grobstein, P., & Chow, K. L. Receptive field organization in the mammalian visual cortex: The role of individual experience in development. In G. Gottlieb (Ed.), *Studies on the development of behavior and the nervous system* (Vol. 3): *Neural and behavioral specificity*. New York: Academic Press, 1976. Pp. 155–193.

Guillery, R. W. Binocular competition in the control of geniculate cell growth. *Journal of Comparative Neurology*, 1972, **144**, 117–130.

Hamburger, V. Anatomical and physiological basis of embryonic motility in birds and mammals. In G. Gottlieb (Ed.), *Studies on the development of behavior and the nervous system* (Vol. 1): *Behavioral embryology*. New York: Academic Press, 1973. Pp. 51–76.

Hasler, A. D. Guideposts of migrating fishes. *Science*, 1960, **132**, 785–792.

Hebb, D. O. *The organization of behavior*. New York: Wiley, 1949.

Hein, A. Acquiring components of visually guided behavior. In A. D. Pick (Ed.), *Minnesota Symposia on Child Psychology* (Vol. 6). Minneapolis: University of Minnesota Press, 1972. Pp. 53–68.

Henry, K. R. Audiogenic seizure susceptibility induced in C57B1/6J mice by prior auditory exposure. *Science*, 1967, **158**, 938–940.

Hilker, D. M., Hee, J., Higashi, J., Ikehara, S., & Paulsen, E. Free choice consumption of spiced diets by rats. *Journal of Nutrition*, 1967, **91**, 129–131.

Hinds, J. W. Early neuron differentiation in the mouse olfactory bulb. I. Light microscopy. *Journal of Comparative Neurology*, 1972, **146**, 233–252. (a)

Hinds, J. W. Early neuron differentiation in the mouse olfactory bulb. II. Electron microscopy. *Journal of Comparative Neurology*, 1972, **146**, 253–276. (b)

Hirsch, H. V. B., & Spinelli, D. N. Visual experience modifies distribution of horizontally and vertically oriented receptive fields in cats. *Science*, 1970, **168**, 869–871.

Hubel, D. H., & Wiesel, T. N. Receptive fields, binocular interaction and functional architecture in the cat's visual cortex. *Journal of Physiology (London)*, 1962, **160**, 106–154.

Hubel, D. H., & Wiesel, T. N. Binocular interaction in striate cortex of kittens reared with artificial squint. *Journal of Neurophysiology*, 1965, **28**, 1041–1059.

Hubel, D. H. & Wiesel, T. N. The period of susceptibility to the physiological effects of unilateral eye closure in kittens. *Journal of Physiology (London)*, 1970, **206**, 419–436.

Hubel, D. H., Wiesel, T. N., & LeVay, S. Functional architecture of Area 17 in normal and monocularly deprived macaque monkeys. *Cold Spring Harbour Symposia on Quantitative Biology*, 1976, **40**, 581–589.

Jacobson, M. A plentitude of neurons. In G. Gottlieb (Ed.), *Studies on the development of behavior and the nervous system* (Vol. 2): *Aspects of neurogenesis*. New York: Academic Press, 1974. Pp. 151–166.

Jerome, N. W. Taste experience and the development of a dietary preference for sweet in humans: Ethnic and cultural variations. In J. M. Weiffenbach (Ed.), *Taste and development: The genesis of sweet preference*. Washington, D.C.: U.S. Gov. Printing Office, DHEW Pub. No. (NIH) 77–1068, 1977. Pp. 235–248.

Johnson, J. I., Hamilton, T. C., Hsung, J.-C., & Ulinski, P. S. Gracile nucleus absent in adult opossums after leg removal in infancy. *Brain Research*, 1972, **38**, 421–424.

Kalmus, H. Genetics of taste. In L. M. Beidler (Ed.), *Handbook of sensory physiology* (Vol. 4): *Chemical senses* (Part 2), *Taste*. Berlin and New York: Springer-Verlag, 1971, Pp. 165–179.

Keidel, W. D., & Neff, W. D. (Eds.) *Handbook of sensory physiology* (Vol. 5): *Auditory system*. Berlin and New York: Springer- Verlag, 1974.

Konishi, M. The role of auditory feeback in the control of vocalization in the whitecrowned sparrow. *Zeitschrift für Tierpsychologie*, 1965, **22**, 770–783.

LeMagnen, J., & Tallon, S. Préférence alimentaire du jeune rat induite par l'allaitement maternel. *Comptes Rendus des Séances de la Société de Biologie et de ses Filiales*, 1968, **162**, 387–390.

Lenneberg, E. H. On explaining language. *Science*, 1969, **164**, 635–643.

Leon, M., & Moltz, H. The development of the pheromonal bond in the albino rat. *Physiology and Behavior*, 1972, **8**, 683–686.

Levi-Montalcini, R. The development of the acoustico-vestibular centers in the chick embryo in the absence of the afferent root fibers and of descending fiber tracts. *Journal of Comparative Neurology*, 1949, **91**, 209–241.

Ling, E. R., Kon, S. K., & Porter, J. W. G. The composition of milk and the nutritive value of its components. In S. K. Kon & A. T. Cowie (Eds.), *Milk: The mammary gland and its secretion*. New York: Academic Press, 1961. Pp. 195–263.

Madison, D. M., Scholz, A. T., Cooper, J. C., Horrall, R. M., Hasler, A. D., & Dizon, A. E. Olfactory hypotheses and salmon migration: A synopsis of recent findings. *Fisheries Research Board of Canada Technical Report*, 1973, **414**, 1–35.

Manning,. A. "Pre-imaginal conditioning" in *Drosophila*. *Nature (London)*, 1967, **216**, 338–340.

Mark, R. *Memory and nerve cell connections*. London and New York: Oxford University Press (Clarendon), 1974.

Marler, P., & Tamura, M. Song dialects in three populations of white-crowned sparrow. *Condor*, 1962, **64**, 368–377.

Marr, J. N., & Gardner, L. E., Jr. Early olfactory experience and later social behavior in the rat: Preference, sexual responsiveness, and care of young. *Journal of Genetic Psychology*, 1965, **107**, 167–174.

Marr, J. N., & Lilliston, L. G. Social attachment in rats by odor and age. *Behaviour*, 1969, **33**, 277–282.

Matthews, M. R., & Powell, T. P. S. Some observations on transneuronal cell degeneration in the olfactory bulb of the rabbit. *Journal of Anatomy*, 1962, **96**, 89–102.

Mistretta, C. M. Topographical and histological study of the developing rat tongue, palate and taste buds. In J. F. Bosma (Ed.), *Third symposium on oral sensation and perception: The mouth of the infant*. Springfield, Ill.: Thomas, 1972. Pp. 163–187.

Mitchell, D. E., Freeman, R. D., Millodot, M., & Haegerstrom, G. Meridional amblyopia: Evidence for modification of the human visual system by early visual experience. *Vision Research*, 1973, **13**, 535–558.

Mize, R. R., & Murphy, E. H. Selective visual experience fails to modify receptive field properties of rabbit striate cortex neurons. *Science*, 1973, **180**, 320–323.

Moore, D. R., & Aitkin, L. M. Rearing in an acoustically unusual environment—Effects on neural auditory responses. *Neuroscience Letters*, 1975, **1**, 29–34.

Moskowitz, H. W., Kumaraiah, V., Sharma, K. N., Jacobs, H. L., & Sharma, S. D. Cross-cultural differences in simple taste preferences. *Science*, 1975, **190**, 1217–1218.

Nachman, M. The inheritance of saccharin preference. *Journal of Comparative and Physiological Psychology*, 1959, **52**, 451–457.

Olson, C. R., & Pettigrew, J. D. Single units in visual cortex of kittens reared in stroboscopic illumination. *Brain Research*, 1974, **70**, 189–204.

Oppenheim, R. W. The ontogeny of behavior in the chick embryo. In D. S. Lehrman, J. S. Rosenblatt, R. A. Hinde, & E. Shaw (Eds.), *Advances in the study of behavior* (Vol. 5). New York: Academic Press, 1974. Pp. 133–172.

Parnavelas, J. G., Globus, A., & Kaups, P. Changes in lateral geniculate neurones of rats as a result of continuous exposure to light. *Nature (London), New Biology*, 1973, **245**, 287–288. (a)

Parnavelas, J. G., Globus, A., & Kaups, P. Continuous illumination from birth affects spine density of neurons in the visual cortex of the rat. *Experimental Neurology*, 1973, **40**, 742–747. (b)

Pettigrew, J. D., & Freeman, R. D. Visual experience without lines: Effect on developing cortical neurons. *Science*, 1973, **182**, 599–601.

Pettigrew, J. D., & Garey, L. J. Selective modification of single neuron properties in the visual cortex of kittens. *Brain Research*, 1974, **66**, 160–164.

Pettigrew, J. D., Olson, C., & Hirsch, H. V. B. Cortical effect of selective visual experience: Degeneration or reorganization? *Brain Research*, 1973, **51**, 345–351.

Pinching, A. J., & Døving, K. B. Selective degeneration in the rat olfactory bulb following exposure to different odours. *Brain Research*, 1974, **82**, 195–204.

Pinching, A. J., & Powell, T. P. S. Ultrastructural features of transneuronal cell degeneration in the olfactory system. *Journal of Cell Science*, 1971, **8**, 253–287.

Porter, R. H., & Etscorn, F. Olfactory imprinting resulting from brief exposure in *Acomys cahirinus*. *Nature (London)*, 1974, **250**, 732–733.

Powell, T. P. S., & Erulkar, S. D. Transneuronal cell degeneration in the auditory relay nuclei of the cat. *Journal of Anatomy*, 1962, **96**, 249–268.

Rabinowitch, V. E. The role of experience in the development of food preferences in gull chicks. *Animal Behavior*, 1968, **16**, 425–428.

Riesen, A. H. Sensory deprivation. In E. Stellar & J. M. Sprague (Eds.), *Progress in physiological psychology* (Vol. 1). New York: Academic Press, 1966. Pp. 117–147.

Riesen, A. H., & Zilbert, D. E. Behavioral consequences of variations in early sensory environments. In A. H. Riesen (Ed.), *The developmental neuropsychology of sensory deprivation*. New York: Academic Press, 1975. Pp. 211–252.

Rutledge, L. T. Synaptogenesis: Effects of synaptic use. In M. R. Rosenzweig & E. L. Bennett (Eds.), *Neural Mechanisms of learning and memory*. Cambridge, Mass.: MIT Press, 1976. Pp. 329–339.

Ryugo, D. K., Ryugo, R., & Killackey, H. P. Changes in pyramidal cell density consequent to vibrissae removal in the newborn rat. *Brain Research*, 1975, **96**, 82–87.

Salas, M., Guzman-Flores, C., & Schapiro, S. An ontogenetic study of olfactory bulb electrical activity in the rat. *Physiology and Behavior*, 1969, **4**, 699–703.

Schiffman, H. R., Lore, R., Passafiume, J., & Neeb, R. Role of vibrissae for depth perception in the rat (*Rattus norvegicus*). *Animal Behavior*, 1970, **18**, 290–292.

Schmitt, F. O., Dev, P., & Smith, B. H. Electrotonic processing of information by brain cells. *Science*, 1976, **193**, 114–120.

Schönfelder, J., & Schwartze, P. Beiträge zur Steuerung der Bursttätigkeit des Bulbus olfactorius. III. Die Ontogenese der Bulbus-olfactorius-Bursttätigkeit bei der Ratte, sowie die Folgen der kompletten Zerstörung der Bulbi olfactorii am ersten Lebenstag für die körperliche Entwicklung dieser Spezies. *Acta Biologica et Medica Germanica*, 1971, **27**, 103–110.

Schwartze, P. Die postnatale Entwicklung der Bursttätigkeit im Bulbus olfactorius des Kaninchens. *Experientia*, 1967, **23**, 725.

Shlaer, R. Shift in binocular disparity causes compensatory change in the cortical structure of kittens. *Science*, 1971, **173**, 638–641.

Stockton, M. D., & Whitney, G. Effects of genotype, sugar, and concentration on sugar preference of laboratory mice (*Mus musculus*). *Journal of Comparative and Physiological Psychology*, 1974, **86**, 62–68.

Strumwasser, F. Properties of neurons and their relationship to concepts of plasticity. In M. R. Rosenzweig & E. L. Bennett (Eds.), *Neural mechanisms of learning and memory*. Cambridge, Mass.: M.I.T. Press, 1976. Pp. 468–474.

Taub, E., Barro, G., Heitmann, R., Grier, H. C., Boretos, J. W., & Cicmanec, J. L. Behavioral development in monkey infants following forelimb deafferentation of exteriorized fetuses at the end of the second trimester of pregnancy. *Neuroscience Abstracts*, 1975, **1**, 786. (Abstract).

Taub, E., Perrella, P., & Barro, G. Behavioral development after forelimb deafferentation on day of birth in monkeys with and without blinding. *Science*, 1973, **181**, 959–960.

Tees, R. C. Effects of early auditory restriction in the rat on adult pattern discrimination.

Journal of Comparative and Physiological Psychology, 1967, **63**, 389–393.

Tretter, F., Cynader, M., & Singer, W. Modification of direction selectivity of neurons in the visual cortex of kittens. *Brain Research*, 1975, **84**, 143–149.

Tschanz, B. Trottellummen: Die Entstehung der persönlichen Beziehungen zwischen Jungvogel und Eltern. *Zeitschrift für Tierpsychologie*, 1968, **4**, 1–103.

Turkewitz, G., Gilbert, M., & Birch, H. G. Early restriction of tactile stimulation and visual functioning in the kitten. *Developmental Psychobiology*, 1974, **7**, 243–248.

Van der Loos, H., & Woolsey, T. A. Somatosensory cortex: Structural alterations following early injury to sense organs. *Science*, 1973, **179**, 395–398.

Van Sluyters, R. C., & Blakemore, C. Experimental creation of unusual neuronal properties in visual cortex of kitten. *Nature (London)*, 1973, **246**, 506–508.

Vince, M. A. Some environmental effects on the activity and development of the avian embryo. In G. Gottlieb (Ed.), *Studies on the development of behavior and the nervous system* (Vol. 1): *Behavioral embryology*. New York: Academic Press, 1973. Pp. 285–323.

Von Noorden, G. K., & Dowling, J. E. Experimental amblyopia in monkeys. II. Behavioral studies in strabismic amblyopia. *Archives of Ophthalmology*, 1970, **84**, 215–221.

Von Noorden, G. K., Dowling, J. E., & Ferguson, D. C. Experimental amblyopia in monkeys. I. Behavioral studies of stimulus deprivation amblyopia. *Archives of Ophthalmology*, 1970, **84**, 206–214.

Warren, R. P., & Pfaffman, C. Early experience and taste aversion. *Journal of Comparative and Physiological Psychology*, 1959, **52**, 263–266.

Weller, W. L., & Johnson, J. I. Barrels in cerebral cortex altered by receptor disruption in newborn, but not in five-day-old mice (*Cricetidae* and *Muridae*). *Brain Research*, 1975, **83**, 504–508.

Westrum, L. E. Electron microscopy of synaptic structures in olfactory cortex of early postnatal rats. *Journal of Neurocytology*, 1975, **4**, 713–732.

Wiesel, T. N., & Hubel, D. H. Effects of visual deprivation on morphology and physiology of cells in the cat's lateral geniculate body. *Journal of Neurophysiology*, 1963, **26**, 978–993.

Wiesel, T. N., & Hubel, D. H. Comparison of the effects of unilateral and bilateral eye closure on cortical unit responses in kittens. *Journal of Neurophysiology*, 1965, **28**, 1029–1040.

Wolf, A. The dynamics of the selective inhibition of specific functions in neurosis: A preliminary report. *Psychosomatic Medicine*, 1943, **5**, 27–38.

INFLUENCES OF EARLY AUDITORY TRAUMA ON AUDITORY DEVELOPMENT

JAMES C. SAUNDERS AND GREGORY R. BOCK

Department of Otorhinolaryngology and Human Communication
University of Pennsylvania
Philadelphia, Pennsylvania

I. Introduction

One of the most comprehensive studies of childhood hearing loss was conducted on 5000 school-aged children in the Pittsburgh area (Eagles, Wishik & Doerfler, 1967; Eagles, Wishik, Doerfler, Melnick, & Levine, 1963). Disregarding middle-ear problems, a 1.6 to 5.0% incidence of hearing loss was observed in this population. Population data like these show that sensorineural hearing losses occur in children and raise the question of where this hearing loss originates. A recent study by Morgan, Charachon, and Brunguier (1971) has dealt with this problem by carefully determining the etiology in 290 cases of partially and profoundly deaf children. An inherited source, arising from genetic, chromosomal, or hereditary-congenital disorders, accounted for 20% of the cases. Acquired hearing loss due to such conditions as rubella, anoxia, prematurity, meningitis, encephalitis, or mumps, and occurring prenatally, during birth, or during childhood accounted for 44% of the cases. About 36% of the cases had a hearing loss of unknown origin. These observations are in general agreement with data published by other authors.

Many workers believe that most of the unexplained cases also have an inherited origin. This conclusion is based in part on the elimination of acquired factors after careful analysis of case histories, from the fact that deleterious traits can be carried as double recessives (Proctor & Proctor, 1967), and on various animal models of inherited deafness (Bosher & Hallpike, 1967; Deol, 1968). However, this conclusion may be an oversimplification since other sources of hearing loss have not been adequately considered. For example, hearing loss due to early acoustic trauma may also contribute to deafness of an unknown origin. The study of the effects of noise on children is not a well-developed area of inquiry, but the information that does exist on the subject has been reviewed by Mills (1975). The specific implications of acoustic trauma on the developing auditory system will be considered in detail in this review.

The present chapter will proceed by presenting an overview of auditory maturation as well as the consequences of acoustic trauma in the adult. This information will provide a basis for considering the consequences of overstimulation damage in an immature auditory system. The concept of a critical period for susceptibility to acoustic trauma will be introduced and the implications of this phenomenon will also be considered.

II. Normal Functional and Anatomical Development of the Auditory System

An important problem in the development of the auditory system is to define the onset of functional capacity and to correlate it with the morphological events that permit function. Generally, the first indication of the cochlear microphonic (CM) potential is taken as a sign that functional capacity has begun. However, the CM response is only an electrical transduction of hydrostatic pressure waves within the fluid-filled spaces of the cochlea. These pressure waves are the end product of a middle-ear system designed to transfer vibrational energy from an air medium to the fluid-filled medium of the inner ear. With the exception of bone conduction, there is no way of stimulating the inner ear if the conductive mechanisms of the middle ear are not functioning. Thus, during the normal course of maturation, the organ of Corti, which is located in the inner ear, could achieve a functional capability and yet be nonfunctional because the middle ear does not have the ability to transfer stimulus energy.

The onset of middle-ear function is not well understood, but normal operation requires that the tympanic membrane be exposed to the pressure waves of airborne sound and that the middle ear be fluid-free. In some species such as the cat, rat, mouse, and rabbit, the ear canal opens after birth. In other species like the guinea pig, chick, duckling, and man the ear canal is open during the late stages of fetal or embryonic development.

It is well established that a fluid-filled middle ear in the adult greatly attenuates the transmission of sound through the middle-ear system (Wever & Lawrence, 1954), and some preliminary data on chick embryos with fluid-filled and dry middle ears indicate that the efficiency of the system greatly improves when the mesenchymal fluid is removed (Saunders, Coles, & Gates, 1973). How much absorption of middle-ear fluids in the embryo or neonate is necessary before the middle ear will work at maximal efficiency is not known. It is possible that abrupt changes in the development of a response recorded from higher levels of the auditory system (e.g., the cochlea and auditory nerve) may not represent maturational events at that level, but may reflect developments in the functional capacity of the more peripheral middle-ear system. It is of interest to note that experiments with 2.5- to 24-hour-old human neonates reveal that the middle ear is free of fluid and functioning normally (Keith, 1975).

The first appearance of the CM response has been reported for a number of species, but because the organ of Corti is in such a dynamic state of development, it has been difficult to determine the morphological event that permits the onset of this response. It was reported in the early literature that the final formation of the internal spiral sulcus, the mature appearance of cochlear supporting cells, and the appearance of Nuel's space and the tunnel of Corti were all highly correlated with the first appearance of either a startle response (Wada, 1923) or the CM response (Larsell, McCrady, & Larsell, 1944; Larsell, McCrady, & Zimmerman, 1935). Larsell et al. (1944) emphasized that CM function does not begin until the pillar cells separate to form the tunnel of Corti. More recent work has continued to support the earlier observations (Ånggård, 1965; Bosher, 1975; Finck, Schneck, & Hartmann, 1972; Lindeman, Ades, Bredberg, & Engström, 1971; Ruben, 1967; Vanzulli & Garcia-Austt, 1963). In addition, there are claims that CM onset is associated with the lengthening of outer hair cells, the opening of the tunnel space, and formation of the

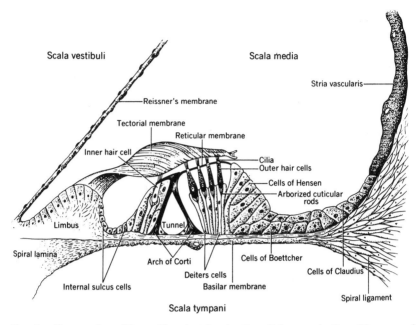

FIG. 1.   Cross section of the cochlear duct showing the cellular organization of the organ of Corti. Endolymph is found in scala media while perilymph is found in scala vestibuli and tympani. Many of the structures described in Section II can be identified in this figure. Reproduced with permission from Gulick (1971).

inner spiral sulcus in fetal guinea pigs, kittens, and puppies (Pujol & Hilding, 1973; Pujol & Marty, 1970). In the mouse, the last major developmental event in the cochlea is the appearance (around Day 10) of efferent nerve endings (Kikuchi & Hilding, 1965). Interestingly, the mouse exhibits its first reflex responses to acoustic stimulation at about this time (Alford & Ruben, 1963; Mikaelian & Ruben, 1965). Finally, there is also evidence that the attachments of the tectorial membrane to both the internal sulcus and the organ of Corti are "released" at the time that CM responses are first seen (Pujol & Hilding, 1973). This morphological event is of prime importance since it would permit the relative motion between hair-cell stereocilia and the tectorial membrane necessary for the production of CM potentials (Dallos, 1973). The implication of these observations is that the onset of CM responses is related to some discrete morphogenetic event within the organ of Corti. Unfortunately, there is relatively little consensus of opinion concerning the nature of this event (the structures described can be located in Fig. 1).

The maturation of auditory function is often studied by measuring a criterion CM or neural evoked response. The criterion represents a fixed level of physiological activity. For example, a 1.0 μV CM response is a frequently used criterion. The dependent variable is the sound pressure level (SPL) at various frequencies needed to elicit the criterion response. At first, these responses are typically elicited over a narrow range of low or middle frequencies and only at very intense stimulus levels. As maturation of the organ of Corti progresses the SPL necessary to elicit the criterion threshold becomes more sensitive and the bandwidth over which responses can be elicited increases. The threshold may improve by as much as 80 dB from first appearance until adultlike thresholds are observed, and the bandwidth in the rat, for example, increases by as much as $5\frac{1}{2}$ octaves (Crowley & Hepp-Reymond, 1966). These general features of peripheral auditory development are shown in Fig. 2 where the maturation of criterion-evoked response threshold in the cochlear nuclei of the chick is seen. The parameter of each curve is incubation age; the increasing bandwidth and sensitivity of the response in progressively older embryos are obvious.

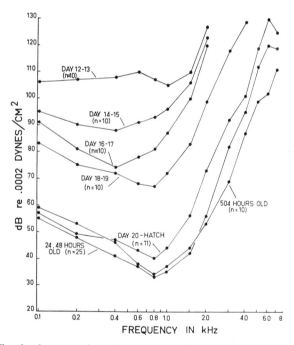

FIG. 2. The development of cochlear nuclei auditory evoked-response thresholds as a function of age in the chick. The days indicate the incubation age of the embryo (20.5-day incubation period), while the hours indicate the time since hatching. Each curve represents the mean of about 10 animals. The large gap between Day 18–19 and Day 20-hatch represents the time the middle-ear fluids are absorbed. The figure is reproduced from Saunders *et al.* (1973).

While these general features of auditory development are common to all
species thus far studied, they occur at dramatically different times and
rates in various animals. The data plotted in Fig. 3 represent a summary of
the available physiological evidence in seven species. The curves trace the
development of threshold sensitivity at a particular test frequency. The
frequency chosen was either the most sensitive in the adult or the one tested
over the widest age range. The essential features of these curves would not
change if other frequencies were plotted. With the exception of the curve for
the chick, all the curves represent the development of CM responses. The
CM threshold at each age was the stimulus sound pressure level (SPL) necessary to elicit a criterion response (e.g. 1.0 μV). In the case of the chick, the
criterion was a fixed level of evoked-response amplitude recorded from the
cochlear nuclei (Saunders et al., 1973).

The data in Fig. 3 demonstrate that the age at which a sound-elicited
response is first observed, and the age at which the response presents an
adultlike appearance, are highly species-specific. Auditory responses were
reported 9–11 days prior to hatching in the chick (Saunders, 1974a; Vanzulli
& Garcia-Austt, 1963) and 49–50 days postpartum in the opossum (Mc-
Crady, Wever, & Bray, 1937, 1940), which is born after a short gestation
period of about 12 days. These responses in the chick and opossum were

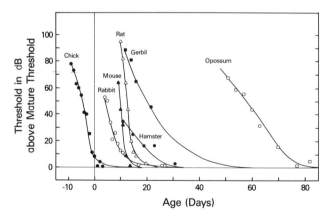

F IG. 3.   Criterion response thresholds in seven species as a function of age. The threshold
was defined from CM potentials recorded from the round window of all species except the
chick where a cochlear nucleus evoked-response threshold was used. To clarify the presentation the curves have been plotted as dB above the most sensitive (mature) threshold. The
frequencies used in each species were: 0.8 kHz in chick, 3.0 kHz in rabbit, 8.0 kHz in mouse,
10.0 kHz in rat, 3.0 kHz in hamster, 4.0 kHz in gerbil, and 7.0 kHz in opossum. The data were
taken from Ånggård (1964), Crowley and Hepp-Reymond (1966), Finck et al. (1972), McCrady
et al. (1940), Mikaelian and Ruben (1965), Stanek et al. (1977), and Saunders et al.
(1973).

mature when the animals were 3 days and 80 days old, respectively. More-over, maturation appears to occur very rapidly in the mouse and rat, but much more slowly in the hamster, gerbil, and opossum. The adaptive signifi-cance of these interspecies differences in the rate of CM maturation is not clear at present.

Another important feature of cochlear development is the onset and growth of the endocochlear potential (EP). This DC resting potential is positive in scala media, is maintained by an active electrogenic ion pump in stria vascularis, and is necessary for the normal generation of the CM potential (Dallos, 1973; Sellick & Bock, 1974). The maturation of the EP has been studied in the mouse, rat, rabbit, cat, and opossum, and the data from these experiments are summarized in Fig. 4. While the general pattern of EP maturation for these five species is similar, the time for EP growth varies from species to species. The most rapid rate of EP maturation occurs at the age of about 9 days in the rabbit, 12 days in the mouse, 13 days in the rat, 14 days in the cat, and 55 days in the opossum. The EP develops relatively slowly in the cat and opossum compared with the other species. A comparison between the data plotted in Figs. 3 and 4 reveals that the growth in sound-generated cochlear potentials (CM) is directly proportional to the maturation of the cochlear DC resting potential (EP).

A light-microscopic examination of the morphology of scala media in the rat at the time that EP begins its most rapid rate of development (Day 11) reveals that the stria vascularis, the tectorial membrane, and the organ of

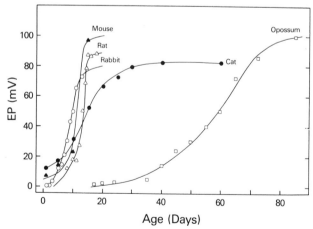

FIG. 4. The maturation of endocochlear potential (EP) in five species as a function of age. The data are replotted from Ånggård (1964), Bosher and Warren (1971), Fernández and Hinojosa (1974), and Schmidt and Fernández (1963).

Corti are fully differentiated (Bosher & Warren, 1971). Apart from Claudius and Böttcher cells, the rat cochlea is completely formed. Light and electron microscopy also indicated that, with the exception of Claudius cells, the organ of Corti in the CBA-J mouse is fully formed by the 8th day (Hilding, 1969; Kikuchi & Hilding, 1965; Mikaelian & Ruben, 1965). The 8th day is also the time when CM responses are first recorded and when the EP begins to show accelerated development (Fig. 4). The maturation of EP responses in the mouse and cat appears to be related to the ultrastructural maturation of marginal, intermediate, and basal cells of the stria vascularis (Fernández & Hinojosa, 1974; Kikuchi & Hilding, 1965).

An analysis of potassium, sodium, and chloride ion concentrations in endolymph and perilymph reveals near adult values by 8 days of age in the rat (Bosher & Warren, 1971). However, between the 8th and 11th days the EP remains at a relatively low level (10 to 20 millivolts). Two explanations have been offered to account for these observations. First, the electrical resistance of the membranes surrounding the membraneous labyrinth remains low and then increases rapidly after Day 11 (thus the voltage gradient after Day 11, between endolymph and perilymph, increases). Second, it may be that the growth in the EP is due to the final maturation of its underlying mechanism (Bosher & Warren, 1971).

Several important ideas are beginning to emerge from the study of EP development. In more general terms it would seem that a correct biochemical environment is essential for the maturation of EP and indeed the cochlea itself (Bosher, 1975; Sobokowicz, Bereman, & Rose, 1974). Moreover the maturation of CM potentials, long assumed to be a function of some specific morphogenetic event along the organ of Corti (e.g., freeing of the tectorial membrane) may in fact be a consequence of EP development.

The maturation of function in the central auditory pathway has been less well studied, but several interesting and important observations have been made. One of these is that action potentials (AP) recorded from the cochlea are first observed several days after the earliest appearance of the CM response. This observation was first reported for the mouse, where a delay of 1 to 2 days between the CM and AP was noted (Alford & Ruben, 1963; Mikaelian & Ruben, 1965). In other species the AP response lags behind the first observation of a CM response by 3 days in the dog (Pujol & Hilding, 1973), 2 days in the guinea pig, cat, and gerbil (Finck et al., 1972; Pujol & Hilding, 1973; Romand, 1971), and 1 day in the rabbit and chick (Ånggård, 1965; Saunders, 1974a; Saunders et al., 1973). An examination of the synaptic junction between hair cells and VIIIth nerve dendrites reveals that they appear mature prior to the first appearance of an AP response in the guinea pig, kitten, and puppy (Pujol & Hilding, 1973). Although the synaptic region appears histologically mature, it has been suggested that the interactions between transmitter substance, membrane characteristics, and extracellular fluids are not yet properly organized to permit a neuronal discharge. Moreover, the AP response represents the discharge of many neural elements and a threshold number of these elements may be necessary for the first detection of that response (Pujol & Hilding, 1973). The results of these experiments indicate that the appearance of CM preceding the first appearance of AP is a general pattern in the maturation of peripheral auditory function. The data also support the hypothesis that hair cells are capable of producing a CM potential prior to the activation of their synapses with auditory nerve fibers.

The maturation of latency in the AP response of the cat and guinea pig, as well as cochlear-nuclei-evoked responses in the chick, have been studied in detail and these data are plotted in Fig. 5. Differences in the first appearance of a neural response in these species extend from 18 days before birth in the guinea pig to slightly after birth in the cat (Romand, 1971). The latency of these responses appears to be mature at birth in the guinea pig, between 6 and 8 days of age in the chick and between 28 and 30 days in the kitten. The improvement in response latency has been related to synaptic efficiency and increasing conduction velocity associated with myelination (Pujol, 1972; Romand, 1971; Saunders, 1974a).

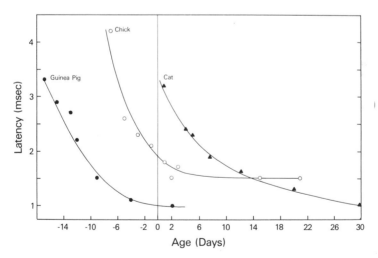

FIG. 5.   Response latency as a function of developmental age in the guinea pig, chick, and cat. The data for cat and guinea pig represent AP latency recorded from the round window using tone-burst stimuli. Click-evoked responses from the cochlear nuclei were used to measure response latency in the chick. The longer latency in the chick reflects the more central recording location. Data replotted from Saunders (1974a) and Romand (1971).

Another observation concerning maturation of the central auditory pathway is that the entire pathway is functional before the synaptic junction between the VIIIth nerve and hair cell is operational. Marty and Thomas (1963), in an ingenious experiment, stimulated the trunk of the auditory nerve and recorded from electrodes situated on the auditory cortex. Stimulation of the nerve in kittens prior to the onset of acoustically evoked AP responses elicited clearly defined evoked activity at the cortical level. These experiments have been replicated on other species and between different synaptic levels of the auditory system (Chaloupka, Záhlava, Mysliveček, & Hassmannová, 1968; Hassmannová & Mysliveček, 1967) and the results continue to support the conclusion that the auditory pathway is at least partially functional prior to the time that it can be stimulated acoustically. These findings suggest the possibility that major organizations of the neural pathway for audition could occur quite independently of any input from the organ of Corti. It should be recognized, however, that in all likelihood there are many elements of the central pathway that have yet to reach complete maturity at the time that this system can be acoustically excited. In fact, recent evidence clearly shows that the waveform of acoustically evoked responses in the auditory cortex of the guinea pig undergoes considerable change from the time it is first detected until it presents a mature appearance (Sedláček, 1976b). Thus, it is plausible to assume that auditory experience from acoustic stimulation can play a role in providing essential "finishing touches" to the final maturation of central auditory function (Gottlieb, 1975, 1976b; see chapter by Mistretta and Bradley, this volume). Another important conclusion from the Marty and Thomas (1963) experiment is that the last region of the auditory system to reach functional competence is the synaptic junction at the base of the hair cell.

The maturation of electrophysiological responses in the central auditory pathway has been examined in the cat, guinea pig, rat, mouse, duckling, and chick (Jewett & Romano, 1972; König & Marty, 1974; Konishi, 1973; Lieff, Permut, Schlesinger, & Sharpless, 1975; Pujol, 1972; Rosowski, Bock, & Saunders, 1976). In general there is agreement, which is consistent with the morphological evidence, that final physiological maturation proceeds systemically from the peripheral auditory nuclei to the auditory cortex. The careful investigation by Pujol (1972) on the maturation of latency at selected auditory nuclei of the cat is perhaps the most cogent demonstration of this principle. Another more recent example is the fact that evoked responses are first detected after 13 days of incubation in the chick cochlear nuclei (Saunders, 1974a, Saunders et al., 1973; but it is not until the beginning of the 18th day that they can be recorded from the cerebral hemispheres (Sedláček, 1976a).

The development of postnatal hearing as defined by a behavioral response to sound has recently been considered in mammals and the ages at which startle reactions first appear has been reported for the guinea pig, cat, rabbit, mouse, rat, dog, mink, and opossum (Foss & Flottorp, 1974). The development of absolute auditory thresholds measured in the quiet and during masking has been reported for mice ranging in age from 11 days to 3 months (Ehret, 1976, 1977). Moreover, the onset of prenatal behavioral responses to sound have been reported for quail, duckling, chick, and gull embryos (Gottlieb, 1968, 1971, 1976a; Impekoven & Gold, 1973). In mammals, at least, the first appearance of a reflex reaction is highly correlated with the appearance of evoked activity in the central auditory pathway, and hence with the functional development of the VIIIth nerve/hair cell synapse. Furthermore, data from a number of sources indicate that the human fetus has a functional auditory system and can respond behaviorally to sound prior to birth. The important question of when hearing begins in man has been considered in detail elsewhere (Eisenberg, 1976; Northern & Downs, 1974). The evidence from studies in which auditory-evoked responses are measured from the skull of 6- to 8-week-old premature babies, and from the skull of the intrauterine fetus, as well as from studies designed to determine the reactivity of the fetus to acoustic stimulation, suggests that hearing capacity may begin as early as 12–16 weeks before birth. The functional significance of fetal hearing in man is not yet clear (Bast & Anson, 1949).

III. The Effects of Intense Sound on Hearing

Acoustic trauma from exposure to pure tones, noise, or impulse sounds can have a profoundly deleterious effect on hearing. The consequences of exposure to intense sound have been considered recently by Kryter (1970), Welch and Welch (1970), Miller (1974), and Mills (1975), and only the salient features of this literature will be described here. Mild exposure conditions may result in a temporary threshold shift (TTS) which completely recovers after removal from the sound. Prolonged exposure to intense sounds can produce a permanent threshold shift (PTS) in which a hearing loss persists throughout life. Acoustic trauma after noise exposure has been extensively studied, but the complex relations between noise spectrum, noise intensity, exposure duration, and hearing loss are not yet completely understood. The effects of noise have been examined at the perceptual and physiological levels, and the use of animal models in recent decades has been successful in revealing basic mechanisms. The following sections will consider some recent evidence concerning the behavioral, physiological, and anatomical effects of noise exposure in adults.

A. The Behavioral Effects of Acoustic Trauma

The threshold of hearing, defined as the minimum audible intensity of a tone, is raised temporarily if an ear is exposed to noise of moderate intensity and duration. The magnitude and persistence of TTS as well as the frequencies affected depend on the specific exposure conditions. Experience with noise of a longer duration and/or higher intensity will result in more severe TTS, while exposure to extreme noise conditions may cause a PTS. Recent work with chinchillas has revealed important principles associated with prolonged noise exposures. Avoidance conditioning and a modified method of limits were used to obtain absolute thresholds of hearing in the quiet (Miller, 1970). Carder and Miller (1972) and Mills (1973) exposed chinchillas to continuous noise for 7 to 9 days. The growth of threshold shift was measured by periodically removing the animals from the noise and testing their thresholds. At the end of the exposure, thresholds were tested until complete recovery was noted or until the thresholds exhibited a stable level. Figure 6 is a composite drawing showing the growth and the recovery of threshold shift at 5.7 kHz after exposure to four levels of a one-octave band of noise centered at 4.0 kHz. The growth of threshold shift reaches a maximum value after 18–24 hours of exposure and then remains asymptotic as the exposure duration increases to 7–9 days. The magnitude of hearing loss at asymptote is systematically related to the noise level and for every 1.0-dB increase in noise SPL there is a corresponding 1.7 dB of threshold shift (Carder & Miller, 1972). The recovery durations also appear to be proportional to the level of threshold shift. Recovery is complete after 2 to 5 days for exposures at 65 and 80 dB and is complete for higher noise levels after 15–30 days. The hearing loss at 90 days was considered permanent (PTS). The occurrence of asymptotic threshold shift has been demonstrated in man (Melnick, & Maves, 1974) and for intermittent noise conditions (Saunders, Mills, & Miller, 1977). Although the relation between noise conditions and the boundary between PTS and TTS in animals is becoming clear, it is not well resolved for man.

While threshold shift has traditionally been used to evaluate the effects of noise, other measures such as speech perception, loudness perception, and the occurrence of tinnitus have also been employed (Miller, 1974; Møller, 1975). Noise exposure causes an abnormal growth in perceived loudness called loudness recruitment and this phenomenon has only recently been shown in experimental animals (Moody, 1973).

B. The Physiological Effects of Acoustic Trauma

The functional changes that accompany exposure to intense sound have been studied throughout the auditory system, and most investigators are in

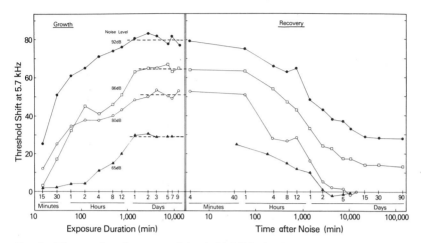

FIG. 6.   The growth and recovery of threshold shift in the chinchilla during sustained noise exposure. The thresholds are plotted for a test frequency of 5.7 kHz and expressed as dB. The parameter of each curve is the octave-band level of the noise. Data are redrawn from Carder and Miller (1972) and Mills (1973).

agreement that the normal processes of sound transduction within the cochlea are disrupted. There are many experiments which indicate a derangement in cochlear microphonic (CM) responses after exposure to intense sound (reviewed by Durrant, 1976).

The chinchilla provides a popular animal model for studying the physiological consequences of noise exposure and has the added advantage that loss in function can be correlated with the behaviorally measured loss in threshold sensitivity. Cochlear microphonic, EP, and AP responses in each cochlear turn of the chinchilla were recently measured after several days exposure to a 95-dB SPL noise (Benitez, Eldredge, & Templer, 1972). These conditions were known to produce about 48 dB of behavioral TTS. The results showed that endocochlear DC potential (EP) was not altered by the exposure. However, CM potentials in the third cochlear turn exhibited a 45- to 50-dB shift in sensitivity. The noise exposure had its greatest effect on the AP responses, and at 48 hours postexposure these potentials exhibited little recovery. These data and others lead to the conclusion that intense noise causes a dramatic loss in normal hair cell function and a general failure of the primary neurons to discharge in synchrony.

Electrophysiological measures of TTS have also been observed in responses recorded from central auditory nuclei (Henderson, Hamernick, & Sitler, 1974; Saunders & Rhyne, 1970). The loss in sensitivity after noise exposure observed in these nuclei is considered only a central reflection of processes originating in the cochlea. However, some recent work suggests the possibility that there is a direct central contribution to TTS (Babighian, Moushegian, & Rupert, 1975; Salvi, Henderson, & Hamernick, 1975). It may well be that sustained afferent activity during exposure to intense sound causes "synaptic fatigue" in central nuclei, and this fatigue takes a relatively long time to recover. The conclusion to be drawn from this section is that the physiological consequences of noise exposure largely result in functional derangements within the organ of Corti. Whether there are primary or secondary effects to the central auditory system is not entirely clear yet.

C. The Anatomical Effects of Acoustic Trauma

The physiological evidence suggests that the anatomical locus of acoustic trauma is the hair cell receptor of the cochlea. Moreover, the biomechanics of basilar membrane movements indicate that hair cells can be traumatized by violent displacements of the cochlear partition. It follows from the specific dynamics of this mechanical action that outer hair cells (in a progression from outer, middle, and innermost rows) are more easily damaged than inner hair cells. Modern histological techniques which make use of surface preparations of the organ of Corti permit precise quantitative evaluation of all hair cells and supporting cell elements on the basilar membrane (Bohne, 1972; Spoendlin & Brun, 1974). These techniques have been extensively applied to examine the cochleas of animals subjected to noise exposures. Only in the chinchilla, however, has it been possible to measure hair cell populations in animals exposed to noise for which the magnitude of threshold shift is known. Electron-microscopic examination of the organ of Corti in chinchillas exposed to moderate noise which is insufficient to produce PTS reveals complex changes in the microstructure (cell membrane) of the hair cell (Bohne, Eldredge, & Mills, 1973; Eldredge, Mills, & Bohne, 1973). It would also appear that these anatomical changes recover with the passage of time (Bohne, 1973). Moreover, it has been reported that hair cell loss occurs (albeit, in very small numbers) after noise exposure, even if the threshold shift exhibits complete recovery (Bohne et al., 1973). The fact that moderate noise levels can produce a hair cell loss with no accompanying indication of threshold shift means that threshold measures of noise-induced hearing loss are insenstivie to small cochlear lesions. Perhaps this pathology is reflected by a perceptual deficit in intensity or frequency discriminations.

With noise exposure conditions sufficient to produce a moderate amount of PTS, the pattern of cellular damage becomes more pronounced and permanent. A substantial number of hair cells may show complete degeneration or severe deformation, and the stereocilia at the top of the hair cell may be fused together and enlarged (Ades & Engström, 1972). The general organization of the organ of Corti, however, remains unchanged. After exposure to extreme noise conditions, there is severe hair cell degeneration and extensive structural damage to the organ of Corti. The formation of scar tissue is also prevalent at the lesion site and all the hair cells and supporting cells may degenerate completely. The noise-induced lesion also extends along the cochlear partition in proportion to the magnitude of the exposure and the frequency spectrum of the noise. These severe structural derangements after intense noise exposures have been documented by Lim and Melnick (1971), Spoendlin (1971), Ward and Duvall (1971), Spoendlin and Brun (1973), and Lidén, Engström, and Hall (1973). Variations in the extent of cochlear pathology following noise exposure are indicated in the schematic diagrams of Fig. 7.

The existing evidence thus suggests that TTS may be associated with some transitory change in cochlear function which may be related to processes localized in the hair cells. In the case of PTS the evidence of extensive and irreversible physical damage along the organ of Corti is convincing. The

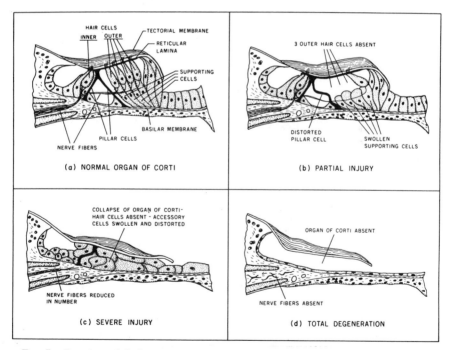

FIG. 7. Drawings of the human organ of Corti are shown that illustrate the normal state, panel a, and increasing degrees of noise-induced permanent injury, panels b, c, and d. Reproduced with permission from Miller (1974).

damage may be the result of extreme mechanical displacement of the basilar membrane during exposure. Our understanding of the effects of noise exposure on hearing would be greatly simplified if the distinction between TTS and PTS were perfectly correlated with permanent or temporary cochlear histopathology, respectively. Unfortunately, the situation is complicated by a gradation of severity of disruption, ranging from the subtle changes in hair cells that accompany low to moderate noise exposures to the severe physical damage that accompanies noise exposure at high levels.

IV. Overstimulation Damage in Children and Young Animals

A. *Effects of Noise on Children*

Most hearing loss observed in children appears to be conductive in origin (e.g., Eagles *et al.*, 1967; Weber *et al.*, 1967), and noise-induced sensorineural losses are not common until about ages 16 to 19. Conductive loss is associated with pathology of the middle ear while a sensorineural hearing loss represents pathology of the inner ear. However, it is important to emphasize that there are many difficulties involved in accurate audiological assessment of young children. Furthermore, even when audiological evidence clearly indicates a sensorineural hearing loss, it is difficult to determine whether the loss is only the result of noise trauma. Mills (1975), for example, concludes that "the incidence of noise-induced permanent hearing loss in children, as measured traditionally, is not known."

Susceptibility of children to TTS has been the subject of several studies (Bess & Powell, 1972; Bess & Poynor, 1974; Fior, 1972), but there is not yet any clear indication in the literature that children differ from adults with respect to severity of TTS induced by noise. What is clear, however, is the kinds and levels of noise to which infants and young children may be exposed. League, Parker, Robertson, Valentine, and Powell (1972), Falk and Farmer (1973), and Douek *et al.* (1976) measured incubator noise and found it to be between 70 and 78 dB. The frequencies between 70 and 250 Hz contained most of the energy. Intensive care units studied by Falk and Woods (1973) ranged between 56- and 73-dB SPL and most of the energy was between 60 and 400 kHz. These sound levels do not seem to be excessive, but as Mills (1975) points out, the infants exposed to them are either premature or in bad health. Moreover, the exposure is continuous and may last for weeks. Children can be subjected to a variety of devices with intense sound levels and, depending on exposure sound pressure level (SPL) and duration, they could cause TTS or PTS. These sounds include model airplane engines (Bess & Powell, 1972), snowmobiles (Bess & Poynor, 1974), cap pistols and real firearms (Marshall & Brandt, 1974), and most seriously, the high-level impulse sound of firecrackers (Ward & Glorig, 1961).

B. Effects of Noise on Young Animals

Most experimental studies of the deleterious effects of noise in young animals have been concerned with the phenomenon of audiogenic seizures, which will be considered in detail in the following section. We are aware of only six published studies which deal with the question of whether susceptibility to noise trauma changes with age. The first is a report by Price (1972, 1976) who exposed young kittens and adult cats to a 5-kHz tone (104- to 124-dB SPL for 50 minutes) and measured the resulting cochlear microphonic threshold deficits. Kittens exhibited greater susceptibility to noise-induced hearing loss, as indicated by CM deficits, than did adult cats.

In another study three different age groups of guinea pigs were exposed to white noise (120-dB SPL for 30 hours): 2-day-old, 8-day-old, and 8-month-old animals (Falk, Cook, Haseman, & Sanders, 1974). Cochlear damage to the organ of Corti was assessed 1 month after noise exposure using the surface preparation technique (Engström, Ades, & Anderson, 1966). Comparison of hair cell counts in noise-exposed cochleas with those from relevant control cochleas indicated that the mean outer hair cell loss induced by noise exposure was 23% in 2-day-old animals, 37% in 8-day-old animals, and 7% in adult animals. The site of cochlear damage induced by noise also appears to vary with development, since Falk *et al.* (1974) noted that maximal damage in young animals occurred in the third turn, whereas comparable noise exposures in adult animals produce maximal damage in the first or basal turn of the cochlea.

The remaining reports are specifically addressed to the question of noise trauma during development (Saunders & Hirsch, 1976; Bock & Saunders, 1977, Stanek, Bock, Goran, & Saunders, 1977) and will be considered in the following section.

C. The Audiogenic Seizure Model

About 6.5% of all epileptic patients suffer from "reflex" or sensory-evoked epilepsy. Most of these patients are susceptible to seizures triggered by visual stimuli, but a small number exhibit seizures when stimulated by sound. The acoustic condition which triggers the seizure varies considerably from patient to patient. In some cases it may be the occurrence of an unexpected sound such as a noise, a buzzer, the ringing of a telephone, or a gunshot, while in other cases it might be a passage of music (musicogenic epilepsy). In general, however, human epileptic seizures triggered by sound are relatively minor, and it is rare for convulsive behavior to occur (for a review of this subject, see Forster, 1970).

Sound-evoked seizures, occurring with much greater frequency and severity than are found in man, have long been known to occur in certain strains of rodents on exposure to an intense sound, such as that produced by an electric doorbell (Donaldson, 1924). These "audiogenic seizures" are characterized by several clearly identifiable stages: a period of vigorous motor activity ("wild running"), followed by myoclonic seizure, followed by myotonic seizure which may result in death, presumably from respiratory arrest. The phenomenon of audiogenic seizure constitutes the most dramatically deleterious effect of noise yet demonstrated in animals and the authors know of no other situation in which exposure to noise alone can directly result in death. It is now known (Henry, 1967; Iturrian & Fink, 1967) that mice from strains which are not susceptible to audiogenic seizure may be rendered susceptible by exposure to a loud sound during a restricted period after birth. This "priming" procedure usually consists of exposing young mice to the sound which is subsequently used to test for seizure occurrence. Although priming itself does not usually result in a seizure, primed mice are likely to exhibit such reactions when re-exposed to the priming sound several days later. Thus, priming provides an experimental model of a dramatic and long-lasting deleterious effect of noise exposure. Furthermore, the effect of priming is such that its deleterious consequences are not immediately apparent. Rather, priming produces a susceptibility to enhanced reaction (seizure) to loud sounds presented some time after the initial exposure.

Early experiments describing the priming phenomenon have been reviewed in detail by Henry and Bowman (1970). The object of the present section is to consider recent evidence concerning the physiological basis of priming and the implications of this evidence for concepts of auditory development and the abnormal growth of loudness perception (loudness recruitment).

1. STIMULUS FACTORS IN PRIMING

The intensity and duration of the priming stimulus are critical in determining its effectiveness. For a given sound intensity, a certain minimal duration of exposure is necessary in order to prime mice effectively. For example, a 20-second exposure to a 103-dB bell is necessary for priming C57BL/6J mice (Henry & Bowman, 1970). Shorter exposures, however, have a cumulative effect, so that an animal may be rendered seizure susceptible by a series of brief exposures (Henry & Bowman, 1970). Similarly, the intensity of the priming stimulus must exceed a certain minimal level in order to induce seizure susceptibility. If the priming stimulus does not exceed this level, then seizures can not subsequently be elicited, regardless of the intensity, of the testing stimulus (Chen, Bock, & Gates, 1974). Moreover, a broad-band sound is more effective than a pure tone as a priming and test stimulus (Bock & Chen, 1972).

The effectiveness of priming does not depend on the animal's state of arousal, since it is equally effective if animals are anesthetized with barbiturate prior to the priming exposure (Henry, 1967). The seizure susceptibility induced by acoustic priming appears to be confined to auditory-induced seizures, since susceptibility to seizures produced by Metrazol or electroconvulsion shock remains unchanged after priming (Henry & Bowman, 1969). Furthermore, the effects of priming are localized to one side of the peripheral auditory pathway. If one ear is blocked during priming then seizures can not subsequently be elicited by exposing that ear to the test stimulus (Fuller & Collins, 1968; Henry, 1972b).

The age at which mice are primed is critical in determining priming effectiveness. For example, the development of audiogenic seizure susceptibility is maximal in C57BL/6J mice if priming occurs between 14 and 20 days of age. There is little or no effect if animals are primed before 12 days of age or after about 30 days of age (Henry & Bowman, 1970). Data from two studies on the effectiveness of priming as a function of age (the "sensitive" or "critical" period) are compared in Fig. 8 for the C57BL/6J strain. Priming appears to be maximally effective at about 18 days of age, regardless of whether the priming stimulus is an electric bell (Henry & Bowman, 1970) or a precisely defined bandwidth of noise (Saunders & Hirsch, 1976).

Priming does not result in immediate susceptibility to audiogenic seizure; susceptibility develops gradually for several days after priming (Willott & Henry, 1974). In the case of C57BL/6J mice, susceptibility is maximal 4 days after priming with a 120-dB bell (Henry, 1972a).

The question of the extent to which priming may alter other aspects of be-

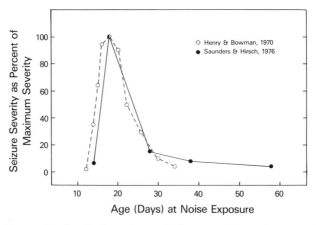

FIG. 8. Curves showing the dependence of seizure severity on the age at which animals are primed. The data are taken from studies by Henry and Bowman (1970) and Saunders and Hirsch (1976). The curves are in close agreement in spite of the differences in priming stimuli (doorbell versus octave-noise band) and in prime-test interval (2 to 24 days versus 5 days).

havior, in addition to audiogenic seizure susceptibility, has received little experimental attention. However, Henry (1972a) has shown that priming results in a decreased threshold for eliciting the Preyer reflex, an effect which also takes several days to develop.

2. THE AUDITORY DEPRIVATION-SUPERSENSITIVITY HYPOTHESIS

Saunders, Bock, Chen, and Gates (1972a) measured CM and VIIIth nerve AP from the round window in primed and unprimed control BALB/c mice. These authors showed that the stimulus SPL necessary to elicit a 1.0 μV criterion CM threshold, for test tones between 0.5 and 25.0 kHz, was significantly raised after priming. In fact, a CM response could not even be detected in 66% of the primed mice. A similar decrement in the AP response was noted, but every primed mouse exhibited an AP, even if the CM response was absent. More recently, Bock and Saunders (1976) measured tone-burst thresholds for inferior colliculus evoked responses in C57BL/6J mice. Mice were primed with a 2-minute exposure to a one-octave (8.0–16.0 kHz) band of 110-dB noise on Day 18. Evoked-response thresholds were measured for tone burst stimuli between 0.5 and 20.0 kHz on Day 23. The data for control and primed animals are presented in Fig. 9. Above 8.0 kHz the threshold sensitivity in primed mice is significantly poorer than that observed in the control animals. At 17.0 kHz the threshold loss in primed mice is 38 dB. These data show that exposure to priming causes a severe loss in the threshold sensitivity of the auditory system. The mice have been significantly deafened by the priming exposure.

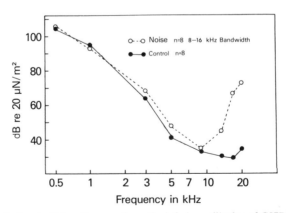

FIG. 9.   Evoked potential audiograms from the inferior colliculus of C57BL/6J mice at 23 days of age. Animals in the primed group were exposed to an octave band of noise (8.0–16.0 kHz) at 18 days of age. Note the high frequency threshold loss in the noise-exposed group. Redrawn from Bock and Saunders (1976).

Increased click-evoked potential thresholds have been reported in the inferior colliculus and cochlear nucleus of BALB/c mice and these reflect the deficit observed in the CM potential after priming (Saunders, Bock, James, & Chen, 1972b). However, the peak-to-peak amplitude of the potential evoked by a click of high intensity is considerably greater in primed mice than in unprimed controls (see Fig. 10). This observation has been replicated in inferior colliculus responses recorded from C57BL/6J mice after priming (Bock & Saunders, 1976; Henry & Saleh, 1973; Lieff et al., 1975).

Furthermore, the enhanced neural responses to loud sound do not occur immediately after priming, but take several days to develop (Willott & Henry, 1974). If it is accepted that "perceived loudness" of a sound is monotonically related to the amplitude of auditory-evoked potentials, then primed mice may be said to exhibit a neural analogue of loudness recruitment. "Loudness recruitment" is the clinical term used to describe an abnormally large increase in perceived loudness with small increases in stimulus intensity. The site of the pathology underlying this disorder is believed to be the cochlea (Dix, Hallpike, & Hood, 1948).

Henry (1972a) suggested that priming might "damage" the olivocochlear efferent system and thereby abolish a gating mechanism which normally protects central auditory nuclei from excessive stimulation. There are two drawbacks to this hypothesis: (a) There is no known neural pathway by which peripheral stimulation could damage this centrally originating neural pathway. (b) Removal of the olivocochlear bundle would be unlikely to produce enhanced central responses to sound since recent evidence suggests

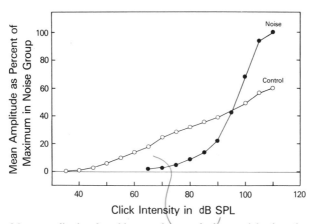

FIG. 10.   Mean amplitude of cochlear nucleus evoked potentials plotted as a function of click intensity in noise-exposed and control BALB/c mice. Redrawn from Saunders et al. (1972b).

that the original concept of the olivocochlear bundle as a peripheral gating pathway may not be correct (Pfalz, 1969). An alternative hypothesis was advanced by Saunders *et al.* (1972a), who suggested that the only *immediate* effect of priming was cochlear damage (destruction of hair cells), resulting in a loss of peripheral auditory sensitivity. It was further proposed that the maturation of connections in the central auditory pathway is dependent on normal auditory input, and that auditory deprivation during this period of maturation would result in abnormal development of central connections. This "abnormal development" could be considered to be analogous with denervation supersensitivity (Sharpless, 1969), with the result that neurons in subcortical auditory nuclei would show enhanced responsiveness to synaptic inputs.

The "auditory deprivation-supersensitivity hypothesis" proposed that two factors are involved in priming: a peripheral process and a central process. Evidence relating to these two aspects of the hypothesis will now be considered.

3. CENTRAL ASPECTS OF PRIMING

Gates, Chen, and Bock (1973) obtained evidence in support of the auditory deprivation-supersensitivity hypothesis of priming by showing that another form of auditory deprivation, which did not involve noise exposure, also induced seizure susceptibility. They showed that destruction of tympanic membranes in 21-day-old BALB/c mice (a procedure which produces a conductive hearing loss of about 30 dB) was successful in rendering the animals susceptible to audiogenic seizure when tested at 27 days of age. McGinn, Willott, and Henry (1973) subsequently confirmed this observation by using ear plugs to produce auditory deprivation in C57BL/6J mice. Another prediction of the hypothesis is that the effect of priming would be attenuated by raising the general 'background' noise level in the environment of primed mice, thereby compensating for their loss in peripheral sensitivity. Some support for this prediction was obtained by showing that intermittent exposure to white noise, interposed between priming and testing for seizure, reduced the effectiveness of priming in BALB/c mice (Bock, Gates, & Chen, 1974).

The auditory deprivation-supersensitivity hypothesis is compatible with most of the characteristics of priming discussed previously. The intensity-duration and bandwidth parameters for an effective priming stimulus are presumably related to the extent of cochlear damage induced during priming. The postpriming development over several days, of both seizure susceptibility and decrease in Preyer reflex threshold would, according to the hypothesis, reflect the time course of the proposed abnormal central maturation.

It is necessary, then, to consider available evidence concerning postnatal development of the mouse auditory system.

Development of the mouse central nervous system has been described by a number of authors. Milonyeni (1967) quantified cell populations in the ventral (VCN) and dorsal (DCN) cochlear nucleus of albino mice from 4 days to 5.5 months after birth. His data show a rapid rise in the cell count of VCN from Day 4 to Day 9, reaching a peak of 19,000 neurons. The count declined from Day 9 to Day 11 and stabilized at about 14,000 cells. The DCN, however, showed only a slight increase in cell count between the 4th and the 11th days, followed by a rapid increase to Day 13. The ensuing cellular degeneration stabilized after Day 17 at about 5000 cells. The observation of cell death in a developing sensory nucleus has been reported by other workers (Rogers & Cowan, 1973; Silver & Hughes, 1973), but its significance is not clearly understood.

Others (Gyllensten, 1966; Gyllensten, Malmfors, & Norrlin, 1965) have presented data which indicate that the mouse cortex undergoes intense differentiation between 15 and 30 days after birth. If the data presented by Pujol (1972) and others (see Section II) on maturation of the central auditory pathway in the cat can be generalized to the mouse, then it would be expected that maturation proceeds in progressively later steps from cochlear nucleus to cortex.

These data on development and differentiation of the central auditory system indicate that, even at the level of the CN, mature organization has not been achieved by the time at which priming becomes effective. It is therefore significant to note that evoked potentials recorded from the inferior colliculus in C57BL/6J mice are developing greater amplitudes during the critical period for priming (Lieff et al., 1975). One plausible explanation of the decline in priming effectiveness which follows the period of maximal sensitivity might be that it is dependent on completion of maturation in auditory nuclei.

Saunders et al. (1972a) speculated that a mechanism similar to denervation supersensitivity (Sharpless, 1969) could account for the enhanced responses of brain-stem auditory neurons to loud sound. Sharpless (1975) has recently reviewed data relevant to the phenomenon of disuse supersensitivity and there appears to be no suggestion in the literature of any developmental specificity in this phenomenon. Such a mechanism might not, therefore, be expected to be related to an animal's developmental state. An alternative proposal is made by Lieff et al. (1975), who postulate that auditory deprivation during development leads to a proliferation of functional synapses in auditory nuclei. This mechanism has the necessary developmental specificity and is congruent with recent data on the development of neural connections (e.g., Cass, Sutton, & Mark, 1973). However, the major difficulty with this proposal is that it predicts that recruitment, and presumably seizures, should be observed in unprimed young mice, since they should have the proliferation of neural connections which is later to be reduced during sensory experience. Nevertheless, the growing body of data on the critical effects of early visual experience on development of the visual pathway (Barlow, 1975) strongly suggests that early auditory experience may have a similarly critical role in auditory development, and some preliminary evidence indicates that this may be the case (Clopton & Winfield, 1974).

The proposed explanations of priming considered in the preceding discussion are concerned only with its sensory consequences, namely loudness recruitment. The relation between the central recruitment effect and the initiation of the characteristic motor patterns observed during audiogenic seizure is not clear at present. However, studies of auditory–motor interactions have shown that auditory stimulation can induce discharges in spinal efferents (Ascher, Jessik-Gerschenfeld, & Buser, 1963; Buser, St. Laurent, & Menini, 1966; Wright & Barnes, 1972). Furthermore, the effect on spinal reflexes of this efferent activity is initially facilitory and depends on the integrity of the inferior colliculus (Wright & Barnes, 1972). Thus it is possible that, in the mouse, recruitment effects in brain stem auditory nuclei could lead to an extreme enhancement of subcortical auditory–motor reflexes.

It must, however, be emphasized that the relationship between the evoked-potential recruitment effect and seizure susceptibility is not simple. McGinn et al. (1973) found that insertion of ear plugs in C57BL/6J mice did not lead to the development of evoked-potential recruitment, although it did induce seizure susceptibility. Furthermore, even though evoked-potential recruitment develops in the genetically susceptible DBA/2J mouse strain, seizures can be elicited before recruitment occurs (Henry & Haythorn, 1975). It could well be that priming of other species will produce the recruitment effects without necessarily producing susceptibility to audiogenic seizure.

4. PERIPHERAL ASPECTS OF PRIMING

The supersensitivity hypothesis as proposed (in Section IV, C, 2) explains why priming is ineffective in mature animals (e.g., after Day 30 in C57BL/6J mice), but does not specify why priming is ineffective in the period immediately postpartum (birth to Day 12 in C57BL/6J mice). If priming produced cochlear damage between birth and Day 12 in C57BL/6J mice, then abnormal central development should ensue. In order to evaluate this problem, it is necessary to consider postnatal cochlear development in the mouse.

The final maturation of the organ of Corti does not occur until after birth in the mouse (Sher, 1971). Structural elements of the basilar membrane present an adultlike appearance between 8 and 10 days after birth (Kikuchi &

Hilding, 1965; Mikaelian & Ruben, 1965), while efferent innervation of the inner ear is not apparent until the 10th day postpartum (Kikuchi and Hilding, 1965). The physiological maturation of cochlear and VIIIth nerve function has been studied in some detail. The CM first appears on the 8th day postpartum, while the first indication of the AP appears on the 9th day (Alford & Ruben, 1963; Mikaelian & Ruben, 1965). During the period from Day 8 to Day 14 the frequency range of the CM response improves by about 4 octaves, from 3.0 to 40 kHz, while the sensitivity of CM at the best frequency (17 kHz) shows an improvement of about 80 dB (see Fig. 3 and Section II). Cochlear responses from Day 14 onward appear adultlike. In summary, histogenesis of the organ of Corti is complete by about Day 10, while functional maturation of the cochlea is complete by Day 14. These data are largely derived from the CBA-J strain and their generality to other strains of mice is not known.

It is important to note that mice studied in these developmental experiments were not selected from inbred strains. A number of inbred strains of mice show severe abnormalities in patterns of auditory development (Deol, 1968). Perhaps the best known example is that of the Shaker-1 mouse, in which the development of cochlear structure and function proceed normally until Day 17 (Mikaelian & Ruben, 1964). Thereafter, a systematic deterioration of the CM response occurs and by Day 22 acoustic stimulation is ineffective in evoking responses in the peripheral auditory system. There is reported evidence that with increasing age DBA/2J and BALB/c mice show losses in inferior colliculus evoked-response threshold sensitivity (Ralls, 1967). Mikaelian, Warfield, and Norris (1974) also showed degeneration in the behavioral thresholds of older C57/b16 mice, while Kocher (1960) reported that hair cell degeneration occurred as a function of age in C57BL/Gr mice. The time course of the degenerative process in DBA/2J, BALB/c, and C57/b16 is longer than that observed in the Shaker-1 mouse, with degeneration first occurring between 50 and 75 days. In the C57BL/Gr strain hair cell loss begins between 250 and 300 days. Degeneration of hearing in the DBA/2J, BALB/c, and C57BL/6J strains is probably not a confounding factor in most studies of priming, since priming and testing for seizure are usually conducted well before the onset of the degenerative process. Nevertheless, investigators should realize this potential problem when using inbred strains of mice. The recent demonstration of a priming effect in 150-day-old BALB/c mice (Gates & Chen, 1973) is difficult to interpret, since priming occurred some time after the onset of threshold deterioration and may therefore represent a complex interaction between genetic cochlear degeneration and priming-induced damage.

The data reviewed in this chapter indicate that responses from the cochlea and VIIIth nerve of the mouse exhibit a mature pattern between the 14th and the 17th days after birth. Thus, the priming stimulus, when presented between Day 18 and Day 21, stimulates a relatively mature hearing organ.

The ineffectiveness of priming between birth and Day 10 is not unexpected, since noise exposure would not be effective in producing cochlear damage before the middle ear is mature. However, if cochlear damage is a necessary prerequisite for priming effectiveness, then priming might be expected to be effective after about Day 10. There appear to be two possible explanations for the ineffectiveness of priming from Day 10 to Day 13 (in BALB/c mice): either the results from developmental studies reviewed in the preceding paragraphs cannot be generalized to C57BL/6J and BALB/c mice, or cochlear susceptibility to overstimulation damage continues to increase after maturation of the middle ear. Indirect support for this latter proposal was obtained by Chen, Gates, and Bock (1973), who found that destruction of tympanic membranes in 14-day-old BALB/c mice resulted in development of seizure susceptibility, whereas noise priming was relatively ineffective at this age.

The question of whether susceptibility of the mouse cochlea to overstimulation damage varies with age was examined in detail by Saunders and Hirsch (1976), who exposed C57BL/6J mice to an octave-noise band (8.0–16.0 kHz, 110-dB SPL, for 2 minutes) at 14, 18, 23, 28, 38, and 58 days after birth. Five days later the mice were anesthetized and electrodes were placed on the exposed round window of the cochlea. The SPL necessary to elicit a 1.0 μV criterion CM response was measured for frequencies between 0.5 and 56.0 kHz. The CM criterion threshold was compared in control and primed mice at each age group. The greatest threshold loss (averaged over all frequencies) occurred in mice exposed on Day 18 (Fig. 11). Exposure on Day 14 or Day 58 did not cause a significant change in CM sensitivity. The time course of this period of increased susceptibility to noise trauma coincides with the time course of susceptibility to priming for audiogenic seizures in C57BL/6J mice (Fig. 8). One interpretation of these results is that the sensitive period aspect of the priming phenomenon is determined by the rate of maturation of the cochlea (Gates & Chen, 1973; Saunders & Hirsch, 1976).

It was noted in the previous section that mice from many inbred strains, including C57BL/6J, develop a progressive hearing loss with age. In order to determine whether this period of enhanced susceptibility to noise trauma might be a more general characteristic of early development, the present authors (Bock & Saunders, 1977; Stanek, Bock, Goran, & Saunders, 1977) exposed groups of hamsters at different ages after birth (between 11 and 75 days old) to an octave-noise band (5.0–10.0 kHz, 120-dB SPL, for 2½ minutes) and measured the resulting CM threshold deficits (Bock & Saunders, 1977; Stanek, Bock, Goran, & Saunders, 1977). The results in Fig. 11 indicate that young hamsters pass through a period of unusual susceptibility to noise

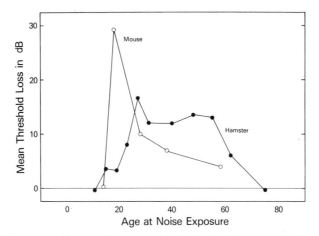

FIG. 11. The curves show cochlear microphonic threshold loss as a function of age at which mice (Saunders & Hirsch, 1976) and hamsters (Bock & Saunders, 1977; Stanek et al., 1977) were exposed to noise. The curve for mice shows the average loss over frequencies between 0.5 and 56.0 kHz while the curve for hamsters shows average loss over the range 0.5 to 3.0 kHz. Exposure stimuli were octave bands of noise: 8.0–16.0 kHz, 110 dB SPL for 2 minutes for mice, 5.0–10.0 kHz at 120 dB SPL, for 2.5 minutes for hamster. In each case the noise exposure-test interval was 5 days.

trauma, the duration of the period being somewhat longer than that observed in the mouse.

The time courses of these sensitive periods to noise trauma are unexpected, since the cochleas of both mouse and hamster (Stephens, 1972) appear to be mature by anatomical and electrophysiological criteria before or during the onset of the sensitive period (see Section II). It would be of considerable interest to determine both the developmental changes which accompany the sensitive period and the generality of this phenomenon in other species.

5. IMPLICATIONS FOR LOUDNESS RECRUITMENT

It has been known for some time that the occurrence of loudness recruitment is a powerful diagnostic tool for differentiating between the receptor or neural origins of various auditory disorders (Dix et al., 1948). It is now widely accepted that loudness recruitment is highly correlated with a cochlear lesion. The typical audiological pattern associated with loudness recruitment consists of a distinct loss in threshold sensitivity, abnormally rapid growth in loudness with increasing stimulus level at mid-range intensities, and, at high stimulus levels, loudness growth that is similar to that reported in the normal ear. This pattern of recruitment is not always so simple and cases of "derecruitment" (relatively diminishing loudness growth) and "overrecruitment" (excessive growth in loudness) have been reported. In fact, Harris, Haines, and Myers (1952) and Carver (1972) describe four types of loudness growth that are all called "recruitment."

Portman, Aran, and Lagourgue (1973) have used electrocochleography to show patterns of recruitment in loudness balance tests. The evoked-response function shows a distinct loss in threshold sensitivity and a remarkably steep rise in response amplitude to mid-range stimulus intensities. Other studies (Bredberg, 1968; Engström, 1958; Hallpike, 1967; Lim & Lane, 1969; Spoendlin, 1969) lend further support to Lurie's (1940) original hypothesis that recruitment is associated with selective lesions of the outer hair cells. Recruitment is associated with various pathologies of the inner ear including Ménières disease and also occurs after overstimulation trauma to the inner ear. Evidence from both behavioral (Henry, 1972a) and physiological tests indicates that primed mice exhibit a form of loudness recruitment. It is therefore tempting to suggest, as Henry and Saleh (1973) have done, that the priming phenomenon offers a convenient experimental model for the physiological study of loudness recruitment. While the present authors agree that priming may offer a potential experimental model, we would suggest two important qualifications. First, the recruitment observed in mice is in fact a dramatic overrecruitment. Overrecruitment is not a frequent occurrence in cases of human loudness recruitment (Carver, 1972). This suggests that other factors must be taken into account when considering the experimentally induced effect in mice. Second, as discussed previously, most of the experimental data on human loudness recruitment indicates that it results from a specific pattern of cochlear damage. Evidence from auditory deprivation experiments suggests that development of audiogenic seizure susceptibility is not necessarily dependent on a specific pattern of cochlear damage, although this may be an additional factor in the noise-priming experiments.

We therefore suggest that the usefulness of priming as a means of producing an experimental model of loudness recruitment must depend on further investigation to determine the precise nature of the developmental events in the auditory system which follow priming and their anatomical locations.

V. Conclusions

The purpose of this review has been to consider the developmental consesequences of acoustic trauma. Unfortunately, there are relatively few facts directly related to this problem and hopefully more data will become available in the future. However, some animal models already exist for studying this problem, and preliminary conclusions can be drawn. In this section we hope to relate the data on auditory development and noise-induced hearing loss (in adults) with recent data on acoustic trauma in young organisms, in order to consider implications for auditory development.

A. The Critical Period for Acoustic Trauma

Until recently it was not known whether young animals were more or less susceptible than adults to noise-induced hearing loss. The organ of Corti is probably resistant to acoustic trauma prior to the time that the tectorial and basilar membranes are capable of some movement. However, shortly after the onset of normal auditory function it would appear that auditory fatigue can occur. In fact, the available evidence indicates that there is a "critical period" of time during which the inner ear is overly susceptible to acoustic trauma. By "overly susceptible" we mean that sound exposures which have relatively little effect on the adult cochlea produce significant derangements in cochlear function when they occur during the critical period. Such a critical period has been directly demonstrated in the C57BL/6J mouse and the hamster, and is indicated in the work of Falk et al. (1974) on the guinea pig. The physiological mechanisms of the critical period are not well understood, but it would appear that hair cells are more susceptible to overstimulation trauma during this time. This conclusion is based largely on changes in CM sensitivity (Fig. 11), which are indicative of hair cell pathology (Saunders & Hirsch, 1976; Bock & Saunders, 1977) and on the occurrence of significant hair cell loss after noise exposure at 8 days of age in the guinea pig (Falk et al., 1974). Moreover, Henry and Saleh (1973) describe preliminary observations of outer hair cell loss in primed C57BL/6J mice. These reports are consistent with the conclusion that noise exposure in adults primarily affects hair cell function (see Section III,C). It is not clear, however, why hair cells should be overly susceptible to acoustic trauma during the critical period. Light and electron microscopic examination of hair cells at about the time cochlear function is mature suggest that they are indistinguishable from adult hair cells (see Section II). We assume that developmental changes in the middle ear or cochlea are associated with the critical period, but we are not yet able to specify these changes. Speculation on the nature of these presumed changes appears to us to be unwarranted until further experimental data are obtained.

The morphological and functional maturation of the auditory system varies greatly among species and presumably there is adaptive value for a given animal to achieve auditory capacity before birth or after birth. This diversity, however, makes it difficult to seek a critical period for susceptibility to acoustic trauma in other species, and particular in those animals which exhibit auditory development before birth. The results from hamster, mouse, and guinea pig experiments suggest that the critical period begins shortly after the auditory system functions normally. Moreover, the duration of the critical period seems to be species-specific. The data plotted in Fig. 3 indicate that the hamster and mouse have a relatively similar age at which the CM response is first seen. However, mature CM responses occur after 14 days of age in the mouse, while in the hamster they are mature around 30 days of age. The slower rate of functional development in the hamster cochlea, relative to that of the mouse cochlea, is reflected in the protracted critical period for acoustic trauma observed in the hamster (Fig. 11).

The important question of whether or not the human infant passes through a period of heightened sensitivity to acoustic trauma has no answer at present. If indeed the critical period follows the onset of auditory function, then the human fetus should be susceptible 12–16 weeks before birth. Fortunately, the attenuating properties of the abdominal wall of the mother shield the fetus from excessive levels of extrauterine sound (Bench, 1968). However, evidence from another species in which auditory development begins during prenatal life, the guinea pig, indicates that the auditory system exhibits mature physiological responses shortly after birth (Fig. 5). The experiment by Falk et al. (1974) shows that hair cell damage from noise exposure is greater 8 days after birth than at 2 days or 8 months. Similar findings have been reported in the guinea pig by Douek et al. (1976). Even though the guinea pig exhibits precocial auditory development it would appear that the critical period extends into neonatal life. This observation suggests that the critical period in man might also extend into early infancy. This conclusion is highly speculative, and supporting evidence of a critical period in other species with functional auditory capacity before birth is not yet available.

The development of normal language and speech in hearing-impaired children has been reviewed recently by Eisenberg (1976) and Northern and Downs (1974). The evidence they present supports the notion that early hearing loss has a severe effect on the acquisition of these skills. There are many ways by which a hearing loss in infants and children can occur (see Section I), and acoustic trauma is only one of them. Nevertheless, noise-induced hearing loss in man may be a contributing factor to abnormal development of language and speech skills.

It seems unlikely that the ear would have specifically evolved a mechanism which rendered it overly susceptible to acoustic trauma during the critical period. Such a mechanism is maladaptive and the probability of hamsters or mice being exposed to high intensity sound in the natural environment is very remote. One interpretation of the critical period, however, is that it represents a time of intensive reorganization of the auditory system. The nature of this reorganization is not known and more experiments are necessary to reveal the peripheral and central aspects of it. The current evidence indicates only that this reorganization leaves the cochlea susceptible to trauma during intense sound exposure.

B. The Peripheral and Central Consequences of Early Acoustic Trauma

Noise exposure in the adult produces pathology which is localized in the cochlea and specifically in the hair cells (see Section III,C). Acoustic trauma in young mice, however, appears to affect two regions of the auditory system: the cochlea and the central auditory pathway. The experiments in which mice and hamsters were exposed to noise early in life show that cochlear function (CM response) is severely damaged. These experiments also report overrecruitment in the relation between stimulus SPL and the amplitude of evoked activity recorded from central auditory nuclei (Fig. 10). The observation of overrecruiting responses suggests that there are important central consequences, as well as peripheral consequences, of noise-induced hearing loss. Further evidence for abnormal central maturation following early noise exposure was previously discussed (Section IV, C) within the framework of the "disuse-supersensitivity" hypothesis. The nature of this abnormal central development is not yet clear and several possibilities have been suggested (Lieff et al., 1975; Sharpless, 1975). The conclusion that must be drawn, however, is that acoustic trauma in young animals results not only in cochlear pathology, but in the abnormal maturation of central auditory connections. The implications for hearing rehabilitation may be serious if early accoustic trauma in man also results in peripheral and central pathology.

C. The Phenomenon of Priming for Audiogenic Seizures

Since the audiogenic seizure phenomenon was first reported in 1924 more than 500 papers have been published on the subject (Henry & Haythorn, 1975). However, only in the last few years have significant strides been made in describing some of the underlying mechanisms, particularly after mice have been rendered susceptible by priming. A number of recent papers have called attention to the more significant aspects of the priming phenomenon (Henry & Saleh, 1973; Saunders, 1974b; Saunders & Hirsch, 1976; Willott & Henry, 1974) and the most important of these is the concept of a sensitive or critical period. The hearing loss associated with early noise exposure, described in this paper, represents one of the few critical period phenomena for which a physiological basis can be shown (cf. the chapter by Whitsett and Vandenbergh, in this volume). As such, the process of priming for audiogenic seizures constitutes one of the most important developmentally specific models for studying critical periods. Moreover, as this review has emphasized, the priming procedure originated by Henry (1967) and Iturrian and Fink (1967) constitutes a powerful and well-developed animal model for studying the effects of noise on young animals. This model has lent significant support to the hypothesis that the developing cochlea passes through a period of unusual susceptibility to acoustic trauma. The significance of this relatively new idea is still not clear although the implications of this critical period for auditory development probably go well beyond those of susceptibility to acoustic trauma.

Acknowledgments

The preparation of this review was supported in part by research grants from the Deafness Research Foundation and by an Otolaryngology Training Grant (NINCDS No. ITOINS–05769-02) to the Department of Otorhinolaryngology and Human Communication. The authors gratefully recognize the assistance of Ms. Gardenia Green, Ms. Page V. Else, Dr. Robert Stanek, and Mr. John Rosowski.

References

Ånggård, L. On the development of cochlear function in rabbit. *Acta Physiologica Scandanavia,* 1964, **60**, 383–384.
Ånggård, L. An electrophysiological study of the development of cochlear function in the rabbit. *Acta Oto-Laryngologica, Supplementum,* 1965, **203**, 1–64.
Ades, H. W., & Engström, H. Inner ear studies. *Acta Oto-Laryngologica, Supplementum,* 1972, **302**, 1–126.
Alford, B. R., & Ruben, R. J. Physiological, behavioral and anatomical correlates of the development of hearing in the mouse. *Annals of Otology, Rhinology and Laryngology,* 1963, **72**, 237–247.
Ascher, P., Jessik-Gerschenfeld, D., & Buser, P. Participation des aires corticales sensorielles à l'élaboration de réponses motrices extra pyramidales. *Electroencephalography and Clinical Neurophysiology,* 1963, **15**, 246–264.
Babighian, G., Moushegian, G., & Rupert, A. L. Central auditory fatigue. *Audiology,* 1975, **14**, 72–83.
Barlow, H. B. Visual experience and cortical development. *Nature (London),* 1975, **258**, 199–204.
Bast, T. H., & Anson, B. J. *The temporal bone and the ear.* Springfield, Ill.: Thomas, 1949.
Bench, J. Sound transmission to the human fetus through the maternal abdominal wall. *Journal of Genetic Psychology,* 1968, **113**, 85–87.
Benitez, L. D., Eldredge, D. H., & Templer, J. W. Temporary threshold shifts in chinchilla. Electrophysiological correlates. *Journal of the Acoustical Society of America,* 1972, **52**, 1115–1123.
Bess, F. H., & Powell, R. L. Hearing hazard from model airplanes. *Clinical Pediatrics,* 1972, **11**, 621–624.
Bess, F. H., & Poynor, R. E. Noise-induced hearing loss and snowmobiles. *Archives of Otolaryngology,* 1974, **99**, 45–51.

Bock, G. R., & Chen, C. S. Frequency modulated tones as priming stimuli for audiogenic seizures in mice. *Experimental Neurology*, 1972, 37, 124–130.

Bock, G. R., Gates, G. R., & Chen, C. S. Priming for audiogenic seizures in mice: Influence of post priming auditory environment. *Experimental Neurology*, 1974, 42, 700–702.

Bock, G. R., & Saunders, J. C. Effects of low and high-frequency noise bands in producing a physiological correlate of loudness recruitment in mice. *Transactions of the American Academy of Ophthalmology and Otolaryngology*, 1976, 82, 338–342.

Bock, G. R., & Saunders, J. C. A critical period for acoustic trauma in the hamster and its relation to cochlear development. *Science*, 1977, 197, 396–398.

Bohne, B. A. Location of small cochlear lesions by phase contrast microscopy prior to thin sectioning. *Laryngoscope*, 1972, 82, 1–16.

Bohne, B. A. *Anatomical correlates of an asymptotic threshold shift (ATS)* (Periodic Progress Report No. 16). Central Institute for the Deaf, Saint Louis, Missouri, 1973. Pp. 15–16.

Bohne, B. A., Eldredge, D. H., & Mills, J. H. Cochlear potentials and electron microscopy applied to the study of small cochlear lesions. *Annals of Otology, Rhinology, and Laryngology*, 1973, 82, 595–608.

Bosher, S. K. Morphological and functional changes in the cochlea associated with the inception of hearing. *Symposium of the Zoological Society of London*, 1975, 37, 11–22.

Bosher, S. K., & Hallpike, C. S. Degenerative process in deaf white cat. Possible relationship to unexplained human congenital deafness. In A. B. Graham (Ed.), *Sensorineural hearing processes and disorders*. Boston: Little, Brown, 1967. Pp. 381–391.

Bosher, S. K., & Warren, R. L. A study of the electrochemistry and osmotic relationships of the cochlear fluids in the neonatal rat at the time of the development of the endocochlear potential. *Journal of Physiology (London)*, 1971, 212, 739–761.

Bredberg, G. Cellular pattern and nerve supply of the human organ of Corti. *Acta Oto-laryngologica Supplementum*, 1968, 236, 6–135.

Buser, P., St. Laurent, J. & Menini, C. Intervention du colliculus inférieur dans l'elaboration et le controle cortical spécifique des décharges cloniques au son chez le chat sous chloralose. *Experimental Brain Research*, 1966, 1, 102–126.

Carder, H. M., & Miller, J. D. Temporary threshold shifts from prolonged exposure to noise. *Journal of Speech and Hearing Research*, 1972, 15, 603–623.

Carver, W. F. Loudness balance procedures. In J. Katz (Ed.), *Handbook of clinical audiology*. Baltimore: Williams & Wilkins, 1972. Pp. 180–203.

Cass, D. T., Sutton, T. J., & Mark, R. F. Competition between nerves for functional connections with axolotol muscles. *Nature (London)*, 1973, 243, 201–203.

Chaloupka, Z., Záhlava, J., Mysliveček, J., & Hassmannová, J. Development of functional abilities of the auditory system. In L. Jilek & S. Trojan (Eds.), *Ontogenesis of the brain*. Prague: Charles University Press, 1968. Pp. 387–393.

Chen, C. S., Bock, G. R., & Gates, G. R. Effect of priming and testing for audiogenic seizures in BALB/c mice as a function of stimulus intensity. *Experientia*, 1974, 30, 153.

Chen, C. S., Gates, G. R., & Bock, G. R. Effect of priming and tympanic membrane destruction on development of audiogenic seizure susceptibility in BALB/c mice. *Experimental Neurology*, 1973, 39, 277–284.

Clopton, B. M., & Winfield, J. A. Early auditory experience modifies unit responsiveness to temporal auditory patterns in the inferior colliculus. *Journal of the Acoustical Society of America*, 1974, 55, 468. (Abstract)

Crowley, D. E., & Hepp-Reymond, M.-C. Development of cochlear function in the ear of the infant rat. *Journal of Comparative and Physiological Psychology*, 1966, 62, 427–432.

Dallos, P. *The auditory periphery*. New York: Academic Press, 1973.

Deol, M. S. Inherited diseases of the inner ear in man in the light of studies on the mouse. *Journal of Medical Genetics*, 1968, 5, 137–158.

Dix, M. R., Hallpike, C. S., & Hood, J. D. Observations upon loudness recruitment phenomenon, with special reference to differential diagnosis of disorders of internal ear and
eighth nerve. *Proceedings of the Royal Society of Medicine*, 1948, **41**, 516–526.

Donaldson, A. H. *The rat: Data and reference tables* (2nd ed.). Philadelphia: Wistar Inst. Press,
1924.

Douek, E., Bannister, L. H., Dodson, H. C., Ashcroft, P., & Humphries, K. N., Effects of incubator noise on the cochlea of the newborn. *The Lancet*, November 1976, 1110–1113.

Durrant, J. D. Effects of noise on the cochlear potentials. In D. Henderson, R. Hamernick,
D. S. Dosanjh, & J. H. Mills (Eds.), *Effects of noise on hearing*. New York: Raven, 1976.
Pp. 179–197.

Eagles, E. L., Wishik, S. M., & Doerfler, L. G. Hearing sensitivity and ear disease in children:
A prospective study. *Laryngoscope*, 1967, Suppl., 1–274.

Eagles, E. L., Wishik, S. M., Doerfler, L. G., Melnick, W., & Levine, H. S. Hearing sensitivity
and related factors in children. *Laryngoscope*, 1963, Suppl., 1–211.

Ehret, G. Development of absolute auditory thresholds in the house mouse (*Mus musculus*).
Journal of the American Audiological Society, 1976, **1**, 179–184.

Ehret, G. Postnatal development in the acoustic system of the housemouse in the light of
developing masked thresholds. *Journal of the Acoustical Society of America*, 1977, **62**, 143–
148.

Eisenberg, R. B. *Auditory competence in early life: The roots of communicative behavior*. Baltimore: University Park Press, 1976.

Eldredge, D. H., Mills, J. H., & Bohne, B. A. Anatomical, behavioral and electrophysiological
observations on chinchillas after long exposure to noise. In J. Hawkins & M. Lawrence
(Eds.), *Advances in oto-rhino-laryngology: International symposium on otophysiology*
(Vol. 20). Basel: Karger, 1973. Pp. 64–81.

Engström, H. On the double innervation of the inner ear sensory epithelia. *Acta Oto-laryng-
ologia*, 1958, **49**, 109–118.

Engström, H., Ades, H. W., & Andersson, A. *Structural pattern of the organ of Corti*. Stockholm:
Almqvist & Wiksell, 1966.

Falk, S. A., Cook, R. V., Haseman, J. D., & Sanders, G. M. Noise-induced inner ear damage
in newborn and adult guinea pigs. *Laryngoscope*, 1974, **84**, 444–453.

Falk, S. A., & Farmer, J. C. Incubator noise and possible deafness. *Archives of Otolaryngology*,
1973, **97**, 385–387.

Falk, S. A., & Woods, N. F. Hospital noise-levels and potential health hazards. *New England
Journal of Medicine*, 1973, **289**, 774.

Fernández, C., & Hinojosa, R. Postnatal development of endocochlear potential and stria
vascularis in the cat. *Acta Oto-laryngologica*, 1974, **78**, 173–186.

Finck, A., Schneck, C. D., & Hartman, A. F. Development of cochlear function in the neonate
Mongolian gerbil (*Meriones unguiculatus*). *Journal of Comparative and Physiological
Psychology*, 1972, **78**, 375–380.

Fior, R. Physiological maturation of auditory function between 3 and 13 years of age.
Audiology, 1972, **11**, 317–321.

Forster, F. M. Human studies of epileptic seizures induced by sound and their conditioned
extinction. In B. L. Welch & A. S. Welch (Eds.), *Physiological effects of noise*. New York:
Plenum, 1970. Pp. 151–158.

Foss, I., & Flottorp, G. A comparative study of the development of hearing and vision in
various species commonly used in experiments. *Acta Oto-Laryngologica*, 1974, **77**, 202–
214.

Fuller, J. L., & Collins, R. L. Mice unilaterally sensitized for audiogenic seizures. *Science*, 1968,
162, 1295.

Gates, G. R., & Chen, C. S. Priming for audiogenic seizures in adult BALB/c mice. *Experimental Neurology*, 1973, **41**, 457–460.

Gates, G. R., Chen, C. S., & Bock, G. R. Effects of monaural and binaural auditory deprivation on audiogenic seizure susceptibility in BALB/c mice. *Experimental Neurology*, 1973, **38**, 488–493.

Gottlieb, G. Prenatal behavior in birds. *Quarterly Review of Biology*, 1968, **43**, 148–174.

Gottlieb, G. *Development of species identification in birds.* Chicago: University of Chicago Press, 1971.

Gottlieb, G. Development of species identification in ducklings: II. Experiential prevention of perceptual deficit caused by embryonic auditory deprivation. *Journal of Comparative and Physiological Psychology*, 1975, **89**, 675–684.

Gottlieb, G. Conceptions of prenatal development: Behavioral embryology. *Psychological Review*, 1976, **83**, 215–234. (a)

Gottlieb, G. The roles of experience in the development of behavior and the nervous system. In G. Gottlieb (Ed.), *Studies on the development of behavior and the nervous system* (Vol. 3): *Neural and behavioral specificity.* New York: Academic Press, 1976. (b)

Gulick, W. L. *Hearing: Physiology and psychophysics.* London and New York: Oxford Press, 1971.

Gyllensten, L. Growth alteration in the auditory cortex of visually deprived mice. *Journal of Comparative Neurology*, 1966, **126**, 463–470.

Gyllensten, L., Malmfors, T., & Norrlin, M. Effects of visual deprivation on the optic centers of growing and adult mice. *Journal of Comparative Neurology*, 1965, **124**, 149–160.

Hallpike, C. S. The loudness recruitment phenomenon: A clinical contribution to the neurology of hearing. In A. B. Graham (Ed.), *Sensorineural hearing processes and disorders.* Boston: Little Brown, 1967. Pp. 489–499.

Harris, J. D., Haines, H. L., & Myers, C. K. Loudness perception for pure tones and for speech. *Archives of Otolaryngology*, 1952, **55**, 107–133.

Hassmannová, J., & Mysliveček, J. Maturation of the primary cortical response to stimulation of medial geniculate body. *Electroencephalography and Clinical Neurophysiology*, 1967, **22**, 547–555.

Henderson, D., Hamernick, R. P., & Sitler, R. Audiometric and anatomical correlates of impulse noise exposure. *Archives of Otolaryngology*, 1974, **99**, 62–66.

Henry, K. R. Audiogenic seizure susceptibility induced in C57BL/6J mice by prior auditory exposures. *Science*, 1967, **158**, 938–940.

Henry, K. R. Pinna reflex thresholds and audiogenic seizures. *Journal of Comparative and Physiological Psychology*, 1972, **79**, 77–81. (a)

Henry, K. R. Unilateral increase of auditory sensitivity following early auditory experience. *Science*, 1972, **176**, 689–690. (b)

Henry, K. R., & Bowman, R. E. Effects of acoustic priming on audiogenic, electroconvulsive, and chemoconvulsive seizures. *Journal of Comparative and Physiological Psychology*, 1969, **67**, 401–406.

Henry, K. R., & Bowman, R. E. Acoustic priming of audiogenic seizures in mice. In B. L. Welch & A. S. Welch (Eds.), *Physiological effects of noise.* New York: Plenum, 1970. Pp. 185–203.

Henry, K. R., & Haythorn, M. M. Auditory similarities associated with genetic and experimentalacoustic deprivation. *Journal of Comparative and Physiological Psychology*, 1975, **89**, 213–218.

Henry, K. R., & Saleh, M. Recruitment deafness: Functional effect of priming-induced seizures in mice. *Journal of Comparative and Physiological Psychology*, 1973, **84**, 885–887.

Hilding, D. A. Electron microscopy of the developing hearing organ. *Laryngoscope*, 1969, **79**, 1691–1704.

Impekoven, M., & Gold, P. S. Prenatal origins of parent-young interactions in birds—A naturalistic approach. In G. Gottlieb (Ed.), *Advances in ontogeny of behavior and the nervous system* (Vol. 1). New York: Academic Press, 1973.

Iturrian, W. G., & Fink, G. B. A conditional convulsive reaction. *Federation Proceedings*, 1967, **26**, 736. (Abstract)

Jewett, D. L., & Romano, M. N. Neonatal development of the auditory system potentials averaged from the scalp of rat and cat. *Brain Research*, 1972, **36**, 101–115.

Keith, R. W. Middle ear function in neonates. *Archives of Otolaryngology*, 1975, **101**, 376–379.

Kikuchi, K., & Hilding, D. The development of the organ of Corti in the mouse. *Acta Oto-Laryngologica*, 1965, **60**, 207–222.

Kocher, W. Untersuchungen zur Genetik und Pathologie der Entwicklung spät einsetzender hereditärer Taubheit bei der Maus (*Mus musculus*). *Archiv für Ohren-, Nasen- und Kehlkopfheilkunde*, 1960, **177**, 108–145.

König, N., & Marty, R. On functions and structure of deep layers of immature auditory cortex. *Journal de Physiologie (Paris)*, 1974, **68**, 145–155.

Konishi, M. Development of auditory neuronal responses in avian embryos. *Proceedings of the National Academy of Sciences U.S.A.*, 1973, **70**, 1795–1798.

Kryter, K. D. *The effects of noise on man.* New York: Academic Press, 1970.

Larsell, O., McCrady, E., Jr., & Larsell, J. F. Development of the organ of Corti in relation to the inception of hearing. *Archives of Otolaryngology*, 1944, **40**, 233–248.

Larsell, O., McCrady, E., Jr., & Zimmerman, A. A. Morphological and functional development of the membranous labyrinth in the opossum. *Journal of Comparative Neurology*, 1935, **62**, 95–118.

League, R., Parker, J., Robertson, M., Valentine, V., & Powell, K., Jr. Acoustical environments in incubators and infant oxygen tents. *Preventative Medicine*, 1972, **1** , 231–239.

Lidén, G., Engström, H., & Hall, J. Audiological and morphological assessment of effect of noise on cochlea and brain stem in cat. *Acta Oto-Laryngologica*, 1973, **75**, 325–328.

Lieff, B. D., Permut, A., Schlesinger, K., & Sharpless, S. K. Developmental changes in auditory evoked potentials in the inferior colliculi of mice during periods of susceptibility to priming. *Experimental Neurology*, 1975, **46**, 534–541.

Lim, D. J., & Lane, W. C. Cochlear sensory epithelium. *Annals of Otology, Rhinology, and Laryngology*, 1969, **78**, 827–841.

Lim, D. J., & Melnick, W. Acoustic damage of the cochlea. *Archives of Otolaryngology*, 1971, **94**, 294–305.

Lindeman, H. H., Ades, H. W., Bredberg, G., & Engström, H. The sensory hairs and the tectorial membrane in the development of the cat's organ of Corti. *Acta Oto-Laryngologica*, 1971, **72**, 229–242.

Lurie, M. H. Studies of acquired and inherited deafness in animals. *Journal of the Acoustical Society of America*, 1940, **11**, 420–426.

Marshall, L., & Brandt, J. F. Temporary threshold shift from a toy cap gun. *Journal of Speech and Hearing Disorders*, 1974, **39**, 163–168.

Marty, R., & Thomas, J. Réponse électro-corticale à la stimulation du nerf cochléaire chez le chat neuveau-né. *Journal de Physiologie (Paris)*, 1963, **55**, 165–166.

McCrady, E., Jr., Wever, E. G., & Bray, C. W. The development of hearing in the opossum. *Journal of Experimental Zoology*, 1937, **75**, 503–517.

McCrady, E., Jr., Wever, E. G., & Bray, C. W. A further investigation of the development of hearing in the opossum. *Journal of Comparative and Physiological Psychology*, 1940, **30**, 17–21.

McGinn, M. D., Willott, J. F., & Henry, K. R. Effect of conductive hearing loss on auditory evoked potentials and audiogenic seizures in mice. *Nature (London), New Biology,* 1973, **244**, 255–256.

Melnick, W., & Maves, M. Asymptotic threshold shift (ATS) in man from 24 hour exposure to continuous noise. *Annals of Otology, Rhinology, and Laryngology,* 1974, **83**, 820–828.

Mikaelian, D. O., & Ruben, R. J. Hearing degeneration in shaker-1 mouse. *Archives of Otolaryngology,* 1964, **80**, 418–430.

Mikaelian, D., & Ruben, R. J. Development of hearing in the normal CBA-J mouse. *Acta Oto-Laryngologica,* 1965, **59**, 451–461.

Mikaelian, D. O., Warfield, D., & Norris, O. Genetic progressive hearing loss in C57/b16 mice. *Acta Oto-Laryngologica,* 1974, **77**, 327–334.

Miller, J. D. Audibility curve of the chinchilla. *Journal of the Acoustical Society of America,* 1970, **48**, 513–523.

Miller, J. D. Effects of noise on people. *Journal of the Acoustical Society of America,* 1974, **56**, 729–764.

Mills, J. H. Temporary and permanent threshold shifts produced by nine-day exposures to noise. *Journal of Speech and Hearing Research,* 1973, **16**, 426–438.

Mills, J. H. Noise and children: A review of literature. *Journal of the Acoustical Society of America,* 1975, **58**, 767–779.

Milonyeni, M. The late stages of the development of the primary cochlear nuclei. *Brain Research,* 1967, **4**, 334–344.

Møller, A. Noise as a health hazard. *Ambio,* 1975, **4**, 6–13.

Moody, D. B. Behavioral studies of noise-induced hearing loss in primates: Loudness recruitment. In J. Hawkins & M. Lawrence (Eds.), *Advances in oto-rhino-laryngology: International symposium on otophysiology* (Vol. 20), Basal: Karger, 1973. Pp. 82–101.

Morgan, A., Charachon, D., & Bringuier, N. Disorders of the auditory apparatus caused by embryopathy or fetopathy: Prophylaxis and treatment. *Acta Oto-Laryngologica, Supplementum,* 1971, **291**, 1–27.

Northern, J. L., & Downs, M. P. *Hearing in children.* Baltimore: Williams & Wilkins, 1974.

Pfalz, R. K. J. Absence of a function for the crossed olivocochlear bundle under physiological conditions. *Archiv für Klinische und Experimentelle Ohren- Nasen- und Kehlkopfheilkunde,* 1969, **193**, 89–100.

Portman, M., Aran, J. M., & Lagourgue, P. Testing for "recruitment" by electrocochleography. *Annals of Otology, Rhinology, and Laryngology,* 1973, **82**, 36–44.

Price, G. R. Loss in cochlear microphonic sensitivity in young cat ears exposed to intense sound. *Journal of the Acoustical Society of America,* 1972, **51**, 104. (Abstract).

Price, G. R. Age as a factor in susceptibility to hearing loss: Young versus adult ears. *Journal of the Acoustical Society of America,* 1976, **60**, 886–892.

Proctor, C. A., & Proctor, B. Understanding hereditary nerve deafness. *Archives of Otolaryngology,* 1967, **85**, 45–62.

Pujol, R. Development of tone-burst responses along the auditory pathway in the cat. *Acta Oto-Laryngologica,* 1972, **74**, 383–391.

Pujol, R., & Hilding, D. Anatomy and physiology of the onset of auditory function. *Acta Oto-Laryngologica,* 1973, **76**, 1–10.

Pujol, R., & Marty, R. Postnatal maturation of the cochlea of the cat. *Journal of Comparative Neurology,* 1970, **139**, 115–125.

Ralls, K. Auditory sensitivity in mice, *Peromyscus* and *Mus musculus. Animal Behaviour,* 1967, **15**, 123–128.

Rogers, L. A., & Cowan, W. M. The development of the mesencephalic nucleus of the trigeminal nerve in the chick. *Journal of Comparative Neurology,* 1973, **147**, 291–320.

Romand, R. Maturation des potentiels cochléaires dans la période périnatale chez le chat et chez le cobaye. *Journal de Physiologie (Paris)*, 1971, **63**, 763–782.

Rosowski, J. J., Bock, G. R., & Saunders, J. C. Frequency selectivity of single neurons in the Mesencephalicus Lateralis pars Dorsalis (MLD) of the neonatal chick. *Journal of the Acoustical Society of America*, 1976, **59**, Suppl. 1, S47. (Abstract)

Ruben, R. J. Development of the inner ear of the mouse: A radioautographic study of terminal mitoses. *Acta Oto-Laryngologica, Supplementum*, 1967, **220**, 1–44.

Salvi, R., Henderson, D., & Hamernick, R. Auditory fatigue: Retrocochlear components. *Science*, 1975, **190**, 486–487.

Saunders, J. C. The development of auditory evoked responses in the chick embryo. *Minerva Otorhinolaryngologica*, 1974, **24**, 221–229. (a)

Saunders, J. C. The physiological effects of priming for audiogenic seizures in mice. *Laryngoscope*, 1974, **84**, 750–756. (b)

Saunders, J. C., Bock, G. R., Chen, C. S., & Gates, G. R. The effects of priming for audiogenic seizures on cochlear and behavioral responses in BALB/c mice. *Experimental Neurology*, 1972, **36**, 426–436. (a)

Saunders, J. C., Bock, G. R. James, R., & Chen, C. S. The effects of priming for audiogenic seizures on auditory evoked responses in the cochlear nucleus and inferior colliculus of BALB/c mice. *Experimental Neurology*, 1972, **37**, 388–394. (b)

Saunders, J. C., Coles, R. B., & Gates, G. R. The development of auditory evoked responses in the cochlea and cochlea nuclei of the chick. *Brain Research*, 1973, **63**, 59–74.

Saunders, J. C., & Hirsch, K. A. Changes in cochlear microphonic sensitivity after priming C57BL/6J mice at various ages for audiogenic seizures. *Journal of Comparative and Physiological Psychology*, 1976, **90**, 212–220.

Saunders, J. C., Mills, J. H., & Miller, J. D. Threshold shift in the chinchilla from daily exposure to noise for six hours. *Journal of the Acoustical Society of America*, 1977, **61**, 558–570.

Saunders, J. C., & Rhyne, R. L. Cochlear nucleus activity and temporary threshold shift in the cat. *Brain Research*, 1970, **24**, 339–342.

Schmidt, R. S., & Fernández, C. Development of mammalian endocochlear potential. *Journal of Experimental Zoology*, 1963, **153**, 227–236.

Sedláček, J. Acoustic and somatosensory evoked responses in the brain hemispheres of chick embryos. *Physiologia Bohemaslovaca*, 1976, **25**, 103–108. (a)

Sedláček, J. Foetal and neonatal development of evoked responses in guinea-pig auditory cortex. *Physiologia Bohemoslovaca*, 1976, **25**, 13–21. (b)

Sellick, P. M., & Bock, G. R. Evidence for an electrogenic potassium pump as the origin of the positive component of the endocochlear potential. *Pflügers Archiv*, 1974, **352**, 351–361.

Sharpless, S. Isolated and deafferented neurons: Disuse supersensitivity. In H. Jasper, A. Ward, & A. Pope (Eds.), *Basic mechanisms of the epilepsies*. Boston: Little, Brown, 1969.

Sharpless, S. Disuse supersensitivity. In A. H. Riesen (Ed.), *The developmental neuropsychology of sensory deprivation*. New York: Academic Press, 1975.

Sher, A. E. The embryonic and postnatal development of the inner ear of the mouse. *Acta Oto-Laryngologica, Supplementum*, 1971, **285**, 1–77.

Silver, J., & Hughes, A. F. W. The role of cell death during morphogenesis of the mammalian eye. *Journal of Morphology*, 1973, **140**, 159–170.

Sobckowicz, H. M., Bereman, B., & Rose, J. E. Development of the organ of Corti of the newborn mouse in culture. *Journal of the Acoustical Society of America*, 1974, **55**, 459. (Abstract)

Spoendlin, H. Innervation patterns in the organ of Corti of the cat. *Acta Oto-Laryngologica*, 1969, **67**, 239–254.

Spoendlin, H. Primary structural changes in the organ of Corti after acoustic overstimulation. *Acta Oto-Laryngologica*, 1971, **71**, 166–176.

Spoendlin, H., & Brun, J. P. Relation of structural damage to exposure time and intensity in acoustic trauma. *Acta Oto-Laryngologica*, 1973, **75**, 220–226.

Spoendlin, H., & Brun, J. P. The block-surface technique for evaluation of cochlear pathology. *Archives of Oto-Rhino-Laryngology*, 1974, **208**, 137–145.

Stanek, R., Bock, G. R., Goran, M. L., & Saunders, J. C. Age dependent susceptibility to auditory trauma in the hamster; Behavioral and electrophysiological consequences. *Transactions of the American Academy of Opthalmology and Otolaryngology*, 1977, **84**, 465–472.

Stephens, C. B. Development of the middle and inner ear in the golden hamster (*Mesocricetus auratus*). *Acta Oto-Laryngologica, Supplementum*, 1972, **296**, 1–51.

Vanzulli, A., & Garcia-Austt, E. Development of cochlear microphonic potentials in the chick embryo. *Acta Neurophysiologica Latino-America*, 1963, **9**, 19–23.

Wada, T. W. Anatomical and physiological studies on the growth of the inner ear of the albino rat. *American Anatomical Memoirs*, 1923, **10**, 1–74.

Ward, W. D., & Duvall, A. J., III. Behavioral and ultrastructural correlates of acoustic trauma. *Annals of Otology, Rhinology, and Laryngology*, 1971, **80**, 881–897.

Ward, W. D., & Glorig, A. A case of firecracker-induced hearing loss. *Laryngoscope*, 1961, *71*, 1590–1596.

Weber, H. J., McGovern, F. J., & Zink, D. An evaluation of 1000 children with hearing loss. *Journal of Speech and Hearing Disorders*, 1967, **32**, 343–354.

Welch, B. L., & Welch, A. S. *Physiological effects of noise*. New York: Plenum, 1970.

Wever, E. G., & Lawrence, M. *Physiological acoustics*. Princeton: Princeton University Press, 1954.

Willott, J. F., & Henry, K. R. Auditory evoked potentials: Developmental changes of threshold and amplitude following early acoustic trauma. *Journal of Comparative and Physiological Psychology*, 1974, **86**, 1–7.

Wright, C. G., & Barnes, C. D. Audio-spinal reflex responses in decerebrate and chloralose anesthetized cats. *Brain Research*, 1972, **36**, 307–331.

EXPERIENTIAL INFLUENCES ON BRAIN ANATOMY AND BRAIN CHEMISTRY IN RODENTS

MARK R. ROSENZWEIG AND EDWARD L. BENNETT

Department of Psychology
University of California, Berkeley
Berkeley, California

Laboratory of Chemical Biodynamics
Lawrence Berkeley Laboratory
Berkeley, California

I. Introduction and Scope

This chapter reviews research that demonstrates significant effects of differential experience on the central nervous system; it also discusses briefly some effects of experience on behavior. The main experiential variable to be considered is interaction of subjects with environments of differing levels of complexity; a few experiments on effects of formal training are also mentioned. We are not concerned here with such variables as stress, early handling, crowding or population density, sensory deprivation, or distortion of sensory input, except as such factors are manipulated to determine whether they may account for the observed effects of experience in environments of differential complexity.[1]

To make clear what we mean by the environmental variables, let us describe briefly some environments used in research with rats. (Most of this research on cerebral effects has been done with laboratory rodents—especially rats—but some references are made to other species.) The typical laboratory rat lives in a small cage with one or two cagemates and with food and water provided *ad libitum*. These conditions are compatible with growth and health that are "normal" by present animal care standards. Of course the rat evolved to live in and deal with much more complex environments. Students of D. O. Hebb at McGill University in the 1950s kept groups of rats in large cages in which varied stimulus objects were placed (e.g., Hymovitch, 1952). Exposure for several weeks to this so-called "free" environment yielded improved problem-solving behavior, as compared with living in the standard colony environment.

We started using a similar environmental complexity (EC) condition in the late 1950s in order to provide extensive opportunities for informal learning. This followed experiments showing small but significant changes in brain chemistry of rats after various types of formal training (Rosenzweig, Krech, & Bennett, 1961), and we hoped that more extensive training would produce even larger cerebral effects that could be used to study brain mechanisms of learning and memory.

In the EC condition, 10 to 12 rats were placed in a $76 \times 76 \times 46$-cm cage along with some stimulus objects ("toys") from a standard pool. Each day six or more objects were placed in the cage. In addition to providing environmental complexity to enrich experience above the standard colony (SC) norm, we also decreased the variety of experience below the SC level by using an impoverished condition (IC) which consisted of housing rats singly in small cages (Rosenzweig & Bennett, 1969; Rosenzweig, Bennett, & Diamond, 1972a).[2,3] Somewhat different enriched conditions have been

---

[1] It should be noted that we are stressing differential *experience* rather than differential environments. As will be shown later in this chapter, differential environments do not cause cerebral effects unless the subjects participate actively (and thus experience) these environments.

[2] The reader who consults some of the earlier articles should be aware of a number of changes of nomenclature. The enriched environment was originally called environmental

used by other investigators (e.g., Volkmar & Greenough, 1972). Ferchmin, Eterović, and Caputto (1970) used more complex cages and arrays of stimulus objects, and also placed older, experienced rats with younger naive rats to facilitate the latter's exploration. Kuenzle and Knüsel (1974) increased group size to 70 as well as using a very complex environment; they referred to this condition as "superenriched."

Previous reviews of effects of differential experience on brain have been prepared by Rosenzweig, Bennett, and Diamond (1972c), Greenough (1976), Bennett (1976), and Rosenzweig and Bennett (1976, 1977). In addition to reviewing work from a number of laboratories, we will furnish new data in certain sections of this chapter.

While surveying cerebral and behavioral effects induced by experience in differential environments, we will consider the following questions:

1. How does age affect the magnitude of the effects?

2. What mechanisms have been proposed to mediate production of these effects? Which of these can be rejected, and which are supported by the evidence?

3. How should effects of differential experience be distinguished from other topics with which this treatment is sometimes confused, such as early stimulation (e.g., research of Denenberg) or sensory deprivation or distortion (e.g., research of Hubel & Wiesel; Blakemore; chapters by Saunders & Bock and Mistretta & Bradley in this volume)?

Footnote 2 (continued)

complexity and training (ECT) but the small amount of training was later found to have no effect and was therefore omitted, so by 1968 (e.g., Rosenzweig, Love, & Bennett, 1968) we were beginning to refer to this simply as the enriched condition (EC). Whereas articles on cerebral effects in the early 1960s referred to "cholinesterase," later articles (e.g., Bennett *et al.*, 1964) state whether acetylcholinesterase or the less specific enzyme cholinesterase was assayed. In earlier articles we referred to a standard sample of "visual cortex," but by 1968 we had begun to employ the more neutral anatomical designation, "occipital cortex" (e.g., Rosenzweig *et al.*, 1968).

[3] As we have stated previously, we use the terms "enriched" and "impoverished" in relation to the standard colony laboratory norm and not in an absolute sense. The seminatural environment (SNE) in a large outdoor enclosure has produced brain values further removed from those of colony rats than has experience in EC (see Section II, B, 1 and Table III). This indicates that the EC condition is restricted in comparison with SNE. Enrichment of experience above the "natural" baseline may stimulate still further development. In the case of human beings "it is, of course, a problem of intense interest, both theoretical and practical, whether enrichment beyond any particular environment that is the norm for a given time and place will alter brain, emotion, and intelligence" (Rosenzweig, 1971, p. 314). Elsewhere (Rosenzweig & Bennett, 1976) we have reviewed research on several degrees of enrichment or impoverishment along two dimensions—social and inanimate stimulation.

II. Cerebral and Behavioral Effects Induced by Experience in Differential Environments

A. Effects on Brain Anatomy

1. MACROSCOPIC EFFECTS

a. Weights of Brain Samples. In our studies on brain enzymes of rats exposed to differential environments, the weights of brain regions were taken by standardized dissection procedures (Rosenzweig, Krech, Bennett, & Diamond, 1962) so that enzymatic activity could be expressed per unit of tissue weight. Several experiments were completed before we noticed that the weights of cortical samples also differed significantly between littermates in the EC and IC environments (Rosenzweig *et al.*, 1962). Since then, weight differences between EC and IC rats have been replicated in many experiments by ourselves and in some by others (e.g., Cummins, Walsh, Budtz-Olsen, Konstantinos, & Horsfall, 1973; Ferchmin *et al.*, 1970).

Table I presents representative brain weight values for the SC group and

TABLE I

DIFFERENCES AMONG EC, SC, AND IC RATS IN BRAIN WEIGHTS (MG) AND BODY WEIGHTS (GM)[a]

	SC Mean ± standard deviation	EC versus SC		IC versus SC		EC versus IC	
		% Diff.[b]	No. EC > SC[c]	% Diff.	No. IC > SC	% Diff.	No. EC > IC
Cortex							
Occipital	66 ± 4	3.3***	58	− 5.6***	25	9.4***	71
Somesthetic	56 ± 4	− 0.9	41.5	− 4.3***	24	3.6***	64
Remaining							
dorsal	290 ± 16	1.0	48.5	− 2.6***	26	3.7***	61
Ventral	246 ± 16	1.5	48	− 1.9*	38	3.4***	58
Total	658 ± 28	1.2**	52	− 2.8***	19	4.2***	72
Rest of brain	833 ± 39	− 0.5	43.5	0.5	47	− 0.9	35
Total brain	1491 ± 65	0.3	47	− 1.0*	30	1.3**	56
Cortex							
Rest	790 ± .020	1.7***	60	− 3.3***	8	5.1***	82
Terminal body							
weight	181 ± 18	− 6.1***	25	5.6***	54	− 11.0***	20

[a]Based on 87 littermate sets of male rats of the Berkeley S₁ stock placed in differential conditions from 25 to 55 days of age.

[b]Percent difference between EC and SC means.

[c]The number of the 87 littermate pairs in which the EC value exceeded the SC value.

*p > .05, **p > .01, ***p > .001. Based on Duncan's New Multiple Range Test.

gives EC versus SC, IC versus SC, and EC versus IC effects. These values are based on rats kept in the experimental conditions from 25 to 55 days of age; similar data from 25 to 105-day experiments are given in Rosenzweig *et al.* (1972c, Table 3). Note that the largest relative difference between EC and IC is found in the occipital cortex (9.4%). The other cortical areas show considerably smaller but nevertheless significant differences. The rest of the brain (or subcortex) shows a smaller EC–IC difference (−0.9%) than does total cortex (4.2%). Because the largest differences have consistently been found in the occipital region, certain other measures to be described later have been made principally or exclusively in this region.[4]

A particularly stable measure of differential experience is the ratio of weight of total cortex to weight of the rest of the brain (cortical/subcortical ratio). This ratio yields, in effect, a value adjusted for covariance of brain weights on body weights (Rosenzweig *et al.*, 1972c, pp. 229–230, 236–237). It should be emphasized that the differences in brain weight between EC and IC rats cannot be attributed to body weight differences; in fact, the brain weights of rats reared in EC environments regularly exceed those of animals reared in IC environments, whereas IC animals achieve higher terminal body weights than do EC animals.

In six recent experiments, the hippocampus was dissected separately from other brain sections in rats that were in EC or IC for either 30 or 25 days, beginning at 30 days of age. The hippocampus was found to be only 1.6% heavier in EC than in IC rats, a statistically insignificant difference.

Differences in weights of brain samples begin to appear after rats have spent only a few days in differential environments. In our earliest experiments we placed rats in the experimental conditions at weaning (25 days of age) and kept them there for 80 days since we supposed that it might take many weeks for measurable effects to occur. Later we found that brain weight differences are somewhat larger after 30 days of differential experience than after 80 days; it may be that rats begin to habituate to the enriched condition after a few weeks. More recently we have tried to determine how short a period is required to produce effects. Significant brain weight effects are first observed after only 4 days in EC or IC (Table II).

Kuenzle and Knüsel compared rats raised in their "superenriched" (SE) situation with others raised in a condition like our EC. In each of three experiments, weight of occipital cortex was significantly greater in SE rats

---

[4]It is not yet clear why the EC–IC cerebral effects are larger in the occipital cortex than elsewhere in the brain. This is not a specifically visual effect, since it occurs even if the experiment is run in total darkness or if the rats are blinded (Rosenzweig *et al.*, 1969). The occipital area is late to myelinate and thus might be plastic over a longer period than are other regions, but myelination is already complete in the adult rats that nevertheless show larger EC–IC differences in the occipital region than elsewhere.

TABLE II

Effect of Duration on EC–IC Percentage Differences[a] in Brain Weights and Body Weights of Rats Put into EC or IC at Weaning

	Duration (in days)											
	1	3	4	8	15	30	45	60	80	100	125	160
No. of pairs	12	11	48	48	58	354	23	40	218	57	70	33
Occipital cortex	2.8NS	-0.3NS	6.6***	4.0**	7.4***	9.0***	9.4***	12.4***	7.2***	10.6***	7.7***	10.6***
Total cortex	-1.2NS	-0.7NS	2.2***	1.9*	5.0***	5.3***	5.8***	4.7***	4.2***	7.3***	5.8***	3.9***
Rest of brain	-0.7NS	-2.9NS	1.9***	0.1NS	1.8***	0.5NS	1.4NS	-0.3NS	-1.0*	1.7*	1.1NS	-1.7*
Total brain	-0.2NS	-1.9NS	2.0***	0.9NS	3.2***	2.5***	3.3***	1.8*	1.2**	4.0***	3.0***	0.6NS
Cortex/rest	-2.1NS	-2.1NS	0.2NS	1.8***	3.1***	4.9***	4.3***	5.0***	5.3***	5.5***	4.8***	5.8***
Body weight	-11.3**	-32.8***	-0.3NS	-7.5***	0.2NS	-8.5***	-8.1**	-4.7**	-7.9***	-3.8*	-7.2***	-5.5*

[a]Percentage differences = $\dfrac{EC - IC}{IC} \times 100$.

*$p < .05$, **$p < .01$, ***$p < .001$; NS $p > .05$. Duncan's new multiple range test.

than in EC rats, the respective differences being 4.4% ($p < .01$), 3.5% ($p < .05$), and 4.9% ($p < .01$). The fact that SE rats exceeded EC rats significantly in this measure indicates that EC is not a limiting or maximal condition; another condition that is more effective than EC is the seminatural outdoor environment to be mentioned later (Section II,B,1).

Formal training has also been found to induce cerebral weight changes, as compared with control conditions (see Section II,A,2,b).

  b. *Thickness of Cortex.*   Rats from the EC environment develop a significantly thicker cerebral cortex than do littermates in IC (Diamond, Krech, & Rosenzweig, 1964) and both differ from littermates in the standard colony environment (Rosenzweig, Bennett & Diamond, 1972c; Walsh, Budtz-Olsen, Penny, & Cummins, 1969). Again, the differences are larger in the occipital area than in other cortical regions. A detailed description of these effects, and of the influences of age and of duration of experience, is given by Rosenzweig *et al.* (1972c, pp. 242–247).

Walsh *et al.* (1969) reported even larger effects of EC–IC rearing on the thickness of the hippocampus than on that of the cortex. However, the hippocampal differences were less reliable than those in the cortex. No evidence of a significant EC–IC hippocampal effect was found, however, by Diamond, Ingham, Johnson, Bennett, and Rosenzweig (1976). As mentioned earlier, we have not found significant differences between EC and IC rearing on hippocampal total weights.

  c. *Dimensions of Cerebral Hemispheres.*   A few findings of altered length and width of the hemispheres have been reported as consequences of differential experience. Altman, Wallace, Anderson, and Das (1968) found that any of several treatments—4 months of operant conditioning, daily handling from Day 2 to Day 11, or rearing in an enriched environment for 3 months after weaning—led to a significant increase in cerebral length but to no change in width. Rosenzweig and Bennett (1969), however, obtained only nonsignificant 1% increases in both length and width in 30-day EC–IC experiments with rats and with gerbils. Walsh, Budtz-Olsen, Torok, and Cummins (1971) reported that the duration of the experiment was an important parameter: In a 30-day EC–IC experiment neither the 1% differences in length nor those in width were significant, although the product of length × width was significant. But following 80 days of differential rearing, the EC–IC differences in length were significant (2.5%, $p < .001$), the difference in width was nonsignificant, and the product of length and width again yielded a significant effect (2.8%, $p < .001$). In a further experiment, Walsh, Cummins, and Budtz-Olsen (1973) reported that the 1.2% difference in length after 30 days was significant ($p < .005$) with a large enough N (22 pairs); nevertheless, the 30-day effect was only half as large as that previously found with 80 days of differential experience. No difference in width was found.

Kuenzle and Knüsel found length of the cerebral hemispheres to be somewhat greater in rats from their "superenriched" condition than in EC. In three experiments, the differences amounted to 0.8% ($p < .05$), 1.0% ($p < .05$), and 0.3% (NS) respectively.

The preponderance of results thus indicates that differential experience can produce small but significant effects in the overall dimensions of the cerebral hemispheres in rats.

2. MICROSCOPIC EFFECTS

As early as the 1890s, Tanzi and then Sherrington had suggested that learning might occur through changes in the synaptic junctions, and in the 1960s anatomical techniques had finally reached a level of precision that permitted investigators to search for neuroanatomical effects of experience at both the light- and electron-microscopic levels.

a. Cell Density and Size. When rats are kept in EC or IC from 25 to 105 days of age, those exposed to EC show significantly more glial cells in a fixed sample of occipital cortex; neurons show only a small and nonsignificant decrease in EC versus IC (Diamond *et al.*, 1976). Although EC does not affect neuron density it does increase the cross-sectional area of neural perikarya and nuclei. Larger changes resulted when exposure to the environments occurred during the preweaning period (6 to 25 days of age, see Malkasian & Diamond, 1971) than during the postweaning period (25 to 105 days, see Diamond, 1967). Both perikarya and nuclei show significant EC–IC differences for the 25- to 105-day group, but only the perikarya shows a significant difference for the 60- to 90-day group (Diamond, Johnson, Ingham, Rosenzweig, & Bennett, 1975a), so the two measures do not always change in comparable fashion in response to environmental conditions.

b. Dendritic Branching. Holloway (1966) made a preliminary study of dendritic branching in layer 2 stellate neurons in occipital cortex of EC and IC littermates. Neurons from EC rats, compared with those from IC, showed a greater number of intersections with multiple concentric rings around the cell body. Similar results have been obtained by Greenough (1975). Greenough also measured the orders of dendrites in terms of branches away from the cell body. "The results were remarkably consistent; in small, medium, and large pyramidal neurons and in stellate neurons, EC rats had consistently more higher-order dendritic branches than their IC littermates (24 of 24 cases in fifth-order branching). SC rats were intermediate but tended to be closer to the ICs in higher-order branching . . ." (Greenough, 1976, p. 265).

Branching patterns of pyramidal cells in different cortical areas were then examined (Greenough, Volkmar, & Juraska, 1973). No differences resulting from differential experience were found in frontolateral cortex; small but reliable differences were found in temporal cortex, which were less than that obtained in occipital cortex. Greenough notes that the regional differences in dendritic branching correspond reasonably well to patterns of differences in brain weight and thickness. This, coupled with the fact that the dendrites account for over 90% of the volume of cortical neurons, suggests that differences in dendritic volume account for most of the EC–IC differences in gross size and weight.

Fiala (1976) and Greenough, Snow, and Fiala (1976) found that giving rats 30 days of EC or IC experience immediately following weaning produced 25% more dendritic branching in hippocampal neurons of the EC rats, as measured by the ring-intersection analysis.

Greenough (1976, pp. 270–272) also investigated dendritic branching in rats given formal training (on either the Hebb-Williams maze or a series of visual discrimination problems) as compared with rats receiving control treatments. Whereas differences between EC and IC rats occur chiefly in the basal dendrites, effects related to training occur chiefly in the outer region of the apical dendrite. These effects of 30 days of formal training were much smaller than effects of 30 days of EC versus IC experience. Rutledge (1976) has reported complex changes in the form of apical dendrites of cats that received conditioning versus control stimulation.

c. Dendritic Spine Counts. EC rats have greater numbers of dendritic spines per unit length of dendrite than do IC littermates (Globus, Rosenzweig, Bennett & Diamond, 1973). The differences are largest on the basal dendrites (9.7%, $p < .01$, based on 40 littermate pairs).

Using very different conditions, Schapiro (1971, pp, 328–329; Schapiro & Vukovich, 1970) found substantial increases in dendritic spines in rat pups subjected to severe and varied stimulation from Day 1 to Days 8, 9, 11, or 13. The pups were given electric shocks, heated and chilled, vibrated, handled, and stimulated with flashes of light and sound pulses (even though their eyes and ears had not yet opened). It seems likely that "stress" is a better designation for this treatment than the original designation of "multidimensional environmental stimulation (handling)." The work of Globus *et al.* (1973) shows that mild environmental treatments are sufficient to induce changes in number of dendritic spines.

d. Synaptic Number and Length. Enriched experience leads to a greater number of dendritic spines per unit of dendritic length and also causes greater dendritic branching. Taken together, these results suggest a considerable increase in total number of cortical synapses in animals with enriched experience. As yet, however, this indication is not supported by direct counts of synapses. Furthermore, the effect of experience may be more specific and differentiated than a simple overall increase in synaptic number.

Bloom (1970, p. 740) reported lack of any consistent difference between

EC and IC rats in number of synapses in the molecular layer (layer 1) of the cortex. It is not clear why the analysis of synaptic number was restricted to the molecular layer, except that counts are easier to make there than in the deeper layers (2–6) where the meshwork of fibers is denser. The choice of layer 1 to look for differences in synaptic numbers may have been unfortunate, as several observations indicate:

(a) In measures of cortical thickness, layer 1 is the only layer in which no EC–IC difference was observed (Diamond et al., 1964).

(b) EC–IC differences in dendritic branching in pyramidal neurons are found chiefly in the basal dendrites (Greenough, 1975) and these, of course, occupy the deeper layers of the cortex.

(c) Similarly, the EC–IC differences in number of dendritic spines per unit of dendrite length are considerably larger in the basal dendrites than elsewhere (Globus et al., 1973). With these points in mind, it is clear that number of synapses should be measured in layers 2–6 to determine whether EC–IC differences occur there.

Individual synapses in deeper layers of the occipital cortex of EC and IC rats have been measured by electron-microscopic techniques by Møllgaard, Diamond, Bennett, Rosenzweig, and Lindner (1971), West and Greenough (1972), and Diamond, Lindner, Johnson, Bennett, and Rosenzweig (1975b). Møllgaard measured the length of the postsynaptic opaque region in type-1 synapses from layer 3 of rats in EC or IC from 25 to 55 days of age. In 12 pairs of littermates from a single experiment, the postsynaptic thickening averaged 52% longer in EC than in IC rats, and there were one-third fewer synapses in the EC rats. West and Greenough also measured the length of the postsynaptic thickenings, and in addition they measured bouton diameter and the length of the region of tight apposition of the pre- and postsynaptic processes of type-1 synapses; these measures were made in layers 1, 4, and 6. The only significant effect found was that EC rats averaged 14% longer postsynaptic thickenings in layer 4. Diamond et al. (1975b) were not able to replicate the findings of Møllgaard but found differences close to those reported by West and Greenough: With 13 littermate EC–IC pairs, length of the postsynaptic thickening in layer 4 averaged 5% greater in the EC rats ($p < .05$); there was also an 8% decrease in number of synapses (NS). West and Greenough also observed an apparent decrease in the number of synapses in their EC rats, but they were inclined to attribute this to the fact that since EC synapses were larger on the average, the probability of their inclusion in measurements was lower since appropriate orientation of the irregular surface of the synaptic cleft in a thin section is lower the longer the synapses (and synapses that could not be seen clearly throughout their length were eliminated from further study). Walsh and Cummins (1976), contrary to the previous investigators, report their EC rats to have not only significantly greater length of synaptic junctions but also significantly greater density of synapses than their impoverished littermates.

Altschuler (1976) reports that 80 days of combined nonspecific and specific training led to a doubling of synaptic density in the hippocampus of the trained rats versus that of the control rats ($p < .001$).

The results to date indicate that postweaning experience in differential environments produces synaptic changes that can be detected by current anatomical methods. Discordances among results cannot be ignored but they may be resolved in terms of differing sites and methods of analysis.

B. Effects on Brain Chemistry

1. CHOLINERGIC SYSTEM

Effects of differential experience on the cholinergic system have been previously reviewed in detail (Rosenzweig et al., 1972c); only a brief review of the topic will be provided here. [5]

Table III presents some previously unpublished results for acetylcholin-

TABLE III

EFFECTS OF SEMINATURAL ENVIRONMENT (SNE), ENRICHED CONDITION (EC), AND IMPOVERISHED CONDITION (IC); PERCENTAGE DIFFERENCES BETWEEN GROUPS IN WEIGHT AND AChE ACTIVITY OF BRAIN SECTIONS[a]

	Weight			AChE/weight		
	SNE versus IC	EC versus IC	SNE versus EC	SNE versus IC	EC versus IC	SNE versus EC
Cortex						
Occipital	11.2***	6.0***	5.0***	−6.0***	−3.4***	−2.7***
Somesthetic	2.1*	1.8*	0.3	−2.0**	−0.8	−1.2
Remaining dorsal	6.1***	3.1***	3.0***	−3.3***	−1.6*	−1.7*
Ventral	4.8***	1.3	3.4**	−3.2***	−1.6	−1.6
Total	5.8***	2.6***	3.1***	−3.6***	−1.9**	−1.7*
Rest of brain	−0.7	−0.8	0.1	1.3*	1.2*	0.1
Total brain	2.1***	0.6	1.4*	−1.1*	−0.2	−0.9
Cortex/rest	6.5***	3.3***	3.1***	−4.8***	−3.0***	−1.8**
Terminal body weight	−10.1***	−7.9***	−2.4*	—	—	—

[a] Results are based on four experiments, each including 12 littermates per condition.

* $p < .05$, ** $p < .01$, *** $p < .001$.

[5] A reader who consults Rosenzweig et al. (1972c) should be sure to employ the errata sheet pasted on the inside front cover of that book, because the volume is marred by many typographical errors, omitted lines, and other errata.

esterase (AChE) activities and weights of brain sections from littermate rats placed for 30 days in either an outdoor seminatural environment (SNE), the enriched condition (EC), or the impoverished condition (IC). Differences between SNE and IC groups were greater than those between EC–IC groups in most measures of tissue weight and of AChE/weight. SNE–EC differences expressed on several of the measures were highly significant: The weights of occipital cortex in SNE rats exceeded those of EC rats by 5.0% ($p < .001$), and AChE/weight of occipital cortex was 2.7% less in SNE than in EC ($p < .001$). On the other hand, ChE activity/weight (not shown in the table) was scarcely affected in these experiments of 30-day duration.

Duration of differential experience has also been investigated in experiments in which enzymatic activity has been measured. Significant EC–IC differences are found in AChE/weight after 30 days in the experimental conditions, but still larger effects are found after 80 days. In the case of ChE/weight, however, EC–IC differences that are often not significant after 30 days, become considerably larger and regularly attain significance after 80 days (Rosenzweig et al., 1972c, pp. 239–240). Brain weight differences, it will be recalled, decline somewhat as duration of the experiment extends beyond 30 days. "Whereas in 1964 we supposed that all of the cerebral effects we measured might be reflecting only different aspects of the same syndrome of changes, it now appears that various measures follow their own time courses and may eventually be shown to represent independent types of change" (Rosenzweig et al., 1972c, p. 239).

Our ideas about the meaning of effects of experience on the activities of AChE and ChE have changed during the course of our research, as we have discussed previously (Rosenzweig et al., 1972c, see especially pp. 271–272). A series of experiments run from 1963 to 1969 showed that the increase of total AChE in the cortex of EC versus IC rats was very small and of doubtful statistical significance. With the more effective enrichment of the seminatural outdoor environment (SNE), however, total AChE activity in occipital and total cortex is now seen to be significantly greater in SNE rats than in IC littermates.

The finding of a clear increase in ChE activity in EC brains was unexpected, and this has been confirmed in numerous experiments. The differential ways in which experience alters AChE and ChE activities suggested that cell counts might reveal an increase in glial cells in EC animals versus their IC littermates. This hypothesis was tested directly and led to the finding of a greater number of glial cells in EC (Diamond, Law, Rhodes, Lindner, Rosenzweig, Krech, & Bennett, 1966). Nevertheless, we wish to be cautious about the interpretation of ChE as an index to glial number. Although neurons do not contain ChE, blood vessel walls as well as glial cells are rich in ChE activity, and further chemical and histological observations are needed to characterize the cerebral changes.

To date at least, the detailed findings of effects of EC, SC, and IC environments on AChE and ChE activities have led to knowledge of structural changes in cortex more than to knowledge of changes in synaptic function.

2. BIOGENIC AMINES

Although the importance of biogenic amines for brain function and behavior is widely recognized, surprisingly few studies of the effects of differential environments on this class of transmitters have been carried out. The paucity of studies probably reflects in part the difficulty of carrying out the reliable analyses necessary to detect relatively small differences in concentrations or activities of components of the biogenic amine system. However, the few studies that have been done indicate that differential environments can bring about modifications in concentrations of selected biogenic amines in brain.

Pryor (1964, quoted in Bennett, Diamond, Krech, & Rosenzweig, 1964) found no significant difference in serotonin concentration of brain (cortex or subcortex) in rats of the S_1 or S_3 Berkeley lines that had been kept in EC or IC from 25 to 110 days of age. Animals run simultaneously did show the usual EC–IC differences in brain weights and AChE activity.

Geller, Yuwiler, and Zolman (1965) found no difference between EC and IC rats in serotonin, dopamine, or 5-HTP decarboxylase/mg protein of whole brain. The IC rats did show increased norepinephrine content of whole brain as well as increased adrenal weight. Subsequent work (Geller, 1971) showed that the norepinephrine differences occurred in the caudate nucleus.

Riege and Morimoto (1970) found that, after 30 days of differential housing, EC rats had a 10% increase of norepinephrine in the cortex coupled with an approximately similar decrease in the hypothalamus-caudate, so that the total brain sample did not show a significant change. Dopamine also showed a similar pattern of change, while serotonin showed a small but significant decrease in the cortex.

The possible role of stress in causing EC–IC differences in biogenic amine levels in brain has been a subject of concern. Geller found evidence that stress occurred during exposure to the IC environment, but he assigned rats to the differential environments at 16 to 21 days of age—earlier than rats are normally weaned. Because of these observations, Riege and Morimoto compared effects of daily overt stress with nonstress over the entire EC–IC period. They found that stress did affect the levels of biogenic amines but in a different pattern from EC–IC effects.

3. RNA and DNA Content

In experiments done in 1964 to determine environmental effects on the RNA and DNA content of brain, we analyzed samples from the occipital cortex of rats exposed to two sets of contrasting conditions—EC versus IC, and rats kept in a normal light–dark cycle versus littermates kept in complete darkness for 80 to 130 days, starting at weaning. The differential environments produced only a small, insignificant difference in RNA/mg but a significant increase in total RNA content. Instead of the expected increase in DNA/weight (due to increased number of small glial cells), we found that the DNA content decreased approximately in proportion to the increase in sample weight of the occipital cortex of the more stimulated rat (the EC or the light-cycle rat). The ratio of RNA to DNA yielded particularly reliable differences between stimulated and restricted groups. The combined results of 80-day EC–IC experiments in which the differential conditions were begun at weaning showed an increase in the RNA/DNA ratio of 5.9% ($p < .01$) in occipital cortex, and the RNA/DNA ratio of the EC rat exceeded the IC in 19 out of 23 littermate comparisons (Rosenzweig et al., 1972c, see especially pp. 251, 253–254).

We discontinued further research on environmental effects of the nucleic acid content of brain until 1973 when the development of a more accurate and relatively rapid method for RNA and DNA analysis made it feasible to investigate more fully environmental influence on the RNA and DNA content of rat brain (Morimoto, Ferchmin, & Bennett, 1974). The RNA/DNA ratio has been shown to be the most reliable chemical indicator of the EC effect; in 90% of more than 550 pairs, the RNA/DNA ratio in occipital cortex of the EC rat has been larger than that of the IC rat, and the average difference is 8%.

We believe that the decrease in DNA content/weight reflects the smaller number of cells per unit of volume that results from greater experience; cell density is reduced because the perikaryon of EC rats is larger than that of IC rats, and there is also greater volume of dendrites in EC rats. We interpret the findings as evidence that the brain, as a consequence of increased behavioral demands, is adapting both anatomically and chemically. The increased total RNA can support heightened chemical synthetic processes (Rosenzweig et al., 1972c, p. 273). We also propose that long-term increases in the RNA/DNA ratio and in total RNA with enriched experience represent the integrated effect of a continuing series of pulses of increased RNA synthesis and other biosynthetic processes resulting from a number of individual learning experiences.

Kuenzle and Knüsel (1974) reported that in each of three experiments, the RNA/DNA ratio in occipital cortex of SE rats exceeded that of EC rats by small but nonsignificant amounts; the SE–EC differences ranged from 1.2%

to 2.6%. Since there was a significant increase in the weight of the occipital cortex in SE rats, as mentioned earlier, the total RNA was also elevated.

The temporal course of changes in RNA with experience was first investigated by Ferchmin *et al.* (1970). They reported a significant increase in RNA content of the cerebrum after 4 days of enriched versus impoverished experience. This was caused in part by an increase in RNA/mg and in part by a small but significant increase in weight of cerebrum. When exposure to the environments was extended to 8 days or more, the increase in total RNA was due almost entirely to the increase in tissue weight.

We have also investigated the time course of EC–IC effects on RNA and DNA levels in brain. In occipital cortex, RNA/weight shows a larger positive EC–IC difference at 4 days than thereafter; it remains positive through the 30-day duration, and thereafter shows only small and irregular effects (Table IV). DNA/weight is lower in EC than in IC rats for all durations greater than 3 days. The RNA/DNA ratio rises more rapidly than the tissue-weight effect, and it remains larger than the weight effect through the 30-day duration; it then becomes somewhat smaller although remaining highly significant.

The RNA/DNA ratio falls off quickly when rats are removed from EC and placed in IC (Bennett, 1976, Table 17.7), whereas the effects in weight and AChE activity show greater persistence (Bennett, 1976, p. 281). Thus, as we had predicted, the RNA/DNA ratio responds sensitively to experiential pressure, rising rapidly when the animal is placed in the enriched condition and declining rapidly when the environmental demands are removed.

In experiments in which rats had to run maze patterns to obtain food and water, RNA/DNA showed generally larger and clearer effects than did the weight measures (Table VIII).

Because the RNA/DNA ratio responds rapidly to environmental demands and to formal training, because this measure is highly reliable and is not too costly, and because small tissue samples can be analyzed thus allowing study of regional differences in effects, measures of RNA and DNA are extremely useful for studies of brain development and of influences of experience and other factors on its development.

4. Gene Activation and RNA Diversity

Several investigators, because of their interest in mechanisms of memory storage, have analyzed RNA diversity as a function of complexity of experience. They have regarded the enriched laboratory environment as one that affords considerable opportunity for learning, in comparison with standard colony or the restricted conditions. It is now generally accepted that new protein must be formed to establish long-term memory (Flood & Jarvik, 1976). However, it has not been definitely established whether this

TABLE IV

Percentage Differences[a] in Occipital Cortex between EC and IC Littermates in RNA, DNA, and Weight as Functions of Duration of Differential Experience and Age at Start

Average age (days) start of differential conditions[b]		Duration (in days)									
		4	8	15	30	45	60	80	100	125	160
27 ± 3 (weaning)	No. of pairs	46	31	44	100	12	12	20	11	53	10
	Weight	6.5**	5.6**	8.6***	8.4***	6.6*	15.3***	12.7***	13.6***	7.6***	10.5**
	RNA/DNA	7.6***	5.8***	10.3***	9.6***	6.7**	5.8**	10.9***	6.3***	4.9***	6.0**
	RNA/weight	4.1***	1.3NS	3.2***	2.4***	-2.8**	-2.2*	3.3NS	-0.2NS	-0.5NS	0.7NS
	DNA/weight	-3.2***	-3.9***	-6.3***	-6.6***	-8.9***	-7.5***	-6.9***	-6.2***	-5.4***	-5.1*
	Total RNA	11.0***	7.1***	12.2***	11.0***	3.7NS	12.8***	15.9***	13.3***	7.1***	11.2***
	Total DNA	3.1*	1.3NS	1.7NS	1.3NS	-2.8NS	6.8*	5.0*	6.6*	1.8NS	4.9NS
63 ± 4	No. of pairs	10			37						10
	Weight	1.0NS			5.2***						9.3**
	RNA/DNA	7.9**			8.3***						10.1***
	RNA/weight	3.5*			2.9***						1.7NS
	DNA/weight	-3.9*			-5.1***						-7.5***
	Total RNA	4.6NS			8.0***						11.2**
	Total DNA	-3.0NS			-0.4NS						0.8NS

304

Starting age (days)	Measure	Exp 1	Exp 2	Exp 3
102 ±18	No. of pairs	12	41	9
	Weight	4.0*	4.7**	8.1*
	RNA/DNA	7.8***	7.1***	7.0**
	RNA/weight	6.4**	1.4**	1.5NS
	DNA/weight	-1.3NS	-5.2***	-5.1*
	Total RNA	10.5***	6.2***	9.8*
	Total DNA	2.5NS	-0.6NS	2.7NS
202 ±15	No. of pairs		24	
	Weight		2.7NS	
	RNA/DNA		9.4***	
	RNA/weight		3.0***	
	DNA/weight		-5.7***	
	Total RNA		5.7**	
	Total DNA		-3.4NS	
303 ±66	No. of pairs	12	22	12
	Weight	0.3NS	3.6NS	6.2NS
	RNA/DNA	5.6**	7.0***	8.8***
	RNA/weight	4.2**	1.7*	4.2*
	DNA/weight	-1.3NS	-4.8***	-4.2*
	Total/RNA	4.4NS	5.4*	10.5*
	Total DNA	-1.2NS	1.3NS	1.8NS

[a] Percentage difference $= \dfrac{\text{EC} - \text{IC}}{\text{IC}} \times 100$.

[b] The standard deviation of starting ages represents variability between experiments.

*$p < .05$, **$p < .01$, ***$p < .001$; NS $p > .05$. Duncan's new multiple range test.

new protein differs qualitatively or quantitatively from the preexisting protein (Barraco & Stettner, 1976; Gaito & Bonnet, 1971).

Since we have found protein content to increase along with cortical weight in EC rats (Bennett et al., 1964), this indicates that quantitative changes occur in protein content as a result of differentiated experience. Levitan, Mushynski, and Ramirez (1972) measured the effects of environmental complexity on in vivo incorporation of L-[³H]leucine into rat cortex. Seven days after rats were placed in the differential environments, the incorporation of leucine into all subcellular fractions of both cortex and hippocampus was higher in EC rats than in the IC rats. After 16 days in the differential environments, the differences were confined to the synaptosomal fraction, and after 35 days no differences were observed. While these experiments confirmed quantitative changes in protein, they provided no evidence for qualitative changes.

Qualitative changes of protein would most probably occur as a result of activation of new regions of DNA leading to a greater diversity of mRNA. Four groups of investigators have therefore searched for changes in the diversity of RNA by DNA-RNA hybridization studies. Mushynski, Levitan, and Ramirez (1973), failed to find evidence for significantly increased diversity. Rats were compared after 7, 20, and 30 days of EC or of IC experience. On the other hand, Uphouse and Bonner (1975) in a preliminary note reported increased RNA diversity in brains of rats raised in an enriched condition as compared to nonstimulated controls. Uphouse and Bonner concluded that although the differences in hybridization between RNA from brains of enriched and nonstimulated rats were in the predicted direction, additional evidence is needed before one can be sure that such differences exist.

Knüsel, Heidelberger, and Kuenzle (1975) assessed differences in gene activation among 20 female rats raised in a superenriched environment for 7 days and a control group of 10 rats maintained in a large cage. Since virtually identical results were obtained with the DNA isolated from enriched or colony-control rats, Knüsel et al. concluded that either gene activation is too low for detection or gene activation is not the basis of memory and learning.

An ongoing collaborative study has produced evidence of significant EC–IC differences in diversity of brain RNA in double-blind experiments using unique sequence molecular hybridization. In this study, RNA diversity is being measured by Grouse and collaborators at NIH in Bethesda in rats that were, for the most part, reared in differential environments in our laboratories at Berkeley (Grouse, Schrier, Bennett, Rosenzweig, & Nelson, 1977). In 40 EC–IC pairs, pooled into 11 subgroups for analysis, the EC rats showed 21% greater diversity than IC rats.

Although it would be tempting to interpret the results to date as reflecting greater diversity of proteins in brains of EC than in those of IC rats, any such interpretation must be guarded by the following considerations. All species of cellular RNA are represented in the total RNA whose diversity is being measured; this includes, among others, heterogeneous nuclear RNA (hn RNA), messenger RNA (mRNA), and ribosomal RNA (rRNA). Much of the diversity resides in the hnRNA, which does not correspond to the diversity of mRNA. It is the mRNA that is translated to produce unique protein molecules. Grouse, Chilton, and McCarthy (1972) have estimated that a maximum of 50% of the total diversity of mouse brain RNA is represented in the mRNA of polysomal fractions. Study of the complex functions of the different RNA fractions is an active area of investigation, and the roles of the different classes of RNA are far from being completely understood at present. We have suggested elsewhere (Bennett, Flood, Orme, Rosenzweig, & Jarvik, 1975) that, at least in cases of strong training, protein synthesis necessary for memory storage occurs using existing mRNA without the formation of new species. Thus, it would be premature to conclude that greater diversity of RNA indicates a greater diversity of protein in the brains of the EC animals as compared with the brains of IC animals.

The question of quantitative versus qualitative changes in the composition of chemical constituents of the brain is central to an understanding of the possible biochemical processes involved in responses to differential experience or training. The increasingly powerful methods now becoming available to study gene expression, coupled with the approach of differential rearing environments, may provide an important tool for studying memory mechanisms.

C. Effects on Electrophysiology of Brain

Latency of evoked responses in occipital cortex was measured in EC and IC rats by Edwards, Barry, and Wyspianski (1969). After 8 weeks in differential environments, the mean latency in EC rats was 56 msec, whereas the mean latency in IC rats was 64 msec ($p < .01$). In a subsequent study, one group was kept in a visually enriched environment for 10 weeks from weaning, a second group had auditory enrichment, and a third group had neither type of enrichment (Mailloux, Edwards, Barry, Rowsell, & Achorn, 1974). Latencies of visual cortex responses were shorter in the visual cortex of rats given visual enrichment as compared with those of the other two groups; only peaks with latencies greater than 100 msc showed significant differences, suggesting that the differences involved cortical processing rather than projection of impulses to the cortex. No significant effects were related to auditory enrichment, either in auditory or in visual cortex. This lack of effect surprised Mailloux *et al.* since they noted our report that blinded or dark-reared rats show effects of EC or IC experience on chemical and anatomical measures in occipital cortex (Rosenzweig, Bennett, Diamond, Wu, Slagle, & Saffran, 1969). The lack of effect of auditory stimulation in the experiment of Mailloux *et al.* is consistent with our conclusion that cerebral changes in rodents are produced by direct interaction with stimuli and that extracage stimulation is ineffective (Rosenzweig & Bennett, 1976, pp. 192–194).

McGinty (1971, pp. 350–353) found that isolation-reared kittens spent less time sleeping than did kittens raised in groups with frequent handling and complex stimulation. When the previously isolated kittens were exposed to a complex environment, the percentages of time spent in both fast-wave (REM) and slow-wave sleep rose sharply. Further experiments showed that a period of novel stimulation caused the increase of sleep time and that neither an equivalent period of sleep deprivation nor the stress caused by restraint produced such an effect.

Tagney (1973) reported that EC rats spent 56% of their time sleeping compared to 45% for ICs. The proportions of sleep time spent in fast-wave or slow-wave sleep did not distinguish the two groups. When IC rats were then transferred to EC, their sleep increased toward the EC level, most of the increase bring in slow-wave activity. Tagney has suggested that the greater sleep time in EC may be necessary for macromolecular synthesis and restoration of brain function after higher levels of waking activity. In this connection, Bloch (1976) has shown that formal training affects sleep patterns in rats. After a training session, the percentage of fast-wave sleep increases, and preventing the occurrence of fast-wave sleep during the 2 hours following training has been found to impair consolidation of memory.

Lambert and Truong-Ngoc (1976b) placed rats in EC or IC for 6 weeks after weaning, then implanted electrodes and took two 3-hour samples of recordings. Not only did EC rats show more total sleeping time than did IC rats, but the EC rats also had a significantly higher proportion of fast-wave sleep, whereas Tagney had reported no difference in this measure. Lambert and Truong-Ngoc (1976a) also found that EC rats had a higher threshold of activation of cortical responses when the reticular activating system was stimulated than did either SC or IC rats. Reticular excitability did not correlate with measures of sleep behavior, so Lambert and Truong-Ngoc (1976b) concluded that environmental experience has independent effects on sleep and on reticular excitability.

D. *Effects on Behavior*

The report by Hebb (1949) that rats reared as pets learned mazes more rapidly than rats reared in laboratory cages provided the impetus for a major effort to investigate and understand the effects of differential experience on subsequent learning or problem-solving behavior. Among reviews of this subject are those by Rosenzweig (1971, pp. 315–323) and Greenough (1976, pp. 260–262). Many of the behavioral differences reported appear to be specific to the species or even the strain tested, to the ages at which differential experience is given, and to the behavioral test employed. Perhaps the most consistent finding (although there are exceptions even here) is that EC rats are superior to SC or IC rats in performance on complex mazes.

Gottlieb (1974) has stated that there is a temporal discrepancy between the behavioral and the cerebral effects of experience. He cited Hymovitch (1952) who reported that exposure of rats to a complex environment from 30 to 75 days of age aided later performance on the Hebb-Williams maze whereas exposure from 75 to 120 days had no effect. This, Gottlieb noted, is in contradistinction to the cerebral effects of complex experience that can be induced even in adult rats. It should be pointed out that Hymovitch's study was conducted with very small groups of rats (only 3 to 6 per condition) and that later experiments with larger groups have not supported his conclusion that enriched experience that begins well after weaning will not affect behavioral test results. Forgays and Read (1962) exposed groups of about 9 rats to a complex environment for 3 weeks beginning either at birth, at Day 22 (weaning), or at Days 44, 66, or 88. All groups were tested on the Hebb-Williams maze beginning on Day 123. All groups except 88–109 were significantly better on the Hebb-Williams maze than the group with no enriched experience. The 88–109 group had scores only very slightly worse than those of the 0- to 21-day group and just missed differing significantly from the control group. Nyman (1967) exposed rats to an enriched environment at 30–40, 50–60, or 70–80 days of age. Eight hours per day exposure at any of the three periods showed significant beneficial effects for later spatial learning, as compared with the control condition. In unpublished experiments, we have found effects of EC versus SC experience on Hebb-Williams maze scores when exposure to EC began after 80 days of age. In six experiments in which differential experience started at 85, 101, or 123 days of age, the ratio of total errors of SC to EC rats was 1.27 ($N = 45$ per group). In six experiments in which differential experience started at around 33 days of age, the ratio of errors of SC to EC rats was 1.18 ($N = 53$ per group). Doty (1972) placed 18 Sprague-Dawley rats in an enriched environment at 300 days of age while keeping 18 littermates in standard laboratory cages. After 360 days of differential experience, the rats were tested on a light–dark active avoidance reversal task, and a passive avoidance task. The EC group was only slightly better than the control rats on the first task, but was significantly better on the latter two tasks. The preponderance of evidence thus indicates that enriched experience that begins well after weaning can alter problem-solving ability as well as cerebral values.

E. Cerebral Effects as a Function of Age of Subjects

1. OBSERVATIONS

How the magnitude of cerebral effects of differential experience varies with age at onset of the experience has not been a major focus of research, but some pertinent information has been obtained. The first EC–IC experiment in which animals were placed in conditions at an age greater than 25 days used the starting age of 105 days when the rats were young adults (Rosenzweig, Krech, & Bennett, 1964). The results were not greatly different from those previously obtained with the 25-day starting age. Later we varied both age at onset and the duration of the EC–IC period. Most of the EC–IC differences in weights of standard brain sections decreased somewhat with age at onset or differential rearing, but even with experiments begun at 290 days, significant effects of differential experience were found (Table V). Similarly, the magnitude of EC–IC differences does not decrease greatly with age of onset of differential experience for AChE, ChE, or cortical thickness (Rosenzweig et al., 1972c) or for RNA/DNA (see Table IV).

An exception to the relative age-independence of effects of differential experience is the report of Greenough et al. (1976) that dendritic branching in occipital cortex was not affected by placing rats in EC or IC for 90 days starting at 90 days of age, whereas significant effects were obtained with 30 days of EC versus IC experience starting at weaning.

Malkasian and Diamond (1971) placed nursing rat pups and their mothers in environments of various degrees of complexity and looked for cerebral effects of early differential experience. They placed litters of rats in one of the following three conditions at 6 days of age: (a) unifamily environment (UFE), the normal breeding colony conditions with a mother and 3 pups in a colony cage; (b) multifamily environment (MFE), 3 mothers with 3 pups each in a large cage; (c) enriched-condition-multifamily environment (EC-MFE), 3 mothers with 3 pups each in a large cage furnished with varied stimulus objects. Three sets of UFE and EC-MFE groups were sacrificed at 28 days. Brain sections were analyzed for thickness of cortex and cross-sectional areas of neuronal nuclei and perikarya. Results are shown in Tables VI and VII, along with comparative values from postweaning EC–IC experiments. Although the number of measures allowing comparisons is rather small, they do indicate greater cerebral responsiveness in the preweaning period than after weaning. Cortical thickness effects are about twice as large with a 22-day preweaning period as with a 30-day postweaning period of differential experience (Table VI).

Cross-sectional areas of nuclei and perikarya suggest even larger differ-

TABLE V
EC–IC Percentage Differences[a] in Brain Weights and Body Weights with Different Starting Ages and Durations

Average age (days) at start of differential conditions[b]		Duration (in days)					
		4	15	30	60	80	160
26 ± 3 (weaning)	No. of pairs	48	58	354	40	218	33
	Occipital cortex	6.6***	7.4***	9.0***	12.4***	7.2***	10.6***
	Total cortex	2.2***	5.0***	5.3***	4.7***	4.2***	3.9***
	Rest of brain	1.9***	1.8***	0.5^{NS}	−0.3^{NS}	−1.0*	−1.7*
	Total brain	2.0***	3.2***	2.5***	1.8*	1.2**	0.6^{NS}
	Cortex/rest	0.2^{NS}	3.1***	4.9***	5.0***	5.3***	5.8***
	Body weight	−0.3^{NS}	0.2^{NS}	−8.5***	−4.7**	−7.9***	−5.5*
61 ± 5	No. of pairs	11	21	160	20	—	12
	Occipital cortex	1.6^{NS}	2.0^{NS}	7.0***	12.0***	—	8.8**
	Total cortex	0.1^{NS}	3.7***	5.0***	3.2**	—	7.8***
	Rest of brain	−0.6^{NS}	0.5^{NS}	1.4***	−0.4^{NS}	—	4.4*
	Total brain	−0.3^{NS}	1.9*	3.0***	1.2^{NS}	—	5.8**
	Cortex/rest	0.7^{NS}	3.2***	3.6***	3.7***	—	3.2*
	Body weight	−0.2^{NS}	−1.2^{NS}	−1.5^{NS}	−3.2^{NS}	—	2.0^{NS}
95 ± 18	No. of pairs	12	—	70	—	45	9
	Occipital cortex	4.0*	—	5.9***	—	10.9***	8.1*
	Total cortex	2.0^{NS}	—	3.6***	—	5.4***	3.3^{NS}
	Rest of brain	0.5^{NS}	—	0.6^{NS}	—	1.7*	−1.6^{NS}
	Total brain	1.1^{NS}	—	1.9***	—	3.2***	0.4^{NS}
	Cortex/rest	1.3^{NS}	—	3.0***	—	3.7***	5.1***
	Body weight	3.5^{NS}	—	0.1^{NS}	—	−0.1^{NS}	−1.2^{NS}
195 ± 10	No. of pairs	—	21	45	21	—	—
	Occipital cortex	—	5.9**	4.2***	3.6*	—	—
	Total cortex	—	5.4***	3.8***	4.7***	—	—
	Rest of brain	—	1.7^{NS}	1.5*	2.9***	—	—
	Total brain	—	3.2**	2.4***	3.6***	—	—
	Cortex/rest	—	3.6***	2.3***	1.7*	—	—
	Body weight	—	1.8^{NS}	0.3^{NS}	0.7^{NS}	—	—
282 ± 47	No. of pairs	12	12	43	12	21	—
	Occipital cortex	0.3^{NS}	6.2^{NS}	3.4*	6.5^{NS}	7.2*	—
	Total cortex	−0.7^{NS}	3.4**	2.0*	0.8^{NS}	3.4*	—
	Rest of brain	0.4^{NS}	0.1^{NS}	−0.7^{NS}	0.7^{NS}	0.7^{NS}	—
	Total brain	0.0^{NS}	1.4^{NS}	0.4^{NS}	0.7^{NS}	1.8^{NS}	—
	Cortex/rest	−1.1^{NS}	3.4**	2.7***	0.2^{NS}	2.8^{NS}	—
	Body weight	−2.2^{NS}	−0.1^{NS}	−2.8^{NS}	−2.4^{NS}	−0.3^{NS}	—

[a] Percentage difference: $\dfrac{EC\text{-}IC}{IC} \times 100$.

[b] The standard deviation of starting ages represents variability between experiments.

*p < .05,   **p < .01,   ***p < .001;   NS p > .05. Duncan's new multiple range test.

TABLE VI
PERCENTAGE DIFFERENCES IN CORTICAL THICKNESS AS A FUNCTION OF AGE AT
ONSET AND DURATION OF DIFFERENTIAL EXPERIENCE

| Cortical area | EC-MFE versus UFE[a] | | | EC versus IC[b] | |
| | Ages (in days) at start and end | | | | |
	6–14	6–19	6–28	25–55	60–90
Occipital cortex					
Difference(%)[c]	6.8	8.0*	10.3***	4.6**	6.2**
No. E > I[d]	4/7	5/7	16/19	23/30	45/70
Somesthetic cortex					
Difference(%)[c]	10.0***	9.7***	6.9**	2.2*	3.6**
No. E > I[d]	6/7	7/7	16/19	20/31	38/50

[a]Enriched-condition-multifamily environment versus unifamily environment (Malkasian & Diamond, 1971).

[b]Enriched condition versus impoverished condition (Rosenzweig et al., 1972c).

[c]Percent difference between enriched condition (either EC-MFE or EC) and impoverished condition (either UFE or IC).

[d]Number of littermate pairs in which the enriched-experience animal (either EC-MFE or EC) has a thicker cortex than the impoverished experience animal (UFE of IC).

*$p < .05$, **$p < .01$, ***$p < .001$.

ences between the magnitude of preweaning and postweaning effects, although few strictly comparable comparisons can be made (Table VII). The one set of MFE versus UFE groups (not shown) yielded no significant differences in any of the brain measures, presumably because the enriched inanimate environment was a necessary factor in the EC–MFE effects.

Large effects of preweaning stimulation on dendritic spine counts have also been reported by Schapiro (1971). But no investigator has counted spines after subjecting older rats to such an overwhelmingly stressful regimen (as Greenough, 1976, p. 257, has termed it), so we do not know whether equally large effects could be induced in postweaning animals.

The study of Malkasian and Diamond (1971) indicates that the brains of nursing rat pups are affected by complexity of a nonstressful environment. More research using preweaning EC seems indicated in order to determine the relative responsiveness of a number of brain measures to preweaning and postweaning experience. While the brain may be somewhat more responsive to environmental influences at early ages than later, it is nevertheless clear that most of the changes reviewed here can be produced at any point during the life span.

While this chapter was in press, we ran experiments in November, 1976, and January, 1977, in order to add to the small amount of information available comparing effects of preweaning versus postweaning exposure to

TABLE VII

PERCENTAGE DIFFERENCES IN CROSS-SECTIONAL AREAS OF NEURONAL NUCLEI AND PERIKARYA
AS A FUNCTION OF AGE AND DURATION OF DIFFERENTIAL EXPERIENCE

	EC-MFE versus UFE[a]			EC versus IC[b]		
	Ages (in days) at start and end					
Area	6–28 (19 pairs)	25–55 (20 pairs)	60–90 (19 pairs)	25–105[b] (12 pairs)	25–105[c] (20 pairs)	105–185 (18 pairs)
Nuclear area						
Occipital cortex						
Difference (%)[d]	25**	1.5	1.5	12.2***	11.7***	−1.4
Somesthetic cortex						
Difference (%)	19*	—	—	—	—	—
Perikaryon area						
Occipital cortex						
Difference (%)	—	—	4.5*	12.5***	—	—
Somesthetic cortex						
Difference (%)	16**	—	—	—	—	—

[a] Enriched-condition-multifamily Environment versus unifamily environment (Malkasian & Diamond, 1971).

[b] Enriched condition versus impoverished condition (Diamond, 1967).

[c] Enriched condition versus impoverished condition (Diamond et al., 1975b).

[d] Percent difference between enriched condition (either EC-MFE or EC) and impoverished condition (either UFE or IC).

enriched or standard colony environments. We found that effects of two weeks of preweaning differential experience on weights and RNA/DNA of brain regions were mainly smaller in magnitude than effects of a similar period of experience that began immediately after weaning. Furthermore, the cerebral effects of preweaning experience could be overcome by the postweaning condition; pups that experienced EC just after weaning showed similar brain measures whether their preweaning condition had been EC or SC. Thus, the preweaning treatment did not produce particularly large or persistent results. A full report of these experiments will be made elsewhere.

2. IMPLICATIONS OF AGE DEPENDENCE

The relative effectiveness of giving access to differential environments at different ages can be considered in terms of the animal's natural habitat and the maturation of its sensory and motor functions. Daly (1973), from the comparative perspective, concludes that laboratory procedures, such as handling, are overstimulative for the nursing rat pup that is "normally confined to the postnatal womb of a hole or burrow," but that the standard condition "becomes an impoverished environment at that stage [weaning] when the young animal would become active over a wider range" (p. 438). Although Daly's conclusion supports the practice of introducing environmental complexity at weaning as we have done in most of our experiments, we believe that a certain amount of additional preweaning complexity may help to simulate the natural condition. In nature the mother rat must leave the nest to forage, the pups stray from the nest and must be retrieved, and the pups begin to explore their surroundings more and more vigorously from about 15 days of age (when their eyes and ears have opened and their temperature regulation improves). The standard colony cage allows space for only the nest. A more natural condition is provided if the litter and nursing mother are placed in a large EC cage with a variety of stimulus objects and a small box for the nest. The mother leaves the nest from time to time to obtain food and water and to explore the objects; when the young begin to venture out from the nest, they also encounter the stimulus objects. Thus the EC situation, without overstimulating the nursing pups, provides some of the stimulation of maternal comings and goings and of a varied environment outside the nest that characterize the natural situation.

What the animal is able to draw from its environmental depends partly on its sensory maturation, which is one of the themes of this volume. Rats sacrificed at 14 days, about 1 day after their eyes had opened, did not show a significant effect of enriched environment in the occipital cortex, although they did show a significant effect in the somesthetic cortex (Table VI). It would be interesting to measure effects in other cortical areas and see if the pattern of effects over areas could be related to differences in developmental stages. To benefit from more complex aspects of the environment, cognitive maturation is probably necessary, and it continues long after sensory-perceptual development is complete. The experimental environments undoubtedly differ along several important dimensions—social and inanimate complexity are among those discussed in Rosenzweig and Bennett (1976)—and much work will be needed to determine the relative effectiveness of these dimensions in relation to the age of the subjects.

F. Comparisons of Effects among Strains and Species

Although research on cerebral effects of experience has been done mainly with laboratory rats, some generality of the effects can be inferred from the fact that similar results have been obtained with several lines or strains of rats and that positive effects have also been found in similar experiments with laboratory mice, gerbils, and feral deermice (*Peromyscus*).

Initial work on brain AChE activity and brain weights showed similar effects in the several lines of rats tested; these were the Berkeley S_1 and S_3 lines (descendants, respectively, of a Tryon maze-bright and a Tryon maze-dull line), the K line (derived from a cross between the S_1 and S_3 lines), and the RDH, RDL, and RCH lines (lines selectively bred by Roderick, 1960, for high and low brain acetylcholinesterase; see also Krech, Rosenzweig, & Bennett, 1960; Rosenzweig et al., 1962). Later we obtained similar effects with rats of the inbred Fischer line and Long-Evans rats. Two kinds of hybrids—S_1 × Fischer and S_3 × Fischer—showed effects of differential experience on brain weights and brain enzymes similar to those previously obtained with the foundation stocks (Rosenzweig & Bennett, 1977).

Other investigators have reported similar EC–IC cerebral differences using still other lines or stocks of rats—Geller (1971) used Sprague-Dawley rats, Walsh et al. (1971) used Wistar rats, Ferchmin et al. (1970) used an albino line maintained at the University of Córdoba, Argentina.

La Torre (1968) used two inbred strains of mice and found brain weights and AChE and ChE activities to show EC–IC differences similar to those reported for rats. Rosenzweig and Bennett (1969) assigned Mongolian gerbils at 30 days of age to the EC, SC, and IC environments and kept them there until 60 days of age. Measures of brain weights, AChE, and ChE showed EC–SC–IC differences rather similar to those obtained previously with rats. Feral deermice (*Peromyscus*) showed EC–SC–IC effects in brain weights, AChE and ChE generally similar to those found with the other species of rodents, although the *Peromyscus* values were more variable than those of the laboratory rodents (Rosenzweig and Bennett, unpublished).

Now that rather similar cerebral effects of differential experience have been obtained with several species of rodents, it will be important to extend this research to other orders of mammals in order to test whether the effects observed to date may be restricted to rodents or may, as seems more likely to us, be even more prominent in animals that are capable of more complex learning and problem-solving behavior (Rosenzweig, 1966, p. 329).

III. Mechanisms Hypothesized to Mediate Production of Cerebral Effects of Differential Experience

We began research with the enriched, colony, and impoverished environments in order to provide differential opportunities for learning (Rosenzweig et al., 1961). We early ruled out several variables—differential locomotor activity, differential handling, and diet—on the basis of control experiments. Subsequently, and in collaboration with David Krech during the period 1958–1966 and with Marian C. Diamond during 1960–1974, we have made a two-pronged attack on the problem, on the one hand studying the roles of various aspects of the informal environments, and, on the other, examining the effects of formal training on brain measures. We have previously reviewed research on possible mechanisms mediating the cerebral effects of differential experience (Rosenzweig & Bennett, 1976; Rosenzweig et al., 1972c, see especially pp. 257–267), and the question has also been discussed by Walsh and Cummins (1975) and by Greenough (1976), so we will not take up most alternative hypotheses here.

A. Distinctions between Effects of Differential Experience and Certain Other Phenomena

The findings reviewed to this point make it possible to distinguish differential experience from two other topics with which it has sometimes been confused. One of these topics is early stressful stimulation (e.g., Denenberg, 1969; Levine, 1971); the other is sensory deprivation or distortion (e.g., Blakemore & Cooper, 1970; Hubel & Wiesel, 1962).

Early handling or stressful stimulation produces clear effects on pituitary-adrenal function and on certain aspects of later behavior (e.g., Denenberg, 1969; Levine, 1971). It should be clear that the causes of these effects must be quite different from those we have been discussing because cerebral effects of differential experience, unlike the handling-stress effects, (a) do not involve stress, (b) are not induced by handling, and (c) because many of the cerebral effects can be produced at any point in the life span. An additional reason for distinguishing between the two is that effects of differential experience can be produced in hypophysectomized rats (Rosenzweig, Bennett, & Diamond, 1972b).

At least three lines of evidence suggest a distinction between effects of sensory deprivation or distortion and those of experience of environments of differential complexity. First, it has been reported that the effects of sensory deprivation or distortion on development of receptive fields in cats or monkeys can be induced only early in the life of the animal (Blakemore & Cooper, 1970; Hubel & Wiesel, 1962), whereas many effects of experience can be caused throughout the life span of rats. Mistretta and Bradley (in this volume) suggest that we overemphasize this difference, but our reading indicates that the sensory effects are more sharply restricted to an early period than are the experiential effects.

Second, the changes in cortical receptive fields have been induced by simply restricting stimulation or by distorting it; no requirement for active participation by the animal has been stated, and it has even been reported that receptive fields can be altered by presenting restricted stimuli to animals that have been immobilized by pharmacological agents (Pettigrew

& Garey, 1974). In contrast, the effects of differential experience on brain measures have been shown to require active participation of the subjects (Ferchmin, Bennett, & Rosenzweig, 1975). We might recall here the findings of Held and Hein (1963) that active locomotion of kittens in a patterned visual environment is necessary for the acquisition of normal sensory–motor coordination; passive movement in the same environment, providing essentially the same visual stimulation, did not result in acquisition of normal behavior.

Third, the amount of visual stimulation in IC, which is not sufficient for full development of the rodent brain, is perfectly adequate for development of normal cortical receptive fields in cats and monkeys. Thus, the effects that are described by such investigators as Hubel and Wiesel, Blakemore, Hirsch, and Spinelli et al. appear to be more specifically sensory and to require much more severe restriction of stimulation than do the effects of differential experience that are the main subject of this chapter.

The value of these comparisons between the effects of the two types of experimental treatment is unfortunately weakened by the fact that to date they have been studied with different orders of mammals. More critical comparisons will be possible when the missing quadrants have been filled in by investigating effects of sensory deprivation or distortion on receptive fields in rodents and by studying effects of differential experience on cerebral measures in carnivores and primates. Meanwhile the present comparison may serve at least to caution against a facile equating of the two types of treatment and of their effects.

B. The Arousal Hypothesis

A further alternative hypothesis for the EC–SC–IC cerebral effects has been developed in detail recently—the arousal hypothesis (Walsh & Cummins, 1975). Walsh and Cummins propose that ". . . a combination of activation of sensory systems and nonspecific activation, or arousal, underlies some proportion of the differential brain effects" (p. 988). Some other proportion of the effects, they feel, is due to learning: "At the present time, one can only conclude that learning is almost certainly involved in the induction of the brain changes resulting from environmental stimulation in general and from environmental complexity in particular, but that the extent of this contribution is almost entirely unknown" (p. 988).

The main support adduced for the arousal hypothesis is that alterations in arousal appear to be concomitants of all brain changes induced by differences in environments. It is certainly true that animals appear to be more active and aroused in EC than in SC, and more so in SC than in IC. (Recall, however, that rats sleep more in EC than in IC.)

Some experiments already mentioned afford evidence with which we can test the arousal hypothesis. In the experiments of Ferchmin *et al.* (1975), animals in the observer condition (OC) group were placed in individual hardware cloth cages inside regular EC cages. The OC rats shared the varied sights, sounds, and smells that were available to their EC littermates. Four times a day, each OC cage was removed from one EC cage to another. This treatment increased activity of the OC rats, and they remained aroused for some time as the EC rats in the new EC cage sniffed and examined them. Yet the combination of sensory stimulation and repeated arousal over a 30-day period failed to produce measurable brain differences between OC rats and their IC littermates; OC did differ significantly from EC. These results demonstrate the necessity for direct interaction with the environment to produce the brain effects; merely "exposing animals to environments rich in sensory stimuli" is not sufficient to cause the brain changes.

In experiments on possible effects of stress some IC rats were taken from their cages each day, carried to another room and given unavoidable electric shocks through the floor bars of a shock compartment. This treatment, which combined arousal with the novel sensory input of the shock compartment, failed to produce measurable brain differences in comparison with other IC rats that remained in their quiet IC cages throughout. Such experiments fail to support the hypothesis that arousal plus sensory stimulation will produce brain changes. If arousal plus opportunity to learn can be shown to produce brain changes, then learning is indicated as the key factor.

C. The Hypothesis That Learning and Memory Storage Are Involved in the Cerebral Effects of Differential Experience

A hypothesis that appears capable of encompassing the observations to date is that the cerebral effects represent mainly an integration or cumulation of a continuing series of pulses of biochemical synthesis that occur as consequences of learning events (Rosenzweig *et al.*, 1972c, p. 269). Arousal would be involved to the extent that it plays a part in learning and memory storage, but not separately from them.

Greenough (1976) has offered the following arguments (with which we agree) to support the hypothesis that these cerebral effects are, in fact, related to learning and memory storage: First, both the behavioral and the cerebral effects of environmental complexity are potentiated by drugs that affect memory formation. Second, Greenough notes that effects of environmental complexity on brain weights and nucleic acids are found after only a few days in the differential environments, and thus the time scale is compatible with that of experiments on learning and memory. Furthermore, brain weight differences occur even when exposure to environmental complexity is restricted to as little as 2 hours per day for 30 days, again a daily period comparable to that of many learning experiments. Third, Greenough points out that behavioral effects of enriched experience seem to be greatest on tasks which are rather similar to the complex environment, especially mazes.

In addition to studying effects of nonspecific experience on brain measures, we have also investigated possible effects of various specific training situations. For example, testing rats for 1 hour per day over a 30-day period in an automatic maze was found to produce small but significant differences in cortical weights when comparisons were made with runway controls or food-box controls.

Our most recent and promising efforts along this direction have been made with mazes introduced into the living situation. A plastic box containing a pattern of barriers is inserted as a story or level into a large cage, 15 cm above the floor. Food pellets are available on the floor of the cage, and water in the upper part of the cage, above the top of the plastic box. To go from food to water, the rat climbs up into the plastic box, traverses the pattern of alleys, and climbs out above at the other end. To eliminate social stimulation entirely, we expose rats individually to the complex maze situation and compare the brain values with those of littermates in EC or IC. Results to date for both weight and RNA/DNA of occipital cortex are shown in

TABLE VIII

EFFECTS OF INDIVIDUAL MAZE EXPERIENCE ON WEIGHT AND RNA/DNA OF OCCIPITAL CORTEX OF RAT

	Conditions[a]		
	EC	ICM	IC
Mean Weight (in mg)[b]	77.6	76.5	73.2
S.D.	5.1	4.8	4.1
Percentage differences in weight (76 paired comparisons):			
EC vs.		1.4	6.0**
ICM vs.			4.6**
Mean RNA/DNA	1.522	1.506	1.430
S.D.	.078	.070	.062
Percentage differences in RNA/DNA (76 paired comparisons)			
EC vs.		1.1*	6.4**
ICM vs.			5.3**

[a]Comparisons between littermates in three conditions: enriched condition (EC), individual rat in complex maze (ICM), and impoverished condition (IC). (N = 76 per condition.)
*$p < 0.10$ **$p < 0.01$.

Table VIII. Individual experience in the complex maze (ICM) produces significant effects that are similar to those of EC.

The experiments with the individual maze raise questions about the possible roles of motor activity in producing the results. We had found early that locomotion in running wheels or alleys does not produce EC effects. Recent results of Ferchmin and Eterović (1977) extend this by showing that training in motor agility does not produce cerebral effects similar to those of free exploration in a complex environment. We have tested this factor directly in recent experiments by adding a condition in which rats had to traverse an empty maze box with no barriers to get from food to water stations. Thus the control condition was exactly like ICM except that there were no maze patterns to learn. The empty box condition did not produce significant effects in brain weights or cortical RNA/DNA, whereas littermates in ICM did show significant effects ($N = 24$ per condition). These experiments, which show clear effects of training (ICM) against a stringent control condition, will be reported in full elsewhere (Bennett, Rosenzweig, Morimoto and Herbert, manuscript).

Arousal may well be an important variable that modulates both strength of learning and formation of long-term memories. In fact, we have done considerable research showing that administering excitant drugs shortly after one-trial training can combat the amnesic effect of an inhibitor of protein synthesis (Flood *et al.*, 1977, 1978). But eliciting or altering arousal does not by itself produce either learning or EC effects. We conclude that, in the light of observations to date, the cerebral effects of experience in differential environments are best interpreted as consequences of learning and memory storage.

IV. Extensions of This Research and Related Investigations

Effects of differential experience are now being studied in a variety of contexts. Enriched experience is being employed as a therapeutic measure to counteract developmental deficiencies that arise from causes as diverse as brain lesions (Will, Rosenzweig, Bennett, Hebert, & Morimoto, 1977; Will, Rosenzweig, & Bennett, 1976), disseminated damage to the brain in experimental cretinism (Davenport, Gonzalez, Carey, Bishop, & Hagquist, 1976), malnutrition (Franková, 1974, p. 226; Winick, 1976), and mental retardation (Bovet, 1976). A recent symposium on this topic was entitled *Environments as therapy for brain dysfunction* (Walsh & Greenough, 1976). The influences of specific environmental factors are being studied in the first 6 months of development of infants (Yarrow, Rubenstein, & Pedersen, 1975). Lack of space prevents a further review of this topic here.

V. Roles of Experience

How can we most accurately characterize the effects of differential experience on cerebral and behavioral measures as reported in this chapter? Gottlieb (1976) has attempted to distinguish three roles of experience in order to avoid terminological and semantic problems and also to clarify some conceptual difficulties. He proposes that experience "can *maintain* (sustain, preserve) ongoing developmental states or particular end points, it can *facilitate* development, and it can *induce* (channel, determine) development" (p. 28). Research surveyed here indicates that experience in environments of varying degrees of complexity can both *maintain* and *modulate* cerebral values (we prefer the term *modulate* to the term *facilitate*, for reasons we will discuss shortly.)

Let us consider an example to see how these concepts can be applied: If we take a rodent that has lived in a standard colony laboratory environment up to 100 days of age, we can then cause the weight of its cerebral cortex either to increase, to remain the same, or to decrease, depending upon whether we place the animal for a few weeks in an enriched environment, or keep it in the colony condition, or place it in an environment more restricted than that of the colony. We might characterize the first result as facilitating growth of cortex, and the second as maintaining the effects of prior development, but the decrease in cortical weight would not seem to fit in any of Gottlieb's categories. To allow for negative as well as positive effects, we would propose that experience can *modulate* cortical development, either increasing or decreasing it, or—within a certain range of stimulation—maintaining the level achieved prior to intervention. It is interesting to note that although Gottlieb (1976) gave mainly positive examples when he suggested the use of the term "facilitation," a few of his own examples were negative: "Exposure to certain sounds can either accelerate or decelerate hatching time in quail embryos.... Prior exposure to light facilitates the young chick's behavioral approach to a flickering light, whereas prior exposure to sound delays the approach to a source of visual flicker...." (p. 32).

While endorsing the attempt to distinguish among different roles of experience, we therefore propose the use of the more inclusive term "modulation" rather than "facilitation" for one class of effects. We also suggest that certain "maintenance" effects may represent only a position on the range of modulation effects rather than belonging to a separate class.

VI. Conclusions

Research in a number of laboratories has demonstrated that significant changes in several aspects of brain biochemistry and brain anatomy are produced when rodents interact with environments that are somewhat more complex than the usual laboratory colony conditions. Such nonstressful enriched experience causes brain changes in both young and adult animals. Although there are indications that preweaning experience may produce larger changes than postweaning experience, the brain remains plastic in many respects long after ages that various investigators have designated as the end points for cerebral development.

Effects of differential experience should be distinguished from effects of early stressful treatment and also from effects of sensory distortion or restriction. Unlike these other effects, most of those caused by differential experience are not limited to early development, they require direct interaction with the environment, and they do not require extreme conditions for their production.

Among the various mechanisms hypothesized to mediate the cerebral effects, learning and memory storage appear best to encompass the data. Several investigators are therefore using experimental environments in studying the anatomical and biochemical mechanisms of memory storage.

Research on effects of differential experience has been extended to experiential therapy for brain lesions, experimental cretinism, and malnutrition. Work with enriching and impoverishing environments is also being done on development of intelligence in children.

We propose that the effects described here represent a modulation of cerebral values through various types of experience.

Acknowledgments

This review was prepared with support from NIH-ADAMHA Grant R01MH26704 and from ERDA.

The research of our laboratories, described in this chapter, has extended over many years, and numerous individuals have made important contributions to it. Particular acknowledgment and appreciation are due Mrs. Marie Hebert, who has made the thousands of brain dissections needed to obtain all of the data summarized in this report. Hiromi Morimoto, assisted by Mrs. Hebert, had done all of the analyses for acetylcholinesterase and cholinesterase, RNA and DNA, and other constituents. Over the past few years, Donald Dryden and Kenneth Chin have been responsible for much of the animal care, maintenance, and behavioral testing. Mrs. Jessie Langford has skillfully kept the records of the project and has patiently and accurately typed and retyped the manuscripts. In addition to these staff members, several students—both undergraduate and graduate—have been active in various aspects of this research; three postdoctoral fellows deserve special mention—Walter H. Riege, Pedro A. Ferchmin, and Bruno E. Will.

Along with the dedication of those who have worked with us, another factor, money, has also been essential. Over the years, several grants have provided much of this support. These have included NSF Grants GB-8011, GB-11840, and GB-30368, grants from NIMH (MH-07903) and NIH-ADAMHA (R01MH26704), and a grant from the Office of Education (OEG-0-9-140398). ERDA (formerly the U.S. Atomic Energy Commission), through the Lawrence Berkeley Laboratory, provided support for this project from its inception.

References

Altman, J., Wallace, R. B., Anderson, W. J., & Das, G. D. Behaviorally induced changes in length of cerebrum in rats. *Developmental Psychobiology*, 1968, **1**, 112–117.

Altschuler, R. Changes in hippocampal synaptic density with increased learning experiences in the rat. *Neuroscience Abstracts*, 1976, **2**, 438. (Abstract).

Barraco, R. A., & Stettner, L. J. Antibiotics and memory. *Psychological Bulletin*, 1976, **83**, 242–302.

Bennett, E. L. Cerebral effects of differential experience and training. In M. R. Rosenzweig & E. L. Bennett (Eds.), *Neural mechanisms of learning and memory*. Cambridge, Mass.: MIT Press, 1976. Pp. 279–287.

Bennett, E. L., Diamond, M. C., Krech, D., & Rosenzweig, M. R. Chemical and anatomical plasticity of brain. *Science*, 1964, **146**, 610–619.

Bennett, E. L., Flood, J. F., Orme, A., Rosenzweig, M. R., & Jarvik, M. *Minimum duration of protein synthesis needed to establish long-term memory.* Paper presented at the Fifth International Meeting of the International Society for Neurochemistry, Barcelona, 1975. (Abstract).

Blakemore, C., & Cooper, G. F. Development of the brain depends on the visual environment. *Nature (London)*, 1970, **228**, 477–478.

Bloch, V. Brain activation and memory consolidation. In M. R. Rosenzweig & E. L. Bennett (Eds.), *Neural mechanisms of learning and memory*. Cambridge, Mass.: MIT Press, 1976. Pp. 583–590.

Bloom, F. E. Correlating structure and function of synaptic ultrastructure. In F. O. Schmitt (Ed.), *The neurosciences. Second study program*. New York: Rockefeller University Press, 1970. Pp. 729–747.

Bovet, M. Piaget's theory of cognitive development, sociocultural differences, and mental retardation. In B. Inhelder (Ed.), *Piaget and his school*. New York: Springer, 1976. Pp. 59–69.

Cummins, R. A., Walsh, R. N., Budtz-Olsen, O. E., Konstantinos, T., & Horsfall, C. R. Environmentally-induced changes in the brain of elderly rats. *Nature (London)*, 1973, **243**, 516–518.

Daly, M. Early stimulation of rodents: A critical review of present interpretations. *British Journal of Psychology*, 1973, **64**, 435–460.

Davenport, J. W., Gonzalez, L. M., Carey, J. C., Bishop, S. B., & Hagquist, W. W. Environmental stimulation reduces learning deficits in experimental cretinism. *Science*, 1976, **191**, 578–579.

Denenberg, V. H. Experimental programming of life histories in the rat. In A. Ambrose (Ed.), *Stimulation in early infancy*. New York: Academic Press, 1969. Pp. 21–43.

Diamond, M. C. Extensive cortical depth measurements and neuron size increases in the cortex of environmentally enriched rats. *Journal of Comparative Neurology*, 1967, **131**, 357–364.

Diamond, M. C., Ingham, C. A., Johnson, R. E., Bennett, E. L., & Rosenzweig, M. R. Effects of environment on morphology of rat cerebral cortex and hippocampus. *Journal of Neurobiology*, 1976, **7**, 75–85.

Diamond, M. C., Johnson, R., Ingham, C., Rosenzweig, M. R., & Bennett, E. L. Effects of differential environments on neuronal nuclear and perikeria dimensions in the rat cerebral cortex. *Behavioral Biology*, 1975, **15**, 107–111 (a)

Diamond, M. C., Krech, D., & Rosenzweig, M. R. The effects of an enriched environment on the histology of the rat cerebral cortex. *Journal of Comparative Neurology*, 1964, **123**, 111–119.

Diamond, M. C., Law, F., Rhodes, H., Lindner, B., Rosenzweig, M. R., Krech, D., & Bennett,

E. L. Increases in cortical depth and glia numbers in rats subjected to enriched environment. *Journal of Comparative Neurology*, 1966, **128**, 117–125.

Diamond, M. C., Lindner, B., Johnson, R., Bennett, E. L., & Rosenzweig, M. R. Differences in occipital cortical synapses from environmentally enriched, impoverished, and standard colony rats. *Journal of Neuroscience Research*, 1975, **1**, 109–119. (b)

Doty, B. A. The effects of cage environment upon avoidance responding of aged rats. *Journal of Gerontology*, 1972, **27**, 358–360.

Edwards, H. P., Barry, W. F., & Wyspianski, J. O. Effect of differential rearing on photic evoked potentials and brightness discrimination in the albino rat. *Developmental Psychobiology*, 1969, **2**, 133–138.

Ferchmin, P., Bennett, E. L. & Rosenzweig, M. R. Direct contact with enriched environment is required to alter cerebral weight in rats. *Journal of Comparative and Physiological Psychology*, 1975, **88**, 360–367.

Ferchmin, P. A., & Eterović, V. A. Brain plasticity and environmental complexity: Role of motor skills. *Physiology and Behavior*, 1977, **18**, 455–461.

Ferchmin, P. A., Eterović, V. A., & Caputto, R. Studies of brain weight and RNA content after short period of exposure to environmental complexity. *Brain Research*, 1970, **20**, 49–57.

Fiala, B. A. *The effects of enriched or impoverished rearing on development of brain and behavior in rats.* Unpublished doctoral thesis, University of Illinois at Urbana-Champaign, 1976.

Flood, J. F., Bennett, E. L., Orme, A. E., Rosenzweig, M. R., & Jarvik, M. E. Memory: Modification of anisomycin-induced amnesia by stimulants and depressants. *Science*, 1978, **199**, 324–326.

Flood, J. F., & Jarvik, M. E. Drug influence on learning and memory. In M. R. Rosenzweig & E. L. Bennett (Eds.), *Neural mechanisms of learning and memory.* Cambridge, Mass.: MIT Press, 1976. Pp. 483–507.

Flood, J. F., Jarvik, M. E., Bennett, E. L., Orme, A. E., & Rosenzweig, M. R. The effect of stimulants, depressants, and protein synthesis inhibition on retention. *Behavioral Biology*, 1977, **20**, 168–183.

Forgays, D. G., & Read, J. M. Crucial periods for free-environmental experience in the rat. *Journal of Comparative and Physiological Psychology*, 1962, **55**, 816–818.

Franková, S. Interaction between early malnutrition and stimulation in animals. In J. Cravioto, L. Hambraeus, & B. Vahlquist (Eds.), *Early malnutrition and mental development* (Symposia of the Swedish Nutrition Foundation XII). Uppsala: Almqvist & Wiksell, 1974.

Gaito, J., & Bonnet, J. Quantitative versus qualitative RNA and protein changes in the brain during behavior. *Psychological Bulletin*, 1971, **75**, 109–127.

Geller, E. Some observations on the effects of environmental complexity and isolation on biochemical ontogeny. In M. B. Sterman, D. J. McGinty, & A. M. Adinolfi (Eds.), *Brain development and behavior.* New York: Academic Press, 1971. Pp. 277–296.

Geller, E., Yuwiler, A., & Zolman, J. F. Effects of environmental complexity on constituents brain and liver. *Journal of Neurochemistry*, 1965, **12**, 949–955.

Globus, A., Rosenzweig, M. R., Bennett, E. L., & Diamond, M. C. Effects of differential experience on dendritic spine counts. *Journal of Comparative and Physiological Psychology*, 1973, **82**, 175–181.

Gottlieb, G. Die Entwicklung des Verhaltens. In K. Immelmann (Ed.), *Grzimeks Tierleben*: *Verhaltensforschung.* Zurich: Kindler, 1974, Pp. 551–570.

Gottlieb, G. The roles of experience in the development of behavior and the nervous system. In G. Gottlieb (Ed.), *Studies on the development of behavior and the nervous system* (Vol. 3): *Neural and behavioral specificity.* New York: Academic Press, 1976, Pp. 25–54.

Greenough, W. T. Experiential modification of the developing brain. *American Scientist*, 1975, **63**, 37–46.

Greenough, W. T. Enduring brain effects of differential experience and training. In M. R. Rosenzweig & E. L. Bennett (Eds.), *Neural mechanisms of learning and memory.* Cambridge, Mass.: MIT Press, 1976. Pp. 255–277.

Greenough, W. T., Snow, F. M., & Fiala, B. A. Environmental complexity versus isolation: A sensitive period for effects on cortical and hippocampal dendritic branching in rats? *Neuroscience Abstracts*, 1976, **2**, 824. (Abstract)

Greenough, W. T., Volkmar, F. R., & Juraska, J. M. Effects of rearing complexity on dendritic branching in frontolateral and temporal cortex of the rat. *Experimental Neurology*, 1973, **41**, 371–378.

Grouse, L., Chilton, M., & McCarthy, B. J. Hybridization of ribonucleic acid with unique sequences of mouse deoxynucleic acid. *Biochemistry*, 1972, **11**, 798–805.

Grouse, L. D., Schrier, B. K., Bennett, E. L., Rosenzweig, M. R., & Nelson, P. G. Sequence diversity studies of rat brain RNA: Effects of environmental complexity on rat brain RNA diversity. *J. Neurochemistry*, 1977.

Hebb, D. O. *The organization of behavior.* New York: Wiley, 1949.

Held, R., & Hein, A. Movement-produced stimulation in the development of visually-guided behavior. *Journal of Comparative and Physiological Psychology*, 1963, **56**, 872–876.

Holloway, R. L., Dendritic branching in rat visual cortex. Effects of extra environmental complexity and training. *Brain Research*, 1966, **2**, 393.

Hubel, D. H., & Wiesel, T. N. Receptive fields, binocular interaction and functional architecture in the cat's visual cortex. *Journal of Physiology (London)*, 1962, **160**, 106–154.

Hymovitch, B. The effects of experimental variations on problem-solving in the rat. *Journal of Comparative and Physiological Psychology*, 1952, **45**, 313–321.

Knüsel, A., Heidelberger, R., & Kuenzle, C. C. Is gene activation in brain neurons the basis of memory and learning? *Bulletin of the Psychonomic Society*, 1975, **6**, 99–101.

Krech, D., Rosenzweig, M. R., & Bennett, E. L. Effects of environmental complexity and training on brain chemistry. *Journal of Comparative and Physiological Psychology*, 1960, **53**, 509–519.

Kuenzle, C. C., & Knüsel, A. Mass training of rats in a superenriched environment. *Physiology and Behavior*, 1974, **13**, 205–210.

Lambert, J.-F., & Truong-Ngoc, A. Influence de l'environnement instrumental et social sur l'excitabilité nerveuse centrale de rat Wistar mâle: Mesure de la réactivité de système réticulo-cortical. *Agressologie*, 1976, **17**, 13–18. (a)

Lambert, J.-F., & Truong-Ngoc, A. Influence de l'environnement instrumental et social sur la structure d'un échantillon du cycle veille-sommeil chez le rat Wistar mâle: Corrélations avec les modifications de l'excitabilité du système réticulo-cortical. *Agressologie*, 1976, **17**, 19–25. (b)

La Torre, J. C. Effect of differential environmental enrichment on brain weight and on acetylcholinesterase and cholinesterase activities in mice. *Experimental Neurology*, 1968, **22**, 493–503.

Levine, S. Stress and behavior. *Scientific American*, 1971, **224**(1), 26–31.

Levitan, I. B., Mushynski, W. E., & Ramirez, G. Effects of an enriched environment on amino acid incorporation into rat brain sub-cellular fraction *in vivo. Brain Research*, 1972, **41**, 498–502.

Mailloux, J. G., Edwards, H. P., Barry, W. F., Rowsell, H, C., & Achorn, E. G. Effects of differential rearing on cortical evoked potentials of the albino rat. *Journal of Comparative and Physiological Psychology*, 1974, **87**, 475–480.

Malkasian, D. R., & Diamond, M. C. The effects of environmental manipulation on the morphology of the neonate rat brain. *International Journal of Neuroscience*, 1971, **2**, 161–170.

McGinty, D. J. Encephalization and the neural control of sleep. In M. B. Sterman, D. J. McGinty, & A. M. Adinolfi (Eds.), *Brain development and behavior*. New York: Academic Press, 1971. Pp. 335–357.

Møllgaard, K., Diamond, M. C., Bennett, E. L., Rosenzweig, M. R., & Lindner, B. Quantitative synaptic changes with differential experience in rat brain. *International Journal of Neuroscience*, 1971, **2**, 113–128.

Morimoto, H., Ferchmin, P. A., & Bennett, E. L. Spectrophotometric analysis of RNA and DNA using cetyltrimethylammonium bromide. *Analytical Biochemistry*, 1974, **62**, 436–448.

Mushynski, W. E., Levitan, I. B., & Ramirez, G. Competition hybridization studies on brain ribonucleic acid from rats reared in enriched and deprived environment. *Journal of Neurochemistry*, 1973, **20**, 309–317.

Nyman, A. J. Problem solving in rats as a function of experience at different ages. *Journal of Genetic Psychology*, 1967, **110**, 31–39.

Pettigrew, J. D., & Garey, L. J. Selective modification of single neuron properties in the visual cortex of kittens. *Brain Research*, 1974, **66**, 160–164.

Riege, W. H., & Morimoto, H. Effects of chronic stress and differential environments upon brain weights and biogenic amine levels in rats. *Journal of Comparative and Physiological Psychology*, 1970, **71**, 396–404.

Roderick, T. H. Selection for cholinesterase activity in the cerebral cortex of the rat. *Genetics*, 1960, **45**, 1123–1140.

Rosenzweig, M. R. Environmental complexity, cerebral change, and behavior. *American Psychologist*, 1966, **21**, 321–332.

Rosenzweig, M. R. Effects of environment on development of brain and of behavior. In E. Tobach, L. R. Aronson, & E. Shaw (Eds.), *The biopsychology of development*. New York: Academic Press, 1971. Pp. 303–342.

Rosenzweig, M. R., & Bennett, E. L. Effects of differential environments on brain weights and enzyme activities in gerbils, rats, and mice. *Developmental Psychology*, 1969, **2**, 87–95.

Rosenzweig, M. R., & Bennett, E. L. Effects of environmental enrichment or impoverishment on learning and brain values in rodents. In A. Oliverio (Ed.), *Genetics, environment, and intelligence*. Amsterdam: Elsevier/North Holland, 1977. Pp. 163–195.

Rosenzweig, M. R., & Bennett, E. L. Enriched environments: Facts, factors and fantasies. In L. Petrinovich, & J. McGaugh (Eds.), *Knowing, thinking and believing*. New York: Plenum, 1976. Pp. 179–213.

Rosenzweig, M. R., Bennett, E. L., & Diamond, M. C. Cerebral changes in response to experience. *Scientific American*, 1972, **226**(2), 22–29. (a)

Rosenzweig, M. R., Bennett, E. L., & Diamond, M. C. Cerebral effects of differential environments occur in hypophysectomized rats. *Journal of Comparative and Physiological Psychology*, 1972, **79**, 56–66. (b)

Rosenzweig, M. R., Bennett, E. L., & Diamond, M. C. Chemical and anatomical plasticity of brain: Replications and extensions, 1970. In J. Gaito (Ed.), *Macromolecules and behavior* (2nd ed.). New York: Appleton, 1972. Pp. 205–277. (c)

Rosenzweig, M. R., Bennett, E. L., Diamond, M. C., Wu, S.-Y., Slagle, R. W., & Saffran, E. Influences of environmental complexity and visual stimulation on development of occipital cortex in rat. *Brain Research*, 1969, **14**, 427–445.

Rosenzweig, M. R., Krech, D., & Bennett, E. L. Heredity, environment, brain biochemistry, and learning. In *Current trends in psychological theory*. Pittsburgh: University of Pittsburgh Press, 1961. Pp. 87–110.

Rosenzweig, M. R., Krech, D., & Bennett, E. L. Strain differences in cerebral responses to environmental complexity and training. *Federation Proceedings*, 1964, **23**, 255. (Abstract).

Rosenzweig, M. R., Krech, D., Bennett, E. L., & Diamond, M. C. Effects of environmental complexity and training on brain chemistry and anatomy: A replication and extension. *Journal of Comparative and Physiological Psychology*, 1962, **55**, 429–437.

Rosenzweig, M. R., Love, W., & Bennett, E. L. Effects of a few hours a day of enriched experience on brain chemistry and brain weights. *Physiology and Behavior*, 1968, **3**, 819–825.

Rutledge, L. T. Synaptogenesis: Effects of synaptic use. In M. R. Rosenzweig & E. L. Bennett (Eds.), *Neural mechanisms of learning and memory*. Cambridge, Mass.: MIT Press, 1976. Pp. 329–338.

Schapiro, S. Hormonal and environmental influences on rat brain development and behavior. In M. B. Sterman, D. J. McGinty, & A. M. Adinolfi (Eds.), *Brain development and behavior*. New York: Academic Press, 1971. Pp. 307–334.

Schapiro, S., & Vukovich, K. R. Early experience effects upon cortical dendrites: A proposed model for development. *Science*, 1970, **167**, 292–294.

Tagney, J. Sleep patterns related to rearing rats in enriched and impoverished environments. *Brain Research*, 1973, **53**, 353–361.

Uphouse, L. L., & Bonner, J. Preliminary evidence for the effects of environmental complexity on hybridization of rat brain RNA to rat unique DNA. *Developmental Psychobiology*, 1975, **8**, 171–178.

Volkmar, F. R., & Greenough, W. T. Rearing complexity affects branching of dendrites in the visual cortex of the rat. *Science*, 1972, **176**, 1445–1447.

Walsh, R. N., Budtz-Olsen, O. E., Penny, J. E., & Cummins, R. A. The effects of environmental complexity on the histology of the rat hippocampus. *Journal of Comparative Neurology*, 1969, **137**, 361–365.

Walsh, R. N., Budtz-Olsen, O. E., Torok, A., & Cummins, R. A. Environmental complexity induced changes in the dimensions of the rat cerebrum. *Developmental Psychobiology*, 1971, **4**, 115–122.

Walsh, R. N., & Cummins, R. A. Mechanisms mediating the production of environmentally induced brain changes. *Psychological Bulletin*, 1975, **82**, 986–1000.

Walsh, R. N., & Cummins, R. A. Electron microscopic observations of occipital cortex in differentially reared rats. *Neuroscience Abstracts*, 1976, **2**, 839. (Abstract)

Walsh, R. N., Cummins, R. A., & Budtz-Olsen, O. E. Environmentally induced changes in the dimensions of the rat cerebrum: A replication and extension. *Developmental Psychobiology*, 1973, **6**, 3–7.

Walsh, R., & Greenough, W. T. (Eds.) *Environments as therapy for brain dysfunction*. New York: Plenum, 1976.

West, R. W., & Greenough, W. T. Effect of environmental complexity on cortical synapses of rats: Preliminary results. *Behavioral Biology*, 1972, **7**, 279–284.

Will, B. E., Rosenzweig, M. R., & Bennett, E. L. Effects of differential environments on recovery from neonatal brain lesions, measured by problem-solving scores. *Physiology and Behavior*, 1976, **16**, 603–611.

Will, B. E., Rosenzweig, M. R., Bennett, E. L., Hebert, M., & Morimoto, H. Relatively brief environmental enrichment aids recovery of learning capacity and alters brain measures after postweaning brain lesions in rats. *Journal of Comparative and Physiological Psychology*, 1977, **91**, 33–50.

Winick, M. *Malnutrition and brain development*. London and New York: Oxford University Press, 1976.

Yarrow, L. J., Rubenstein, J. L., & Pedersen, F. A. *Infant and environment: Early cognitive and motivational development*. New York: Wiley, 1975.

Section 4

EPILOGUE

This volume has described various physical substances and sensory-stimulative events which are of prime importance in the normal and abnormal development of the brain and behavior. As in previous volumes in this series, the "fit" between the neural and behavioral findings is often far from perfect, but we nonetheless have a valuable compendium of facts, issues, and future directions for our understanding of early influences on neural and behavioral development.

The teratogenic literature reviewed in Section 1 gives us a fairly good conceptual hold on the notion of critical or vulnerable periods of development, especially as applied to structural maturation in the prenatal period. When a toxic substance invades an area of the body at a time when the cells therein are actively proliferating to form the specific organ in question, the result is malformation in that particular area. The same substance at a later time does not cause gross structural alteration, although it may cause subsequent behavioral disturbances or deficiencies, presumably through a persisting alteration of neurochemistry and/or electrophysiology. The ability of toxic substances to alter behavior is not so sharply delimited to particular periods of development as is their ability to alter gross structure. Nor are the behavioral correlations inevitable or necessarily highly consistent. The greatest amount of consistency is perhaps found in the hormonal regulation of sexual behavior, where sex-appropriate hormones tend to facilitate sex-typical behavior, especially if the individual's genotype corresponds to the hormone, but even if the genotype does not correspond, some effects are observed. That is, the experimental manipulation of hormone conditions has shown that genotypic sex can be overriden by the substitution or subtraction of the relevant hormones during early development. Thus, species- and sex-typical brain, behavior, and sex organs are dependent upon the availability of the appropriate sex hormone during development.

A most important theoretical implication of the preceding work is the

331

regulation of genetic activity during individual development by factors considerably removed from the genes. When, in Section 2, we come to the matter of the influence of nutrition on the growth of the brain during early (prenatal) development, we come face-to-face with the fact of external environmental factors modulating genetic activity in a way which will perhaps influence the individual's perceptual, learning, social, and cognitive ability throughout life. Admittedly, the human and animal evidence to date does not support such a long-lasting effect of early malnutrition, except perhaps in extreme cases of "kwashiorkor" (severe infantile malnutrition with edema), as indicated, for example, by the work of Birch, Piñeiro, Alcalde, Toca, and Cravioto (1971), or prolonged and severe malnutrition during the first 2 years of life (e.g., Hertzig, Birch, Richardson, & Tizard, 1972; Richardson, Birch, Garbie, & Yoder, 1972). The other side of the coin is also very important: the as yet largely unexplored effects of "supernutrition" on optimal brain development broached tentatively by Zamenhof and van Marthens in Section 2. The point here is that actual brain development may be, in many cases, below the optimal, in the sense that it is below the genetic potential of the individual. "Supernutrition" is not the same as "overnutrition"; the former refers to quality, as well as to quantity, tailored to individual needs.

The animal experimentation on undernutrition has failed as yet to show any long-lasting, irreversible deficits in the learning ability of prenatally malnourished rodents. There is a quantitative delay or lag in behavioral development and learning ability but these are eventually rectified. A possibly critical procedural deficiency in the animal experiments has been the use of standard learning tasks and simple conditioning paradigms which may insufficiently tax the highest "cognitive" functions of the malnourished animals. For example, the fact that certain problems in the Hebb-Williams maze bring out learning deficiencies that otherwise go undetected suggests that psychological investigators in the malnourishment field might do well to become more innovative in their design of behavioral problems for their animals to solve (e.g., McCullough & Blackman, 1976). More cognitively oriented problems such as those described by Razran (1971) in relation to configural and symbolic learning could prove useful in this connection.

In the final section of the volume, in the context of a discussion of sensory-stimulative influences on neural and behavioral development, we once again face the important distinction between critical and sensitive periods of development. The early periods in which the immature organism is especially vulnerable to the damaging effects of traumatic overstimulation are "critical" in three respects: (1) the peculiarly high state of vulnerability to structural damage which is (2) never again repeated during the course of development, and (3) the fact that damage during this period makes the

organism behaviorally deficient at a later stage. In these respects the
defining behavioral features of critical periods for auditory trauma, as
described by Saunders and Bock in Section 3, are the same as those for
exposure to drugs and radiation and malnutrition during early development,
where the behavioral deficits appear later than the treatment and are clear
if not always consistent or persistent. (The effects of hormones would seem
to fit more closely the sensitive-period notion described immediately
below.)

When we turn to the question of nontraumatic sensory stimulation and
environmental enrichment, while there would certainly appear to be early
periods of maximum susceptibility to these factors–in the sense that it may
take less of a "dose" and/or a shorter time to achieve the same effects
earlier than later on—the fact that the mammalian and avian organisms
discussed in these contexts seem to remain behaviorally "sensitive" to these
treatments virtually throughout their entire life makes it more appropriate
to conceptualize nontraumatic sensory stimulation and general environmental enrichment as operating during sensitive rather than critical periods
of development.

The "fine tuning" role of experience seems assured for all sensory
modalities and behavioral functions examined to date–it seems indubitable
that the presence of relevant stimulation during early development is
beneficial and that the absence of such stimulation is detrimental to sensory-
perceptual function and behavioral competence. Thus, there would seem to
be no further necessity for demonstrations of those kinds but, rather,
for the specification of the relevant aspects of the stimulating environment
in relation to specific sensory-perceptual and behavioral functions,
especially in regard to species-typical outcomes. Further demonstrations of
"plasticity" merely for the sake of the demonstration no longer seem
fruitful or necessary.

A very significant issue concerns our conceptualization of the effects of
sensory stimulation and environmental enrichment. Specifically, should
these effects be considered on top of, or beside, learning (strictly defined),
or should they be included under the broad umbrella of "learning," even if
vaguely defined? This is an important problem because it concerns our
conceptual clarity and precision on the behavioral and neural "mechanisms" involved; i.e., the specifics of the role of experience in development.
As one example of the problem, the "learning" that goes on in immature
organisms during perceptual development would not seem to fit important
features of the Pavlovian (classical) or Skinnerian (instrumental) versions
of conditioning. The "memory" which is brought about by S–R conditioning
procedures, involving deprivation, reward, and/or punishment, is very probably different, and thus mediated differently, than that brought about by

environmental enrichment. These are important matters for future incisive analytic discussion, so that our understanding of the similarities and differences of developmental conceptions and those of learning can be mutually enriched. It hardly needs pointing out that our most widely applied notions of learning (i.e., the various types of conditioning) are based on studies of adult animals. In most cases, these adult-based principles are merely applied to young organisms to see if they work, not to understand the very likely developmental "idiosyncrasies" of immature organisms. For these various reasons, it would seem that developmental conceptions and those of adult learning and memory might be kept conceptually distinct, at least for the time being. This is not to imply that it is not valuable to try to establish links between the means or effects of environmental enrichment and those of learning, provided that the uniting categorization does not inadequately represent, or otherwise obscure, significant differences in the factual or conceptual content of either area. For example, it should be noted that maturational variables are very important components of developmental conceptions, whereas they are rarely accorded any formal importance in theories of learning (conditioning). On the other hand, extrinsic reward and punishment do not seem to play key roles in the early development of species-typical behavior, even when such behavior has a strong experiential basis (Gottlieb, 1976).

Finally, the concept of an enriched environment or environmental enrichment (or environmental complexity), as it applies to nonhuman animals, could benefit from a more critical appraisal. Although the full details of the Berkeley group's exciting study of rodents in a seminatural habitat have not yet been published, the report that these animals exceed the so-called environmentally enriched (EC) laboratory animals on various measures of cortical structure and function is very telling (see the chapter by Rosenzweig & Bennett, in this volume). When viewed in the context of species-typical development, one would conceptualize the results from the seminatural habitat (SNE) as approximating the species-typical norm of cerebral development, with the environmentally enriched laboratory situation (EC) representing one grade below the norm, the usual caged condition (SC) two grades below the norm, and the impoverished condition (IC) possibly three grades below the species-typical norm. This conceptualization in no way detracts from the Berkeley group's excellent and important demonstrations of the effects of differing environments on cerebral development, but it does rob the term environmental enrichment of the connotation that the effects exceed the typical norm of cerebral development for the species. The latter is a separate and highly significant question that must be dealt with in the context of naturalistic environments as the baseline. While many may assume that the species-typical environment of a domestic laboratory rat is the standard colony cage, it turns out that the behavior of domestic rats is indistinguishable from wild rats whn they are placed in a naturalistic habitat (Boice, 1977).

As with the tentative concept of "upernutrition" in optimizing species-typical brain growth, it would be mot interesting to determine if a "super-normal" natural environment (whatever that may be) can actually boost cerebral attainment beyond the species-typical norm. Such studies as these will begin to put real meat on he otherwise bare bones of the genetic concept of a reaction norm and the related developmental notion of neural and behavioral potentialitis (Kuo, 1976); that is, in order to flesh out our under-standing of development we need studies of genuine enrichment, as well as studies of deprivation.

References

Birch, H. G., Piñeiro, C., Alcalde, E., Toca, T., & Cravioto, J. Relation of kwashiorkor in early childhood and intelligence at school age. *Pediatric Research*, 1971, **5**, 579–585.

Boice, R. Burrows of wild and albino rats. *Journal of Comparative and Physiological Psychology*, 1977, **91**, 649–661.

Gottlieb, G. Conceptions of prenatal development: Behavioral embryology. *Psychological Review*, 1976, **83**, 215–234.

Hertzig, M. E., Birch, H. G., Richardson, S. A., & Tizard, J. Intellectual levels of school children severely malnourished during the first two years of life. *Pediatrics*, 1972, **49**, 814–824.

Kuo, Z.-Y. *The dynamics of behavior development* (enlarged ed). New York: Plenum, 1976.

McCullough, M. L., & Blackman, D. E. The behavioral effects of prenatal hypoxia in the rat. *Developmental Psychobiology*, 1976, **9**, 335–342.

Razran, G. *Mind in evolution*. Boston: Houghton, 1971.

Richardson, S. A., Birch, H. G., Garbie, E., & Yoder, K. The behavior of children in school who were severely malnourished in the first two years of life. *Journal of Health and Social Behavior*, 1972, **13**, 276–284.

AUTHOR INDEX

Numbers in italics refer to the pages on which the complete references are listed.

SUBJECT INDEX

A

Age, differential experience and, 310, 312–314

Aggressive behavior, sexual differentiation in, hormonal influences on, 88–90

Amino acids, prenatal brain development and, 154–155

Amphetamine, prenatal development and, 25–26

Arousal hypothesis, differential experience and, 317–318

Audiogenic seizures, 265–276
  priming for, 266–268, 270–275, 279–280

Auditory deprivation-supersensitivity hypothesis, 268–270

Auditory experience, brain and behavioral development and, 216–219

Auditory system, normal development of, 250–259

Auditory trauma, 259
  anatomical effects of, 262–264
  audiogenic seizures and, 265–276
    priming for, 266–268, 270–275, 279–280
  behavioral effects of, 260
  critical period for, 277–279
  effects on children, 264
  effects on young animals, 265
  peripheral and central consequences of, 279
  physiological effects of, 260–262

Avoidance conditioning, undernutrition and, 200–203

B

Barbiturates, prenatal development and, 26–28

Behavior
  auditory trauma and, 260
  differential experience and, 308–309
  effect of teratogens on, 17–21
  prenatal stress and, 113–116
    hormonal manipulations and, 121–126
    open-field activity, 134–137

Behavioral development
  early sensory experience and, 215–216
    approaches to study of, 236–240
    auditory, 216–219
    gustatory, 219–223
    mechanisms for structural and neurophysiological effects, 232–235
    neural plasticity, learning, and memory and, 235–236
    olfactory, 223–226
    tactile, 226–229
    visual, 229–232
  radiation and, 36–37, 54, 68–69
    correlation with brain abnormalities, 59–61
    degree of nervous system malformation and, 57–59
    dosage and developmental stage and, 55–57
  undernutrition and, 193
    methods for producing, 193–195
    motor development, 196–197
    reflex development, 195–196

CONTENTS OF PREVIOUS VOLUMES

A
B
C 8
D 9
E 0
F 1
G 2
H 3
I 4
J 5